Interfaith
Spiritual Care
Understandings and practices

For Helmut Weiss
ecumenically-minded and collaborative pioneer
in the field of intercultural and interfaith spiritual care

Interfaith
Spiritual Care
Understandings and practices

Daniel S. Schipani and
Leah Dawn Bueckert, editors

Published by Pandora Press
Kitchener, Ontario
In collaboration with the SIPCC
Society for Intercultural Pastoral Care and Counseling
Gesellschaft für interkulturelle Seelsorge und Beratung
Düsseldorf, Germany

Interfaith spiritual care
Understandings and practices

Copyright © 2009 Daniel S. Schipani and Leah Dawn Bueckert
Published by Pandora Press
33 Kent Avenue
Kitchener, Ontario N2G 3R2
Toll Free: 866.696.1678
Web site: www.pandorapress.com

Book design by Mary E. Klassen. The photograph "Sunrise in Nebraska" is the creation of Sara R. Klassen and is used by permission. The editors chose the image of the dawn as a fitting symbol of the promise of a new day in interfaith spiritual care.

All Pandora Press books are printed on Eco-Logo certified paper.

Unless otherwise indicated, the scripture quotations in this book are from the New Revised Standard Version of the Bible, copyright © 1989 by the Division of Christian Education of the National Council of Churches of Christ in the USA, and are used by permission.

Library and Archives Canada Cataloguing in Publication

Interfaith spiritual care : understandings and practices /
Daniel S. Schipani and Leah Dawn Bueckert, editors.

Includes bibliographical references.
ISBN 978-1-926599-07-6

1. Hospital patients—Pastoral counseling of. 2. Pastoral medicine.
3. Spiritual care (Medical care). 4. Religious pluralism. 5. Cultural
pluralism. I. Schipani, Daniel S., 1943- II. Bueckert, Leah Dawn

BV4335.I58 2009   259'.411   C2009-900843-2

Contents

Part II: Interfaith spiritual care in diverse cultural contexts

Introduction

Globalization[1] and the manifestations of post-modernity[2] are key factors that inform the social context of spiritual care practices in our time. The growing presence of a plurality of faith expressions (religious as well as non-religious)[3] in our culture is indeed a major dimension of the social reality. Spiritual care specialists, both as clinicians and as pastoral theologians, need to work within, and reflect upon such reality in the light of normative claims of their faith traditions. Actually, spiritual caregivers

---

[1] The globalization process under way includes political, economic, technological, and cultural dimensions. Interconnected systems of communication, transportation, and political organization tend to weave our world together into a single global locality. Indeed, globalization is restructuring the ways we live in diverse areas such as sexuality, family life, and the socialization of youth. See, Anthony Giddens, *Runaway World: How Globalization is Reshaping Our Lives* (New York: Routledge, 2000). For a comprehensive introduction to the subject of globalization, see David Held, Anthony McGrew, David Goldblatt, and Jonathan Perraton, *Global Transformations: Politics, Economics, and Culture* (Cambridge, U.K.: Polity Press, 1999). We agree with authors such as Robert J. Schreiter that *globalization* is the broad category to use in describing the signs of the times, *postmodernity* needing to be viewed within such a larger conceptual framework. See, for instance, Schreiter's *The New Catholicity: Theology Between the Global and the Local* (Maryknoll: Orbis Books, 1997), especially chapter 1.

[2] We work with a straightforward account of postmodernity: a pluralist society in which not only are many theories and worldviews tolerated and accepted but there is also a profound suspicion of grand theories and theologies, of systems which make claims to truth (which are viewed as inadequate to reality and coercive). As an ideology, *postmodernism* celebrates the pluralism and fragmentation of so-called postmodern societies as a condition in which "true freedom" is possible. Further, postmodernists typically highlight alternative ways of knowing, restate the human value of emotions and feelings, wonder and mystery, and appreciate the experience of a "second naivete" (with an emphasis on the significance of living in the master stories as stories rather than as factual historical accounts). For an overview of the different sources and expressions of postmodernism, and an evaluation from a Christian perspective, see Stanley J. Grenz, *A Primer on Postmodernism* (Grand Rapids: Eerdmans, 1996).

[3] We adopt the understanding of *faith* as a human universal that may or may not find expression in terms of a specific religious tradition and content (especially beliefs and rituals). It is the understanding articulated by James W. Fowler in his classic work: *Stages of Faith: The Psychology of Human Development and the Quest for Meaning* (San Francisco: Harper & Row, 1981). See also Fowler's *Faithful Change: The Personal and Public Challenges of Postmodern Life* (Nashville: Abingdon Press, 1996).

1

have always had to engage in interfaith communication even if they have not always reflected critically and constructively on such phenomenon in a systematic way.[4] Some of them, however, have taken advantage of the contributions of *intercultural* study to pastoral care and counseling, which offers an opportunity for further exploration of *interfaith* spiritual caregiving as a structurally analogous experience.[5] As documented in the first part of this book, Christian spiritual caregivers are especially challenged to transform their religious and theological language while remaining focused on caring well for care receivers regardless of their religious affiliation, the nature of their faith broadly speaking (including religious and non-religious humanism) and the overall quality of their spirituality.[6]

The main question that the book addresses is, what is desirable and appropriate in the interfaith caring relationship? The research and writing project leading to this publication was designed to address this question with the following goals in mind: to explore the dynamics of interfaith spiritual care as a work of practical and pastoral theology; to identify reliable guidelines for the competent, and duly contextualized, practice of interfaith spiritual care; and to invite further cooperation on this subject among practitioners and scholars.

Throughout this study we worked intentionally within the frame-

---

[4] An exception is the collection of essays in Robert G. Anderson and Mary A. Fukuyama, eds. *Ministry in the Spiritual and Cultural Diversity of Health Care: Increasing the Competency of Chaplains* (New York: The Haworth Pastoral Press, 2004). See also, Sue Wintz and Earl P. Cooper, *Learning Module for Cultural and Spiritual Sensitivity and Quick Guide to Cultures and Spiritual Traditions* (2000) www.professionalchaplains.org. These valuable resources, however, do not include a systematic consideration of theological foundations and perspectives for interfaith spiritual care; further, they do not address the epistemological and methodological issues involved in the interplay between the human sciences and theology, which is essential for an adequate understanding and an effective practice of interfaith caregiving from a theological perspective.

[5] During the last two decades a number of books addressing the challenges of intercultural caregiving have been published in North America, especially in the areas of counseling and psychotherapy. Recent research connects issues of cross-cultural communication and spirituality, as documented, for example, in Mary A. Fukuyama and Todd D. Sevig, *Integrating Spirituality into Multicultural Counseling* (Thousand Oaks, Ca.: Sage, 1999). On the one hand, *interfaith* spiritual caregiving can be viewed and practiced as a special form of *intercultural* caregiving, as caregivers and care receivers share meaning and values. On the other hand, the former presents unique features pertaining not only to the specific content of the verbal and non-verbal interactions between caregiver and care receiver but, especially, to the norms that guide and help to evaluate the very quality and effectiveness of those interactions.

[6] The term *spirituality* is meant here as the overarching construct, connoting a fundamental human potential as well as need for meaning and value and the disposition for relationship with a transcendent power. *Faith* is used by us as denoting patterned ways of being *spiritual* in terms of Fowler's contribution.

work of practical theology as a discipline with its four main tasks and dimensions.[7] Those tasks and dimensions are reflected comprehensively in the following pages: observation of interfaith care situations (*empirical-descriptive* dimension); interpretive analyses (hermeneutic or *interpretive* dimension); consideration of clinical as well as ethical-theological norms of good care (*normative* dimension); and identification of guidelines for excellent practice (*pragmatic-strategic* dimension).

This project aims to enhance the practice of spiritual caregivers in the hospital and other settings as they encounter the growing plurality of faith traditions and expressions among care receivers and colleagues. The book is therefore intended for chaplains, pastors, Clinical Pastoral Education students and other caregivers, such as counselors and psychotherapists, both in training and already in practice.

Content of the book

The first part of the present volume stems from an unprecedented year-long seminar sponsored by the Lutheran Hospital of Indiana-Pastoral Care Division and Associated Mennonite Biblical Seminary-Pastoral Care and Counseling Program. Our collaboration provided a unique opportunity to reflect systematically on pastoral care in interfaith situations in the hospital setting.[8]

Chapters 1 and 2 under "Identity and vocation of the spiritual caregiver" present first-person accounts and reflective observations of the dynamics of interfaith communication in spiritual caregiving. They address questions regarding what actually goes on in interfaith care, and what the key issues are that we can identify in a given interfaith encounter, especially focusing on the caregiver as a ministering person. They also include interpretive analysis and the overall orientation of interfaith care.

Chapters 3 and 4 under "Bases for a theological framework for interfaith spiritual care" deal with biblical and theological norms. This focus on the normative dimension and task of our practical theological strat-

---

[7] The source for the reference to the structure and overall approach of practical theology as a discipline is Richard R. Osmer and Friedrich L. Schwitzer, eds., *Developing a Public Faith: New Directions in Practical Theology* (St. Louis: Chalice Press, 2003), 1–11.

[8] The original study, for which Lutheran Hospital of Indiana served as the main hosting clinical setting, took place from September 2006 to August 2007. Seminar-style meetings consisted primarily in the presentation and discussion of interfaith care situations. The records of our work together include a wealth of material, some of which was presented and discussed in several international conferences in 2005–2008: the Canadian Association for Pastoral Practice and Education (Winnipeg and Niagara Falls), the Society for Intercultural Pastoral Care and Counseling (Dusseldorf, Hamburg, and Bratislava), the International Academy of Practical Theology (Berlin), and the Latin American Association of Theological Schools (Buenos Aires).

egy illumines the key question of what criteria we identify for *excellence* and *faithfulness* in interfaith spiritual care from a Christian perspective. It further suggests that we should consider additional or alternative ethical and theological norms represented by other theological traditions.

Chapters 5 to 9 make up the section "Other windows to competent ministry practice" and illustrate the following issues: how spiritual caregivers can approach an interfaith situation and remain engaged as reflective practitioners; the benefits of consultation and group case discussion; and commonalities and differences in interfaith care provided in public and faith-based hospitals.

The second part of the book offers a partial view of the expanding field of interfaith spiritual care. The essays included reflect the commonalities and differences encountered in various culturally-specific settings in diverse countries.

Chapters 10 and 11 present two North American perspectives which complement the contributions found in part one of this volume. "Different lyrics but the same tune: Multifaith spiritual care in a Canadian context" makes the case that spiritual caregivers must have a truly multifaith orientation grounded in the common process of faith and orienting one's life around one's faith. "Competencies for pastoral care in multicultural and multifaith societies" offers abundant practical information and tools by focusing on the realities of the Hawaiian context.

Chapter 12, "Interfaith spiritual care: A view from Brazil," discusses the emerging challenge of interfaith care in a largely Catholic country, seen from a Protestant (Wesleyan-Methodist) perspective. The picture presented here partially resembles that of other Latin American countries with strong Christian majorities (primarily Catholic, with growing Evangelical and Pentecostal movements) and various indigenous regional expressions of religion and spirituality.

Chapter 13, "The sacralization of identity: An interfaith spiritual paradigm for chaplaincy in a multifaith context," demonstrates the relevance of Hans Mol's social scientific paradigm (a general theory of religious and spiritual beliefs) as applied to interfaith chaplaincy in Australia. It documents the results of research involving Christian chaplains caring for people of other faiths and draws implications for further study and for more effective education of spiritual caregivers.

Chapters 14 to 17 consider the heterogeneous reality of interfaith care in four European countries. The research reported in "How it is that you, a Jew, ask a drink of me ...? A study of interfaith care in a Norwegian context" explores the role of Lutheran pastors as spiritual caregivers with Muslims and conversation partners of their religious leaders. The increasing need for clinically competent and theologically informed interfaith care in the face of growing numbers of Muslim, Buddhist, atheist and other care seekers, is considered in "Interreligious and intercultural pastoral care and counseling: Notes from a German perspective;" the essay includes verbatim material and analysis. The chapter, "Individualization-Migration-Globalization: A Protestant perspective on interfaith spiritual care in the hospitals of Switzerland" demonstrates the value of intercontinental dialogue (the Swiss spiritual care situation and the Stanford-USA model) for changing the paradigm and improving the practice of interfaith care; special attention is given to social context and theological integrity. Finally, a three-part contribution, "The junction of the seas: Interfaith spiritual care in the Netherlands," introduces an inclusive model of spiritual care grounded in values such as professionalization and intentional interculturalization; this chapter also presents a gender specific approach from a Muslim perspective, and an educational model aimed at fostering community in a multifaith society.

The epilogue represents a call to spiritual caregivers to keep growing in three-dimensional *wisdom*—knowing, being, and doing—as we face the challenges and possibilities of interfaith care in the years ahead.

Readers will discover that the collection of essays is heterogeneous in both content and form. We deliberately tried to preserve the "voice" and the communication style of each of the contributors to this book because such diversity in fact resembles the plurality of experiences and perspectives that define intercultural and interfaith encounters. We regret, however, that for this project it was not possible to include contributions from colleagues representing a variety of religious and nonreligious (e.g. humanist) traditions and other geographical areas. It is our desire and our plan to engage in a more inclusive, properly *multicultural* and *multifaith*, conversation and collaboration in the near future.

Finally, this book furthers the collaborative pastoral theological reflection presented in our previous work, *Spiritual Caregiving in the Hospital: Windows to Chaplaincy Ministry.* [9] It is fitting, then, to paraphrase the very last words in that book, which may serve as a twofold guiding principle for understanding and practicing interfaith spiritual care: on the one hand we affirm the essential place of clinical and professional competence; on the other hand, given our theological convictions, we claim that, ultimately, the source of all healing and life-giving transformation is not the excellence of our ministry but the Spirit of grace and wisdom

---

[9] See Leah Dawn Bueckert and Daniel S. Schipani, eds. *Spiritual Caregiving in the Hospital: Windows to Chaplaincy Ministry* (Kitchener: Pandora Press, 2006), pp. 245–263.

with whom we are partners.[10]

Gratitudes

We are grateful for the many ways in which Associated Mennonite Biblical Seminary (AMBS) and the Pastoral Care Division of Lutheran Hospital of Indiana (LHI) supported the research and writing project documented in the first part of this book. Special thanks go to two wonderful partners at LHI whose collaborative spirit and competence as pastoral caregivers, supervisors, and pastoral theologians contributed to make the project a successful and enjoyable endeavor: John D. Peterson, Pastoral Care Division Director, and Joseph F. Viti, Program Manager of Clinical Pastoral Education. We also wish to acknowledge the contribution of a number of CPE students who, together with chaplains Roseann Bloomfield and Victor F. Kolch (Pastoral Services Manager), participated in the year-long seminar on interfaith spiritual care held at LHI.[11] Carol Demland, Pastoral Care Division's administrative assistant, graciously provided valuable logistic support during that time.

We are also grateful to many colleagues and friends who joined us in the conversation on interfaith care and, especially, to those who contributed essays for the present volume. Many thanks go to the Society for Intercultural Pastoral Care and Counseling (SIPCC)[12] whose members encouraged and supported our research endeavors and gave an unqualified endorsement to the publication project. We wish to recognize particularly the founder and president of the SIPCC, Rev. Helmut Weiss, to whom the book is dedicated.[13]

Several people helped us during the final phases of the writing and publication process: Joanne Gallardo, Cara Lynn Pfeiffer, Carrie Martens, and Rosalie Grove provided secretarial and copy-editing assistance; Mary Epp Klassen designed the cover and the book and prepared it for

[10] Ibid., 263.

[11] Participants during different stages of the year-long seminar included resident chaplains Lindsay Beeson, Russell Dewell, David Griebel and Sr. Sharlene Kakkattil; and CPE students Steve Evans, Brad Foster, Sheryl Nicholson, Paul Spira, and James Walker.

[12] The Society for Intercultural Pastoral Care and Counseling was formed in 1995 and its central office is located in Dusseldorf, Germany. Currently the SIPCC members represent over thirty countries around the world. The purpose of the Society is to encourage and support international collaboration and mutual learnings in the fields of pastoral care and counseling, with special focus on the dynamics of interculturality. Visit www.sipcc.org.

[13] An ordained minister of the Lutheran Church in Germany, Helmut Weiss has been involved in the education of pastors and other church workers for over thirty-five years. He has organized numerous international seminars and conferences and has taught courses on intercultural pastoral care and counseling in several countries in Europe and Asia.

publication; Christian Snyder of Pandora Press literally made the book a reality. Last but not least, we wish to acknowledge the financial support given for AMBS's interfaith care research by individual donors that ensured timely publication.

The editors

Part 1

Pastoral and practical theology of interfaith spiritual care

An unprecedented collaborative study involving a theological school and a regional hospital

A journey of soul companioning
Personal, vocational, and ministry reflections

Joseph F. Viti

Christian caregivers in a hospital setting soon discover that there is a growing need to minister to others regardless of their religious affiliation, lack of religious affiliation, the nature of their faith, and their type of spirituality. Interfaith ministry is at the forefront of the practice of pastoral care. In this essay I document the value of integrating soul companioning as a key component of interfaith ministry. I have come to understand the effectiveness of soul companioning from my own personal, vocational, and ministerial journey. Personal, vocational, ministerial, and soul companioning are the main headings of this chapter. I begin by sharing about the roots of my personal interfaith journey which I trace back to my childhood experiences when I was exposed to a diversity of culture and faith. These experiences were foundational. During my theological formation at the Catholic Theological Union my approach to theological truth became ecumenical. As I responded to my calling as a chaplain, I initially understood the value of forming a pastoral relationship as the basis for an inclusive ministry to a diversity of faiths. But it is precisely the faith beliefs of the chaplain rooted in theological conviction that set the tension off in ways that hinder ministry as illustrated by the verbatim I present between a Christian chaplain and a Jewish patient. The tension evolves from differences between religious beliefs and relationships into the tension of ministering to a stranger. The ensuing dynamic becomes less theologically focused and more relationally centered. Biblical references such as Genesis 18:1–15, Luke 24:13–35, and Matthew 35:31–46 underline the value of hospitality as a way to relate to strangers by understanding their spiritual needs and po-

Joseph F. Viti, M.Div., is a supervisor and Program Manager of Clinical Pastoral Education, Pastoral Care Division, at Lutheran Hospital of Indiana, Fort Wayne, Indiana.

tential. The focus of hospitality is coming to know the stranger as a person with spiritual needs as well as resources. The person, not doctrine or dogma, becomes the focal point of attention. Finally, this leads to the pastoral relationship of soul companioning. As a soul companion the chaplain encourages patients to take responsibility for their beliefs by giving them the freedom to get in touch with the spiritual needs of their soul.

Personal journey

I was raised in a small town in eastern Pennsylvania called Nazareth. It was in this town that I learned to appreciate diversity from a social and religious point of view. I have memories of a peaceful, clean, charming town of friendly people. I was born in 1945, so I am referring to the decades of the fifties and sixties. Comparatively speaking, it was a more simple lifestyle back in those days. The environment was very safe. Sometimes homeowners forgot to lock their doors at night, and felt perfectly safe. The impact of the immigrants from Europe was still experienced by the way the economy of Nazareth was carved up. Most of the bars and barber-shops in town were owned and operated by the Italians, most of the retail was in the hands of the Jewish people, and the surrounding farms in the outlying districts were owned by the famous Pennsylvania Dutch. My dad was a barber, and I can still remember some of his Pennsylvania Dutch customers trying to teach me a few words in Dutch when I would hang around my dad's barber-shop as a boy. They succeeded in teaching me how to say dog, cat, and potato in Pennsylvania Dutch (hund, katz, and grumberr). My folks, who originated from Italy, really got a "kick" out of that. There was a rich diversity among the entrepreneurs of Nazareth. Nazareth was surrounded by many limestone-rich quarries from which the cement industry thrived. The Nazareth Cement Company employed thousands of workers. The cement industry had an impact on the trade of the store owners. The store owners had to deal with the ups and downs of the cement industry as well as the income of the farmers. So the store owners had a lot to talk about among themselves because they were bonded together by the economy of a small town. Their conversation produced a thriving relationship. When my dad, mother, brother, and I returned home from our three-week vacation in Italy during the summer of 1965, all of the store owners gathered in my dad's barber-shop on the Monday morning he reopened his shop. They all welcomed him back, and they wanted to hear all about his experience revisiting the land of his boyhood. That gathering in my dad's barber-shop symbolized a caring social community. They felt a sense of bonding.

What comes to mind about the former shop owners of Nazareth is the common ground they discovered in their struggles as entrepreneurs. Despite their cultural and religious differences they discovered a common language that fostered values of respect and mutuality. When they spoke to one another they listened with sensitivity, understanding, and validated experiences. The inherent differences did not prevent them from affirming one another's humanity and supporting each other in the struggles they faced as entrepreneurs.

We lived around the corner from the Moravian church. The Moravians, a Protestant group, founded the town back in 1740. They predated the Revolutionary War. One Sunday morning I innocently walked into the Moravian church before their worship service. The janitor recognized me. He walked over to where I was sitting, took me by the hand, and walked me down the stairs to the Sunday school. The janitor and the Sunday school teachers all knew who I was. They were aware that I was the barber's son whose family was Italian and Roman Catholic. They saw no harm in letting me stay and participate with the other children in their weekly Sunday school. I had a wonderful time and took a great interest in Sunday school. I returned several times on my own. When my parents found out about what I was up to on Sunday mornings, they were shocked beyond words. When I expressed my great delight with Sunday school, my sister, Nancy, and brother, Victor, begged our parents to accompany me the next Sunday. My parents consented, which was a surprise. Eventually the Moravian pastor, who was one of my dad's customers, invited the entire family to join the Moravian church. Our family quickly became the subject of a lot of talk around town. "Can you imagine this Italian Roman Catholic family considering joining the Moravian church?" When the Roman Catholic priest heard about what was going on, he approached my dad for a stern conversation. He said you need to make a decision. You are either Roman Catholic or Moravian, not both. He forced us to make a definitive decision. I have a vague memory of my family sitting around the kitchen table talking about what we were going to do. My dad wanted to join the Moravian church because he anticipated lots of new customers to his barber shop. My sister, brother, and I wanted to join the Moravian church. We liked Sunday school. My mother is the one who made the decision. She said, "I was born a Catholic, and I will die a Catholic." And that was it! The decision was made.

As I look back on my experience with the Moravian church, I had many pleasant memories of learning about God in ways that were fun and educational. One of the first seeds of faith was planted in me by a

Protestant church. It was, for me, a rich, lively, exciting experience. I was not aware of it at the time, but it was a soulful experience. God became present to me in a way that was relevant and diverse even though I innocently crossed over some boundaries. I was also fortunate I had parents who were willing to go with the spirit and not the rules. Their openness put our family in a position to consider options about where we were going to worship and how we were going to express our faith. I learned that there is more than one way to practice one's faith without impunity and judgment. At a very early age it was clear to me that there is not one way to God but several!

All of this freedom I was experiencing as a young boy came to a crashing head when I entered Catholic school at the fourth grade level. From kindergarten through third grade I attended public school. When I was about ten years old the Catholic church in Nazareth, Holy Family Church, completed construction on a brand new school, grades one to eight. My mother and dad decided to transfer us children from public school to Holy Family Parochial School. My Roman Catholic education began with the fourth grade. At some point during religion class I recall being taught that the church of Jesus Christ subsists in the Catholic church, because the Roman Catholic church had the unbroken line of apostolic succession and the fullness of the Eucharist. During the days prior to The Second Vatican Council, we were taught that there was no salvation outside the Catholic church. I understood that as much as any child could, but I really had trouble with that when the religious sisters who taught us counseled us not to play with Protestant children. The religious sisters were aware that most of the children at Holy Family School lived in neighborhoods populated by families who belonged to the Catholic church. They may have overlooked students like my brother, sister, and I who lived in a primarily Protestant neighborhood. I recall that when my sister, Nancy, and my brother, Victor, attended public school, a Jewish girl who lived down the street from us would, now and then, stop by our house on the way to school, and we would all walk to school together. Looking back on that experience, I am certain that the religious sisters had our best interests at heart. It does, however, bring up an interesting issue. I wonder how people of other Christian faiths felt when they heard that the Catholic church taught no salvation outside the Catholic church. Some felt indifferent. Some felt challenged. Others may have felt hurt and offended. There are times when churches adhere to a particular doctrine that brings up relational issues. The doctrine of no salvation outside the Church caused conflict between me and my playmates in our neighborhood. I wonder what they would have thought if I had told them about no salvation outside the Catholic church. How would that have influenced our relationship as playmates? Doctrine was potentially cancelling out relational values I had developed, and the relational values were threatening to the doctrine. There was a tension between the doctrine I learned at the Catholic school and the relationships I had spontaneously developed as a child. My brother, sister, and I quietly ignored what the religious sisters said and continued to enjoy our Protestant/Jewish playmates. I felt encouraged when the Vatican II document, "Dogmatic Constitution on the Church (Lumen Gentium)," emphatically stated that there is salvation outside the Roman Catholic church.[1]

My childhood experience sharply focuses the pastoral care dilemma. Pastoral care is relationally driven. There are times when the pastoral relationship is threatened because of doctrinal differences not only within Christian churches, but even more so in non-Christian churches such as Jewish, Islamic, Buddhist, and Hindu. I certainly accept the teachings of the Roman Catholic church and want to be faithful to its magisterium. In this country people live in a diverse society including different cultures and different belief systems. With the influx of Hispanics, Asians, Hindus, Buddhists, and Muslims we continue to be a "melting pot" after a fashion. Proclaiming that there is only one way to God tends to create too many distinctions between right and wrong, inclusive and exclusive, the saved verses the damned. There are many expressions of Christianity and, perhaps, the multiplicity is pointing to the many faith needs that are met in different ways. If we listened to one another with sensitivity and openness we could deepen the truth about what we believe. Division does not create an understanding. Reaching out to one another does.

While studying for my M.Div. degree at the Catholic Theological Union in Chicago, Illinois, I had a discussion with a religious woman about ecumenism. During our discussion she said that no one Christian church had the fullness of the truth about who God is, what we are to believe about God, and how we are to go about our eternal salvation. She compared the Christian church to a diamond. Not any one church has the fullness of the truth, but each church is like a facet of the diamond. If you turn the diamond in a particular direction to let the light shine through the diamond, you may get the Lutheran expression. If you turn the diamond another way, you may get the Methodist expression. If

---

[1] Walter M. Abbot and Joseph Gallagher, *The Documents of Vatican II* (New York: Guild Press, 1966), 33–35.

you turn the diamond again, you may get the Roman Catholic expression, and so on. Together, as one diamond, we all have the truth. That made sense to me. It was then that I realized that the truth was found not by reinforcement of the doctrine/dogma of any one religious denomination, but by studying the differences and/or gaps between them.

Vocational journey

As a student of Clinical Pastoral Education (CPE) at Allentown State Hospital, a state-run institution for the mentally ill, I soon realized that mental illness does not discriminate among Protestants, Catholics, Jews, or Muslims. I was dealing with our weak human nature. Many of the patients I ministered to reached out to God, at times, in delusional ways; and at other times, in ways that were sane. My ministry did not consist in trying to figure out who believed what, but the key to my ministry was to establish a rapport of trust. There was a strong relational component driving my ministry. I believed God worked through my ministry in an incarnational way. God became present through the confusion and delusion of the person of the patient and through me. Looking to the patient to establish the agenda was a way to relate to the spiritual needs of the patient that did not necessarily involve doctrine and/or differing beliefs. A ministry of healing driven by relationship was the priority.

However, I have discovered as a supervisor for the Association of Clinical Pastoral Education (ACPE) that there are times when the relational quality of pastoral care relationships is not sufficient to bridge the gap. Below is a verbatim that illustrates the problem. This verbatim was presented in a scheduled case study conference by a CPE student during a unit of CPE. Feedback was given to him by me and the peer group.

The patient is an 87-year-old woman known as Mrs. Wheatley. At the time the verbatim was written she was a resident of a nursing home recovering from a broken ankle. She is Jewish. The chaplain, a Christian, is making a random visit. This was the third time the chaplain visited Mrs. Wheatley. He describes her as a vibrant person of 87 who is now showing signs of depression because she is adjusting to many life changes. Her fractured ankle was caused by a spell of dizziness which led to a fall. The physical cause of the dizziness is not known at the time of the visit. After rehabilitation at the nursing home, the plans are that she will live with her son who has recently moved into a new home. The chaplain has discovered that Mrs. Wheatley recently lost her brother-in-law who died in Los Angeles, California. She grieved his death. She wanted to travel and attend the funeral, but could not due to the fractured ankle. The chaplain did not know about the death of her brother-in-law. He discovered it during the visit. The chaplain's goal was to comfort her with his presence. Mrs. Wheatley had been in this room for approximately two weeks, so she does not have many of her personal belongings in the room. As the chaplain entered the room, he could tell from the patient's appearance that she was grieving. She was well dressed, well groomed, and wearing some makeup.

Dialogue

P = Patient

C= Chaplain

C1: Good morning, Mrs. Wheatley. How are you?

P1: Not very well, my brother-in-law just died yesterday.

C2: I am sorry to hear that. Were you close?

P2: Yes, but he was in L.A. And now I won't be able to go to the funeral like I would have if I weren't here.

C3: Is your sister still living?

P3: Yes

C4: How is she doing?

P4: She'll get through it; she has to be strong. I was, when my husband passed away.

C5: When did he die?

P5: In 1989.

C6: Do you miss him?

P6: Oh my yes, but we had a good life.

C7: Does your brother-in-law's death conjure up memories and feelings from when your husband died?

P7: Some.

C8: What else are you feeling now?

P8: Bad because I can't be there for my sister.

C9: Is there a sense of guilt at not being able to be there?

P9: Yes.

C10: Does your sister know where you are, and what has happened to you?

P10: Yes.

C11: Do you think she is upset with you for not being able to come out?

P11: No, I do feel bad. I know that she isn't angry with me, but I was close to her husband and I feel bad about not being able to be there for the funeral to say good-by.

(At this point her roommate was brought back into the room with her two daughters. The conversation came to an end.)

C12: Can I stop back, and see how you are doing in a few days?

P12: I would like that, thank you.

Assessment of the pastoral visit

The chaplain was deeply motivated to help Mrs. Wheatley, but he experienced a theological distance because he is Christian and she is Jewish. The chaplain could have brought up that issue, but did not. It is ignoring the "elephant" in the room. This may explain why the visit is brief, and why he did not follow the patient's agenda. It also explains why the chaplain did not offer a prayer. The chaplain claims that despite the theological distance, he enjoyed visiting with Mrs. Wheatley. Generally the chaplain did not focus on the relationship between Mrs. Wheatley and her brother-in-law. Instead he inquires about grief over the loss of Mrs. Wheatley's husband who died in 1989. He also raises the issue of the relationship with her sister. This was a valid concern, but the chaplain's timing is bad, because he uses the relationship with her sister to distract from dealing with the funeral. Below is a detailed critique of the verbatim based on the feedback the chaplain received.

Because of what Mrs. Wheatley says in P2, the chaplain, in C3, had an opportunity to ask Mrs Wheatley what going to the funeral means to her. Instead, he changes the subject and focuses on Mrs. Wheatley's sister. Instead of asking, "Is your sister still living?" he could have asked a more timely question such as, "How would the funeral be a source of consolation to you?" It may have been helpful for her grief to draw that out. There may have been some specific parts of the funeral that she would have found meaningful. In C4, the chaplain continues to focus on Mrs. Wheatley's sister. In P4, the chaplain learns new information concerning the death of the patient's husband. In C7, the chaplain pursues the possibility that Mrs. Wheatley continues to have some feelings of grief over the death of her husband who died in 1989. In P7, Mrs Wheatley indicates that she continues to experience feelings of grief over her husband's death, but her feelings are not that intense that she wants to continue to reflect on them. At this point it is safe to say that the chaplain is not following the patient's agenda as he could, but is pursuing his own agenda. Finally in C8, the chaplain invites Mrs. Wheatley to focus on her feelings, "What else are you feeling now?" In P8, Mrs. Wheatley shares feelings about her sister, and this leads to feelings of guilt Mrs. Wheatley has about not being there for her sister. In P11, Mrs. Wheatley brings up the topic again, on her own initiative, about her sadness over not being there for the funeral. This is the second time Mrs. Wheatley has brought up this topic because this is a soul-felt desire. Her feelings of grief about her brother-in-law and how she relates them to her faith in Yahweh come together here. There is significant meaning for her here.

In her book, *Listening for the Soul*, Jean Stairs says it well: "The goal of soul companionship is to help people listen for the soul and for the presence of God in their daily work and lives."[2] The chaplain focused on his agenda because he felt threatened by religious differences. We see here the strength of Mrs. Wheatley's soul struggling for solace despite the chaplain's hesitation to honor her agenda. The chaplain missed an opportunity to become her soul companion. He could have responded to her without threat to his beliefs merely by being personally present to her. Soul companioning could have been significant here because the concern could have been placed on the spiritual needs of Mrs. Wheatley, not on doctrinal or dogmatic differences. He could have found common space and holy ground with her despite religious differences. I will discuss more on soul companioning later on in the article.

If Mrs. Wheatley cannot go to the funeral, then how will she say goodbye to her brother-in-law whom she is close to? The chaplain may have wanted to do this, but the visit was interrupted by the roommate coming back into the room. Because the chaplain perceives a *theological* distance, there is also a *relational* distance. During the critical evaluation among the CPE students, the chaplain, who made the visit, openly expressed feelings of conflict over ministering to Mrs. Wheatley. He wanted to reach out to her, but felt hindered by theological differences. It is interesting to note that he does not ask Mrs. Wheatley if she would like him to contact her rabbi. The chaplain does feel a sense of relating to Mrs. Wheatley's grief. He does not know how to go about bridging the gap, however.

By bringing up the theological differences, the chaplain could have shared his unfamiliarity with the Jewish funeral. This would have created an opportunity for Mrs. Wheatley to bridge the gap. It is not the obligation of patients to educate chaplains. We have a mandate to educate ourselves about religious differences. But by expressing theological

---

[2] Jean Stairs, *Listening for the Soul* (Minneapolis: Fortress Press, 2000), 142.

differences, the chaplain is bringing the limits of his ministry out in the open where something can be done to recognize and validate the difference as being OK. Because the chaplain does not verbalize the difference, it becomes a shadow of the ministerial event. Shadows have a way of blocking the light which can illuminate the limits of pastoral relationships as a spark of knowledge and information that can begin to take away those limits. It could place the chaplain in a position of openly claiming how he is prepared to minister, and how he is not prepared. This openness could be the foundation of bridging the chaplain-patient relationship. Sharing of limits would open up the dialogue for the benefit of the patient and the learning of the chaplain.

Prayer is one way the chaplain has of elevating the death of Mrs. Wheatley's brother-in-law to a higher power. It is one of the ways chaplains communicate that they represent the wisdom and authority of faith. The chaplain may not have prayed with Mrs. Wheatley because he felt he may have to compromise his faith in the Trinity, particularly Jesus Christ. This is one of the limits of interfaith ministry that many chaplains fear. The thinking goes something like this, "If I minister to a non-Christian, what beliefs am I going to have to give up? Will I discover myself ministering in a way that compromises my faith? What will I have to accept that I will regret?" In this particular ministerial event the chaplain could have read a psalm from the Hebrew Scriptures which are also part of the Christian Scriptures. He could have asked Mrs. Wheatley to offer a prayer. He could have asked Mrs. Wheatley if she would object to invoking the Universal God. Biblically, one could argue that Jesus Christ is Jewish. I do not believe that God is Roman Catholic or Lutheran or Methodist or Episcopalian or Muslim or Buddhist or Hindu. God is God. We will never truly understand who God is. God is beyond our understanding and our knowledge. When chaplains minister to patients, a window of opportunity opens up for God to "enter the room," so to speak. Whether or not God enters the room with divine presence, grace, or healing, is up to God. We have no control over God. We can invoke the Divine with prayer. The chaplain could have prayed to the God who is in the room, or the God who is present to the ministerial event.

Ministry journey

I believe that God is present to ministers of pastoral care through their calling. In his article, "Spiritual Windsurfing," John Janka says that the call of ministry "is to believe in the revealed truth so deeply that we are fundamentally changed by it and compelled to invite others to live as though this truth is the only reality of consequence in their lives."[3] This understanding of call takes into account that ministers not only believe in their call, but are also willing to commit their life to it. The commitment implies that the meaning of their life revolves around this call. It is what puts "wind" in their vocational sails. It is a reason to get up in the morning, and a prayer of hope that is said before sleep. It can become a passion for life that one struggles with, fails at, succeeds at, and that even makes our souls bleed. We feel so strongly and deeply about our calling that we want to invite others to become impacted by it, and take up that same divine "spark" for their lives. We hope others will be as moved by it as we are so that it impacts the way they live their lives. We hope they develop values and priorities that influence their lifestyle. Ultimately we hope our ministry leads the people we serve to have a deeper relationship with God, and helps them on their spiritual journey.

Sometimes, it is this very deep commitment that can become an obstruction to interfaith ministry. The chaplain who ministered to Mrs. Wheatley felt that he was a stranger to her Jewish faith and was faced with compromising his commitment. When chaplains tend to back away from interfaith ministry, they see that as self-care, that is caring for their faith and giving testimony to their integrity and authenticity. Care for one's faith and pastoral care begin to compete. There is a tension that develops. Ministering to a person of a different faith for the first time, can be a threatening experience for some chaplains. I recall when I took my first unit of CPE at Virginia Baptist Hospital in Lynchburg, Virginia, I experienced a threat to my Roman Catholic morality when I made a pre-surgery visit one particular evening. I knocked on the door of a private room. The door was ajar. I was invited to enter by a couple who was in the room. The woman was sitting in bed sipping a glass of champagne, and her husband was sitting in a chair next to the bed also enjoying a glass of champaign. I was delightfully surprised, and asked them what was going on. They explained to me that the wife was having her fallopian tubes tied the next day. They were no longer going to have children. As a married couple, they were celebrating the end of one era in their lives, and now they were moving on to the next phase of their marriage and family life. They wanted to honor and celebrate the event with a glass of champaign. As a Roman Catholic, I strongly disagreed with that form of birth control; and so I said some words of congratulations, and removed myself from the room as quicky and graciously as I

[3] John Janka, "Spiritual Windsurfing: Exploring the Context for Evaluation" in *Congregational Resources* (Bethesda, MD: Alban Institute, 2004), 2.

could. I did not even offer to say a prayer for the wife that the surgery would go well. My quick departure was an indication that in my own mind I judged the surgery to be wrong. As I look back on that ministerial event, I shudder at my lack of sensitivity and regard for the couple. If I would do anything differently, I would tell them that I am Roman Catholic, and although I cannot celebrate with them in fact, I want to celebrate with them in spirit. In certain instances of morality the lines of difference are not always black and white. There are gray areas. This instance was one of them. Just because someone else disagrees with me, how is that a threat to my morality? There is a value to being a non-anxious presence at those times to honor and respect others, to honor and respect each other in our differences. In a parallel way, when I minister to someone who is not Christian, it is a matter of being sensitive to differences and caring for differences. That approach is more pastoral than being judgmental, aloof, distant, and feeling threatened. People who believe differently than we do are considered strange to us because we are not familiar with what they believe. We do not feel we are on common ground with them, and that makes us feel uncomfortable. We become hesitant to relate to them. As ministers of pastoral care we need to develop a ministry to the stranger.

Ministering to the stranger

Whenever I minister to a person who is not Christian, who is Jewish, Muslim, Buddhist, or Hindu, I am ministering to a stranger from a pastoral point of view. The stranger symbolizes faith. As Parker Palmer says, "Faith is a venture into the unknown, into the realms of mystery, away from the safe and comfortable and secure."[4] Faith is stepping into mystery. Mystery is who God is. Becoming acquainted with God is departing from those areas of our lives that are comfortable and secure. Relating to God is a "stretch." Sometimes, when we believe in God, we make ourselves vulnerable to the challenges God has for us. When chaplains step into a hospital room to visit a patient, they are entering the realm of Mystery. Patients in a hospital are often in physical, emotional, and spiritual crisis. They look to the chaplain to guide them through confusing feelings they may have about their relationship to God. Chaplains can do little to prepare for the visit. They need to become spontaneous and go with the "flow" of what the patient wants to deal with. The authority in the room becomes the patient and his or her spiritual agenda. As we

---

[4] Parker J. Palmer, *The Company of Strangers* (New York: The Crossroad Publishing Co., 1997), 56.

read in the book of Hebrews, "Keep on loving one another as Christian brothers and sisters. Remember to welcome strangers in your homes. There were some who did that and welcomed angels without knowing it." Hebrews 13:1–2. The stranger is a key figure in certain biblical stories of faith: Genesis 18:1–15, Luke 24:13–35, Matthew 25:31–46.

In Genesis 18:1–15, strangers appear to Sarah and Abraham to announce that Sarah, who is beyond the childbearing years, will give birth to Isaac, the second patriarch of the Jewish people. As the story unfolds, it becomes evident that the strangers are angels who have come to announce God's promise to Abraham and Sarah. They struggle with the message the strangers deliver. The only way they can validate their message is with their faith. But Abraham did welcome the strangers by showing hospitality. When he saw the three strangers, he ran to meet them, bowing down to them until his face touched the ground (verse 2). In verse 3, he invites them into his home to serve them. He brings them water so they can wash their feet, and invites them to rest under the shade of the sacred trees at Mamre (verse 4). He tells them that they have honored him by coming to his home, and asks Sarah to bake bread for them. He then picks out a tender, fattened calf from the herd, and asks a servant to prepare it for the strangers. He serves this food to the strangers with milk and cream (verses 5–8). By being attentive to the needs of strangers they become less strange and more familiar. Hospitality recognizes that the stranger has needs. Knowing the needs of another is the beginning of knowledge that makes the stranger less of an unknown person and more of a known person whom we can help. Creating an atmosphere of comfort gives strangers the message that they are welcomed. Despite the fact that I do not know you; I want to treat you with honor and respect. I want to be concerned for your well-being. I want to put you at ease. This hospitality creates the atmosphere for dialogue and establishes the possibility of the non-judgmental listening Carl Rogers speaks about for arriving at understanding.[5] After the strangers ate, they asked Abraham where Sarah was. Abraham replied that she was in the tent. One of the strangers then announced to the couple that nine months from now Sarah will have a child. After Abraham offered hospitality, the strangers communicated their message. If Abraham and Sarah had not offered hospitality to strangers, they could have missed the message of fulfillment.

When chaplains minister to patients of a different faith, they are strangers to one another. A learning curve for chaplains is how to effec-

---

[5] Carl R. Rogers, *Client Centered Therapy* (Boston: Houghton Mifflin Company, 1965), 45.

tively participate in the ministry of strangers. As Henri Nouwen points out in his book *Reaching Out*, we need to take the initiative to establish hospitality. If we do not, the potential remains there for the chaplain to become infected with fear and hostility, threatening the chaplain's faith and blocking dialogue and understanding.[6] It does not mean that we become so attentive to their needs that strangers become "putty" in our hands. It means that we allow them free space where strangers can be themselves without having to change.[7] From a pastoral point of view, Christian chaplains offer strangers—Jews, Muslims, Hindus, Buddhists, and others—hospitality which does not charm them into accepting our God, but opens up an opportunity that gives them the freedom to accept and find their God in a deeper way and discover a new message that addresses their spiritual needs.

In Luke 24:13–35, the risen Jesus and the two disciples on the road to Emmaus discover themselves as strangers. Not only do they not recognize one another, but the two disciples are deeply distressed about the outcome of the life of Jesus. In verse 21 they express their distress by saying, "And we had hoped that he would be the one who was going to set Israel free!" After the two disciples continue to express their regret, sorrow, disillusionment, and confusion, Jesus explains the scriptures to them, beginning with the books of Moses and the writings of all the prophets (verse 27). As they came near the village, Jesus acted as if he were going to travel on, but the two disciples asked Jesus to stay with them. They recognized Jesus in the breaking of the bread. Jesus disappeared from their sight. "Wasn't it like a fire burning in us when he talked to us on the road and explained the Scriptures to us?" (verse 32). Their regret, sorrow, disillusionment, and confusion turned to enlightenment and enthusiasm as they ran all the way back to Jerusalem to tell the eleven apostles that they recognized Jesus in the breaking of the bread (verse 35). The two disciples, perhaps out of their desperation, offered hospitality to someone who looked like a stranger. They invited him into their home and sat down to eat with Jesus. It is in the breaking of the bread that they recognized Jesus as the risen Lord. Jesus offered hospitality to the two disciples by being attentive to their feelings of regret, sorrow, disillusionment, and confusion. He took the time and patience to explain the Scriptures to them. In a sense he informed their faith and invited them to believe from a different point of view. The two disciples freely affirmed their new-found faith in the breaking of the bread.

---

[6] Henri J. Nouwen, *Reaching Out* (New York: Image Book Doubleday, 1986), 69.

[7] Ibid., 71.

The hospitality became mutual and the two disciples arrived at a new experience of recognizing who Jesus really is. The stranger of Jesus brought the two disciples beyond their limits to a new faith and a new vision. The vision inspired them and reignited their faith, motivating them to tell others. Strangers may look like shadows, but they have the potential to enlighten truth, reignite passion, and deliver a vision for life. Jesus touched the souls of the two disciples as he taught them, "Wasn't it like a fire burning in us when he talked to us on the road and explained the Scriptures to us?" (verse 32). Jesus was a soul companion for them.

In Matthew 25:31–46, Jesus emphasizes the value of "welcoming the stranger" (verse 38). In this passage the stranger is used to represent all those who suffer and are considered among the lowliest.[8] It is their strangeness which makes us hesitant to minister to them. We feel anxious and threatened by them. What is significant here is that Jesus identifies with the stranger. "I tell you, whenever you refused to help one of these least important ones, you refused to help me" (verse 40). As spiritual caregivers we need to take our soul companioning very seriously.

Soul companioning

Jean Stairs defines soul as "the spiritual essence of one's existence expressed through body, mind, or any other facet of our being."[9] In Genesis 2:7, soul could be understood as the breath of life God gave to Adam. Soul, in the Hebrew language means, "neck."[10] The neck contains the jugular vein, nerves that are connected to the brain and spine that connects the rest of the body to the head. Soul then gives us a vital connection to God as the life force, a sense of wholeness, but also a sense of interior presence about ourselves. When someone touches our soul, they reach the center of who we are. In John 4:1–42, we have the story from the Christian Scriptures about Jesus touching the soul of a Samaritan woman, one who, according to the custom at that time, was not permitted to speak with Jesus, a man and a Jew. When Jesus asks the woman for a drink of water she replies, "You are a Jew and I am a Samaritan, so how can you ask me for a drink?" (verse 9). This limited them in their conversation with each other. The Samaritan woman was also limited by her lifestyle of broken relationships which may have caused her to be

---

[8] Palmer, *The Company of Strangers*, 64.

[9] Stairs, *Listening for the Soul*, 10.

[10] For a reference to the Hebrew meaning of "soul," see Eugene H. Peterson, *Christ Plays In Ten Thousand Places* (Grand Rapids, MI. Eerdmans, 2005), 36.

defensive due to her self-esteem issue.[11] So the relationship between Jesus and the woman does not get off to a good start. Jesus listens to her objections, such as, "I am a Samaritan, so how can you ask me for a drink?" (verse 9). "You don't have a bucket, and the well is deep. Where would you get that life-giving water? It was our ancestor Jacob who gave us this well; he and his sons and his flocks all drank from it. You don't claim to be better than Jacob, do you?" (verses 11–12). Despite all of her objections, Jesus holds her attention with his promise of living water. In verse 14, Jesus promises to give the Samaritan water that is life-giving and will have eternal life. In verse 15, the woman expresses a great desire for this living water. She says, "Then I will never be thirsty again, nor will I have to come here to draw water" (verse 15). Up until this point in their conversation, Jesus is emphasizing the spiritual, and the Samaritan woman is more concerned with the practical and mundane. Jesus then asks her to call her husband in verse 16. Jesus helps her to understand her need for the spiritual freedom he is giving witness to. Jesus heard the nonverbal misery and unhappiness in her objections. Jesus reflects to her what he has heard from the conversation. He pinpoints that relational area in her life that is causing her emotional pain. He surprises her with his knowledge of her sexual life which is personal, private, and potentially shameful.[12] Jesus implies that he has a sense about her false patterns of connectedness.[13] He does not relate to her in an accusatory way of blaming, punishing or judging, but relates to her in a way that gives her the opportunity to know herself from a new perspective. She becomes free to fully know herself, see herself, and be herself.[14] With this new self-knowledge she, without shame, goes to her neighbors to say, "Come and see the man who told me everything I have ever done" (verse 30). Through the conversation Jesus helps the woman come to know herself more deeply and get in touch with her longing for relationships that are freeing, not binding. In a sense Jesus hears her into speech, "Come and see the man …" Her proclamation reflects her new-found freedom from shame. Jesus addresses the personal areas of her life that hinder her from spiritual freedom.

Soul companioning is significant for chaplains ministering to people

---

[11] See the reference to the Samaritan woman at the well in Jeanne Stevenson-Moessner, *Through the Eyes of Women* (Minneapolis: Fortress Press, 1996), 329.

[12] For a reference to how Jesus helps the Samaritan woman to see herself, see Margaret Guenther, *Holy Listening* (Boston: Cowley Publications, 1992), 50.

[13] Stevenson-Moessner, *Through the Eyes of Women*, 28.

[14] Margaret Guenther, *Holy Listening* (Boston: Cowley Publications, 1992), 50.

of different faiths because the concern is placed on the spiritual needs of the person rather than on the religious differences. Soul companioning helps chaplains listen for the spiritual misery patients may be experiencing, and how they can help without changing or compromising their own faith convictions. Just as Jesus heard the Samaritan woman into speech, chaplains do the same with people of other faiths (Isaiah 50:4). Chaplains listen carefully to the person they are ministering to, but are also open to the promptings of the Spirit. This requires chaplains to educate themselves about the various beliefs and religious practices of Jews, Muslims, Buddhists, Hindus, and other people. It also requires chaplains to have a non-anxious presence. On the one hand if I anticipate that my belief is going to be threatened, I may become anxious. On the other hand why should what another believes cause me to become afraid? I do not want to have a weak and dependent faith. I need an autonomous faith that can stand on its own. Chaplains who minister to others of different faiths need a conversant faith. A conversant faith is one that can dialogue and sort out differences that can enhance our beliefs and values, and differences that are irreconcilable.

In conclusion, I wish to restate some guidelines for soul companioning inspired by Jean Stairs's contribution. First of all, the goal of a soul companion is to listen for the soul and the presence of God who is active in their lives.[15] Chaplains need to establish a rapport with the patient, listen for feelings, reflect feelings, express empathy, and identify spiritual issues that the care-receiver is concerned about. Chaplains do not need to take responsibility for the patient's religious (or non-religious) faith as such. They need to be attentive to how God is active in the patient's soul. Patients can take responsibility for their own beliefs. For example, in the verbatim presented above, Mrs. Wheatley was really concerned about missing the funeral. This was the cry of her grief touching her soul. She wanted to attend the funeral but could not be there due to her fractured ankle. The chaplain could have explored other ways in which she could bring closure and comfort to her brother-in-law's death that would be in keeping with her Jewish faith. The Jewish beliefs that are related to her grief are her responsibility, not the chaplain's. The chaplain is personally present to invite Mrs. Wheatley to reflect on her grief. The chaplain's responsibility is pastoral presence, understanding, and unconditional caring.

Secondly, Stairs reminds us that soul companioning affirms the com-

---

[15] Stairs, *Listening For The Soul*, 142.

monality of our human experience.[16] Soul companioning can provide a way of coming together that rises above differences. In the verbatim above, both the chaplain and Mrs. Wheatley share the common human experience of grieving. We as a society are divided by social status, ethnic backgrounds, what neighborhoods we live in, financial incomes, and so on. There is enough that divides us, compartmentalizes us, isolates us. Grief becomes the common ground both the chaplain and Mrs. Wheatley can stand on with some comfort. In spiritual matters we can be present to one another in ways that bring clarity of meaning and new understanding that comes out of empathy. Soul companioning opens up the opportunity to make meaning out of one's spiritual crisis in a way that can be recognized, validated, and affirmed as a human experience elevated to a level of faith. If the patient is comfortable with his/her faith, he/she can validate the new spiritual meaning that develops out of the chaplain-patient relationship. It was unfortunate that the chaplain did not offer to include prayer in his ministry to Mrs. Wheatley.

Thirdly, Stairs states, "Soul companioning expands our spiritual vision and helps us cross boundaries."[17] "If someone says he loves God, but hates his brother, he is a liar. For he cannot love God, whom he has not seen, if he does not love his brother, whom he has seen" (1 John 4:20). Stairs points out that soul companioning challenges the chaplain to become more inclusive in a way that respects differences.[18] Chaplains are on a learning curve all the time. We are not experts, we are learners about how God interacts with us during crisis. Soul companioning provides an opportunity to learn truths beyond our awareness and to discover new meaning "outside of the box," if you will. It is a way to be aware of the truth that is beyond us, and that sometimes comes to us in a way we did not expect. The chaplain who ministered to Mrs. Wheatley might have discovered that by soul companioning Mrs. Wheatley in her grief, he would have learned more about how empowering the offer of hospitality can be. He would have learned something new in a way that is not threatening but truly revealing. When chaplains so respect the people they serve, they are likely to be more open to interfaith differences and, ultimately, more open to the very Spirit in whose name they serve.

---

[16] Ibid., 143.

[17] Ibid.

[18] Ibid.

Stepping into the borderlands
Prayer with people of different faiths

Leah Dawn Bueckert

When I was a child, our family owned a small, hardcover book entitled *Dolls from Many Lands.*[1] Each page of the book featured a drawing of a doll from a certain country along with a simple description of that culture. Pedro was from Mexico, Katrinka was from Holland, Vanya was from Russia, Luisa was from Argentina. According to my mother, by the time I was two or three years old I had memorized the names of each of the dolls and the countries they came from. My orientation to a positive view of diversity started young, in spite of the fact that I grew up in a predominantly Caucasian, middle class, Mennonite community. Since those early storybook days I have traveled overseas and have encountered people from a variety of cultures and faith traditions. My experiences in contexts where Caucasians were a *minority* have been relatively few and brief, but cultural diversity has been very much a part of my work, study, and friendship circles.

In this essay I offer a close look at three conversations I had as a resident chaplain with a Muslim man, two Hindu men, and a Jewish woman in the hospital. With these steps into the "borderlands" I hoped to play some part in the healing process. Somewhat awkward yet sincere, I initiated these encounters, guided by a conviction that I later found stated well by Peter Dula. In his essay, "A Theology of Interfaith Bridge Building," Dula emphasizes that borderlands can be places of growth and promise when we choose to *inhabit* them instead of fearing and avoiding

Leah Dawn Bueckert, M.Div., serves as Spiritual Care Coordinator with the North Eastman Health Association in Manitoba, Canada. She is based in the community of Beausejour, Manitoba.

[1] Written by Renee Bartkowkski, illustrated by Dorothy Grider (Chicago: Rand McNally & Co., 1975).

them.[2] He proceeds to reveal, through the lens of theologian Karl Barth, "that engaging persons of other faiths hospitably is an imperative for Christians."[3]

Sharing such hospitality may include praying with people of different faiths. Prayer is a common mode of expression for people from a variety of worldviews and traditions. Prayer is a way of articulating our deepest pain, deepest joy, greatest fears, greatest hopes, and our most closely held values. It is an acknowledgment of the limitations and deep longings of our human selves. Prayer is an act of faith in which the one praying decides to trust that care and healing are, or will be, somehow available.

Praying with people of different traditions is grounded in a Christian ethic of care. When their ministry is informed by an ethic of care,[4] chaplains serve patients and families as they would hope to be cared for themselves, while keeping in mind not to make assumptions based on their own preferences. They are attentive to the question: what does good news look like for this person? A Christian ethic of care is based on the biblical paradigm of shalom, namely, the integration of peace and justice that characterizes holistic well-being. In prayer we seek the realization of this well-being for individuals and for all of humanity. In the Judeo-Christian tradition, God understands the human plight as recounted during the Exodus journey of the Israelites and as seen in the life, death, and resurrection of Jesus. God promises to be a Companion in the midst of suffering, through the Holy Spirit. An ethic of care recognizes that human beings exist not in isolation but in relationships. We seek to support care receivers' experiences of right relationships. When a chaplain prays by drawing from the care receiver's own expressed needs and resources, evidence of a therapeutic relationship may well become a vehicle of grace and healing.

Extending welcome to care receivers of faiths different than ours may generate feelings of insecurity and anxiety. Questions about our own spiritual integrity may surface. We may feel uncomfortable if we are unfamiliar with certain cultural and religious traditions. While it is helpful and important to become more familiar with the customs and beliefs of di-

---

[2] Peter Dula, "A Theology of Interfaith Bridge Building," in *Borders & Bridges: Mennonite Witness in a Religiously Diverse World*, edited by Peter Dula and Alain Epp Weaver (Telford: Cascadia Publishing House with Herald Press, 2007), 160–70.

[3] Ibid., 161.

[4] For a discussion of the "ethic of care" and its significance for a Christian understanding and practice of life and ministry see Leah Dawn Bueckert and Daniel S. Schipani, "The ethic of care in spiritual caregiving," in *Spiritual Caregiving in the Hospital: Windows to Chaplaincy Ministry* (Kitchener: Pandora Press, 2006), 233–44.

verse traditions, we must remember that people of any heritage—ourselves included—will have their own particular ways of interpreting and living the tradition. Our task is to learn how we might partner with them in drawing upon their values and beliefs in meaningful ways, whether they are religious or nonreligious. This may be easier said than done at times.

Often we can become perplexed even by people we know quite intimately. On the one hand, we may be able to guess how our spouse, friend or family member will respond to the events of life. On the other hand, we can still be surprised. Do we really know what goes on in their "heart of hearts"? Do they know what goes on in ours? How easy is it to fully express our sense of being loved or our experience of significant loss? These questions speak to a tension that is part of being human: the tension between familiarity and mystery. It is captured well by the following quote regarding the possibility of sharing religious experiences:

> We know from both hermeneutics as well as on the basis of our own personal experience that we cannot completely understand another person with regard to the most profound things.... Understanding what is going on in another person is not a question of 'all or nothing,' however.[5]

Meaningful encounters with people of other faiths require that we avoid the dichotomy demonstrated by the liberals' tendency towards superficial tolerance and the conservatives' tendency towards unreflective certitude—both at the expense of sincere engagement.[6] We aim beyond tolerance towards engagement and care, and beyond certitude towards admiration. By being candid about who we are as spiritual caregivers, and by being receptive to patients and families as they reveal who they are, we help build the trust and positive curiosity necessary for meaningful encounters.

A central feature of the role of spiritual caregivers is attentiveness to the stories of care receivers. As we invite patients and families to tell us about their lives, we begin to understand what they value and hold dear. By paying attention to these things we learn how to care for them, remembering that we glimpse the "tip of the iceberg." Amidst the expressed fears, hopes, and longings is the stuff that prayer is made of. In prayer we

---

[5] Jerald D. Gort, Hendrik M. Vroom, Rein Fernhout, & Anton Wessels, editors, *On Sharing Religious Experience: Possibilities of Interfaith Mutuality* (Grand Rapids: William B. Eerdmans, 1992), 5.

[6] Dula, "A Theology of Interfaith Bridge Building," 162.

are always walking on holy ground.

When I first started as a chaplain I hesitated or neglected to offer spoken prayer because I did not want to come across as imposing my own faith practices. In my subsequent experiences I have been surprised by how frequently an offer to pray is welcomed by patients and families from diverse religious traditions as well as by those who identify themselves as nonreligious. In wondering about why this might be, I offer a few observations and hypotheses:

- Many people who do not affiliate with a religious community still pray or appreciate someone praying for them.

- Christianity has directly and indirectly shaped North American consciousness so that people may have a certain degree of familiarity (for better or worse) with what they will be receiving from me when they accept my offer to pray.

- Patients may not feel like they have the freedom to refuse the offer even if they would prefer to.

- The relationship that develops between the care receiver(s) and me is such that they feel they can trust that my motivation is one of care and not proselytism.

- People of diverse denominations or faith traditions hold the conviction that "there is one God."

- Members of cultural minorities that I encounter often seek to minimize the ways in which they feel marginalized by the society around them

- Regardless of religious affiliation, people welcome prayer because it is a way of at least *trying* to give expression to "the most profound things" at a time of painful isolation. It may be a search for assurance that one's deepest needs will somehow be met in the midst of human limitation.

- Perhaps most important when it comes to *sharing* prayer, is the gift of knowing that one has been heard and cared for. When care receivers' own expressed concerns are woven into the chaplain's spoken prayer, their sense of isolation may be lessened and they may gain strength from knowing they have an ally in their healing process.[7]

---

[7] It is implied, of course, that caregivers must remember that not everyone will welcome prayer and the caregiver must respect this. Prayer is inappropriate when it stems from the chaplain's need to do so rather than from the development of the caregiving relationship and the patient's needs and spiritual resourcefulness.

These and other dynamics may be at play within care receivers when it comes to prayer. A Christian ethic of care motivates us in discerning whether or not to pray with patients and families of faith traditions and worldviews different than our own.[8] This chapter focuses on prayer in three case studies that detail a few such interactions I had in the hospital. The cases are not meant to be "picture perfect" examples of how to conduct a visit in an interfaith situation. Rather, I offer them as accounts of conversations I actually had, including my weaker moments, for the sake of demonstrating what I learned from the experiences. Each of the vignettes is followed by a reflection on the nature of the visit. Positive outcomes of these situations are noted alongside observations about what could have been done better or differently. Group discussions with colleagues in pastoral care at Lutheran Hospital of Indiana informed some of these reflections.

Before proceeding with the cases, a few words about the cultural context that shapes me and my practice of spiritual caregiving will suffice as a preface to the three accounts. We all approach others through the lens of our own worldview, values, and assumptions. Awareness of our own biases and convictions should lead us to clarity about the guidelines behind our own practice of caregiving. In turn we are also reminded that the patients and families we serve are likewise shaped by their cultural contexts, values, and convictions.

My cultural context

Born in the 1970s to Mennonite parents, I grew up in a mid-sized prairie town in Manitoba, Canada. Mennonites from different conferences made up a large percentage of the population of my hometown. The word "Mennonite" is derived from the name Menno Simons, a Dutch Roman Catholic priest who became a leader in the sixteenth century Reformation/Anabaptist movement. One key feature of Anabaptist faith was expressed by another sixteenth century reformer, Hans Denck, who stated that the life of faith involves following Christ daily in life.[9] By following the example of Jesus, Mennonites believe we are called to extend hospi-

---

[8] For a helpful discussion on the value of praying with patients, see "The Use of Prayer" in Sharon Fish & Judith Allen Shelly, *Spiritual Care: The Nurse's Role* (Don Mills: InterVarsity Press, 1978), 95–106. This volume is written explicitly from a Christian perspective. The language is dated in terms of gender inclusiveness.

[9] Werner O. Packull, "Hans Denck: Fugitive from Dogmatism," in Hans-Juergen Goertz, ed., *Profiles of Radical Reformers: Biographical Sketches from Thomas Muenster to Paracelsus* (Scottdale: Herald Press, 1982), 62–71. See also W. Neff, "Denk (Denck), Hans," in *The Mennonite Encyclopedia*, vol. 2, Harold S. Bender and C. Henry Smith, editors (Scottdale: Mennonite Publishing House, 1956), 32–35.

tality *to* and accept hospitality *from* those within and outside our usual sphere of contact.

Another aspect of the Mennonite perspective, inspired by Jesus' own practice, is a commitment to nonviolent resistance in response to violence. Violence is a response primarily motivated by fear—fear of the unknown, fear of loss. Part of a Mennonite understanding of interfaith spiritual care includes the belief that building relationships with people from other traditions diminishes fear and violence.[10]

In addition to my theological formation, I also grew up alongside two interconnected socio-political phenomena: globalization and postmodernism. Increasingly, we live side by side with people from many different cultures. This has contributed to a growing awareness that the stories, customs, and traditions we live by influence the way we perceive each other and the world. In the years after I moved away from my hometown, I lived in North American neighborhoods that were much less homogenous than the one I came from. I encountered people whose beliefs and lifestyles were very different than mine.

We have a unique opportunity in the twenty-first century to welcome diversity in ways that transform threat into a sense of wonder and richness. This is easier said than done, however. Spiritual caregivers in the hospital face daily the challenge and responsibility to support the faith and hope of care receivers while ministering with integrity out of their own convictions and membership in a faith community. I, as a Mennonite, must be mindful of the theological convictions that guide my spiritual caregiving practice. What I believe affects, in every way, the kind of care I offer. At the same time, I must be willing to behold the world of those I care for and allow them to teach me, from the wisdom of their own experience. In so doing, I begin to learn how I might address their spiritual needs and partner with them in drawing upon their own resources.

Case #1: Nasim Hafeez[11]

Fifty-year-old Nasim Hafeez was taking time off from his work in construction to care for his eighty-year-old father. Mr. Hafeez, Sr., was an intensive care patient who had been admitted following a heart attack. While making rounds through intensive care, I caught Nasim's eye from where he sat beside the hospital bed. My first guess about his ethnicity

---

[10] For a summary of the Mennonite stance regarding nonviolence, see "Article 22: Peace, Justice, and Nonresistance" in *The Confession of Faith in a Mennonite Perspective* (Scottdale: Herald Press, 1995), 81–84.

[11] All names have been changed to protect the privacy of the people featured in the case studies.

was that perhaps he was from India. I said hello and introduced myself. Nasim invited me to enter the room. He told me his name and briefly related the events leading up to his father's hospitalization. Mr. Hafeez, Sr., was sedated and on a respirator, having gone through bypass surgery. Nasim looked concerned but calm.

"He is doing better," Nasim said with a hopeful tone. "He's on the respirator but he is really breathing on his own. They are probably going to take that tube out today."

"That sounds like good news," I said.

"Yes, he's doing okay. He had a heart attack and they had to do bypass surgery. He is always very active and healthy."

"He stays in good shape."

"Yes. That's why this was a surprise. He is strong, so he will get better."

"And you are able to take the time to be here?"

"Yes. I am here every day. My brother comes too. He lives with my brother. He'll be coming soon," Nasim paused then said, "My mother died in this hospital."

"Oh, she did?"

"Yes, she had a stroke. She was here for a few weeks. There was too much blood on her brain. We were here then, too."

A respiratory technologist, along with two students, wheeled into the room with his computer and indicated that they were going to do a test to determine if Mr. Hafeez was ready to be weaned off of the respirator. He addressed Nasim and said they would need him to translate. It took a few minutes for them to get set up. Nasim told me that his father spoke Urdu.

"Say a prayer for him?" Nasim requested, nodding over at his father.

I agreed and we bowed our heads while the respiratory team made preparations. "God of life and love, we ask for your blessing upon Mr. Hafeez. We give you thanks for the healing that is already happening since his surgery and pray that you will continue to work through the hands of the nurses and doctors and other staff here at the hospital, restoring Mr. Hafeez in body, soul, and spirit. May he know of your care also through the support of his family and friends; we thank you for his sons who are here with him. In your grace and mercy, hear our prayer. Amen."

After the prayer, the respiratory technologist began. He had Nasim tell his father to take a few deep breaths and blow out as hard as he could. The technologist measured his breathing and made positive comments about the situation. Within ten minutes the test was done and Nasim was told that the doctor would be in to confirm the next steps.

"Sounds like your father did well, according to the technologist."

"Yes. We'll see what the doctor says."

"Yes," I paused, "Is there anything you need right now?"

"No. I am fine. Thank you. How long have *you* been here?"

"Almost a year."

"And are you a minister?"

"I am a chaplain with the hospital full time and I worship with a Mennonite Church."

"Oh yes. I know the Mennonites."

"And you? Is there a faith community you belong to?"

"We are Muslim. But we are all God's children."

"Yes. We are all loved by the same God."

"Yes. There are so many stereotypes about what Muslims are like. But it is a political Islam that people see—the political Islam is not the true Islam. We pray in the name of Jesus."

"You do?"

"Yes!"

"I didn't know that."

"Many people do not know that, but we do. We believe that Jesus was the Son of God. Jesus did not have a human father. Mohammad did. So Jesus is the Son of God. There are Muslims who will not say that. But nobody can speak against Jesus. In Pakistan, if anyone says anything against Jesus or Abraham or Mohammad, they can be sent to jail."

"Really."

"Yes. There are laws governing what people can say," Nasim paused, "I know the Mennonites. I work in construction and there are Mennonites who work with me. Right now we are building a mosque together."

"Oh, you are? What do your Mennonite co-workers say about that?"

"They say, 'Jews, Christians, and Muslims all share the same God.' The

Jews believe from Abraham up until Jesus—they don't believe Jesus is the Son of God. Christians believe from Abraham up until Mohammad—they say it stops with Jesus. From the time of Abraham, every prophet was told about who would come next. Jesus received a revelation about Mohammad. That is what we believe."

"Well I appreciate your sharing about it. I have learned some things I did not know before! When we live and work side by side with people of different faiths it is good when we can get to know each other."

"Yes. I enjoy working with the Mennonites."

The cardiologist entered the room to speak with Nasim.

"Mr. Hafeez, I will be on my way," I said, extending my hand to him and he shook it. "It was good to meet you."

"Thank you. If you ever want to stop by and say a prayer for my father, you are most welcome to."

"Thank you. I will do that. Bye."

It is clear that I was graciously received by Nasim Hafeez. Two significant matters surface in this encounter. First, Nasim was confronting the possible loss of someone he loves. Second, he was experiencing this as a Muslim in a Christian context at a time of vulnerability. All of us experience death and loss as part of the human condition. Beyond this common ground, however, each situation is unique and it is important to respect cultural and religious differences. Nasim needed assurance that his father would receive the best care possible; he also needed to know that he would be respected even though his religious convictions were different, in some significant ways, than those of most of the staff at the hospital. As he kept vigil with his father, who was hanging in the balance between life and death, Nasim also needed the freedom to draw upon his faith as a source of strength and hope.

My purpose as chaplain in this encounter was to offer spiritual support by listening and praying, as requested, and by exploring Nasim's faith as a source of nurture and guidance. With his request for a prayer early in the visit he expressed a desire to make supplication to God for his father's recovery. He made this request before he knew anything about me other than my being a Christian spiritual caregiver, symbolized by the cross on my navy blazer. I did not know his religious background, if any, at that point and, therefore, I intentionally refrained from using the words "in Jesus' name" to close the prayer. Our subsequent conversation revealed that he personally, though he was a Muslim, would not have been offended if I had prayed in Jesus' name in his presence.[12]

Regardless of how much we know about any religious tradition, this encounter demonstrates that every person within that tradition will have a unique way of interpreting the connection between their spirituality and their life circumstances.[13] I maintain that it is important for spiritual caregivers to make decisions about the religious language we use based on our fullest understanding of what would be meaningful for the people in our care in that moment.[14] I do not need to audibly pray the words "in Jesus' name" as if the prayer is incomplete without them. As a Christian, my prayers are always in Jesus' name, whether or not I explicitly say the words.[15] I pray those words explicitly when I am with people whose faith and worldview are similar to mine because we are more likely to share an understanding about why those words are meaningful. In this particular conversation with Nasim I would like to have asked, in retrospect, about his own experience of prayer.[16]

If I had asked Nasim more about his mother's death in this same hospital, we might have talked about what gave him hope in the midst of that experience. We might have talked about that time in light of Nasim's father, now on a respirator. Experiences with mortality, grief, hope, and love are fundamentally human. We are all dependent and interdependent, regardless of religious affiliation. At the same time, religious dis-

---

[12] It is important to keep in mind, of course, that praying "in the name of Jesus" may mean something very different to a Muslim than to a Christian.

[13] For a helpful discussion about learning from the patient see Elizabeth Johnston Taylor, *What Do I Say? Talking with patients about spirituality* (Philadelphia: Templeton Foundation Press, 2007), 111.

[14] For a discussion of this challenge see Leah Dawn Bueckert and Daniel S. Schipani, "Interfaith Spiritual Caregiving: The Case for Language Care," in Bueckert and Schipani, editors, *Spiritual Caregiving in the Hospital*, 245–63.

[15] For me to pray in Jesus' name stems from my belief that God was uniquely present in Jesus of Nazareth—in his care for the sick, the suffering and the outcast, in his non-violent and wise challenge of the powers of domination. When I pray in Jesus' name, I ask that God's will be done as seen in the life and faith, death and resurrection of Jesus who sought redemption and healing for all.

[16] One of the "Five Pillars of Faith" in Muslim tradition is to pray five times a day, accompanied by ritual cleansing. It is important for caregivers to help make this possible, according to the abilities of the patient, by providing a pitcher of water and a basin to wash with, for example. Prayers emphasize praise of Allah Most Compassionate, Most Merciful instead of personal requests, as the latter could be considered criticism of Allah's will for the person praying. Following is an example of a prayer that might be offered. "O Allah, Lord of the people, remove all harm, give care, for you are the one who cures. There is not curing except your curing—a curing that leaves no illness. (Bukhari)." Mary M. Toole *Handbook for Chaplains: Comfort My People* (New York: Paulist Press, 2006), 23–9. See also Neville A. Kirkwood, *A Hospital Handbook on Multiculturalism and Religion: Practical Guidelines for Health Care Workers*, revised edition (Harrisburg: Morehouse Publishing, 2005), 28–40.

tinctions regarding these experiences are very significant and must be taken into consideration.

I understood that Nasim communicated some sadness and anger about some people's perception of him as a Muslim. Perhaps the source of these feelings came from life in North America amidst a prevailing negative attitude towards Muslims. Had I been more aware of the possible reasons why Nasim was showing interest in establishing common ground, such as expressing the right to be treated with respect as a "visible minority," I could have been more conscious to be an advocate for him with other hospital staff. I might have done this by asking Nasim how he was experiencing the staff's treatment of him and his father and if there were things being overlooked in relation to the customs of his family and tradition. I could also have asked if he was affiliated with a particular mosque or worshipping community and, if so, whether or not this was a support to him at this time. I wanted him to have the assurance that we as staff would work together with him to provide care that would respect his faith and culture. I hoped that, through our encounter, Nasim had a sense of being heard and cared for. My motivation was for the sustaining power of his faith to be enhanced during our visit and throughout this difficult time.

Case #2: Tarak Ajit Maruti

Tarak Ajit was a 43-year-old Hindu man. He was being treated on the neuro-medical surgical unit following a stroke. Originally from India, he was currently living in Indiana. I had visited Tarak once before but, because of the language challenge, we had some trouble communicating. When I looked into the room this time, another man was with him. Tarak was lying in bed with the head of the bed slightly raised. He was in a single room; the window blinds were open. The visitor was standing at the foot of the bed. During our conversation I learned that this man was Tarak's friend Peter, also from India but having lived in the United States for a longer period of time. He was fluent in both Hindi and English.

"How have you been since the last time we talked?" I asked. Tarak responded with a question mark on his face. I started again, "How are you?"

"Fine," he answered.

"Have you been doing exercises?" I inquired, trying to open a conversation that connected with the first time I met him. Peter interpreted my question.

"Yes," Tarak answered affirmatively.

"In the mornings," Peter added.

"What kind of exercises do you do?" Peter again interpreted my question. Tarak began to lift his left arm up and down with his right hand. "Arm exercises. And walking?"

Peter answered, "He uses a walker and somebody supports his left side."

"Are you here when he does his exercises?" I asked Peter.

"No, I'm not here in the morning."

"How did the two of you meet?" I asked.

"We come from the same place in India and we have the same last name."

"Oh really? But you met here in Indiana?"

"Yes. A friend of his is also my friend and so we met. I am looking for a job and I heard that he was in the hospital. So I came here to be with him—I like to be here when he needs help."

Turning to Tarak I said, "Good to have friends, isn't it?" Tarak nodded. "Last time we talked you told me that you are Hindu."

"Yes," Tarak replied.

"As a Christian, I'm interested to know more about what it is like to be Hindu." Tarak smiled and nodded. "It must be different to be here in Indiana where there aren't very many people who are Hindu— different than in India where, what, 70 percent of the population is Hindu?"

"In India?" Peter asked.

"Yes."

"Oh, about 80 percent are Hindu, 13 percent are Muslim, and the rest are Christian and others."

"Oh, I see," I said. "That must be a different experience."

"Yes. It's different." Peter replied, "but I go into a church."

"A Christian church?"

"Yes. There is one God. Whether I am in a temple or in a mosque or in a church—Krishna, Rama, Jesus—it's all the same God."

"Different names for one God," I said.

"Yes—different names for one God. That's what I believe."

"What about you?" I asked, looking at Tarak. Peter interpreted my question.

Pointing up with his finger Tarak said, "One God."

"I also believe that." I stated. "Do you also pray in the Hindu tradition?" Peter interpreted and then said, "Yes, we pray."

"What is it like for you to pray? How do you pray?" Peter chuckled and interpreted for Tarak. Tarak put his hands together and bowed his head.

"Do you know what he is saying?" Peter asked me. "He is saying when we go into the temple we stand in front of the god, we put our hands together—like you—and bow our head—the same. In a temple there is a statue, in a mosque there may be nothing, in a Christian church there is a statue of Jesus. The method doesn't matter, it's what is in the heart that's important."

"Yes, God knows the heart." I replied. Looking at Tarak I asked, "What do you pray for?" Peter interpreted and Tarak touched his arm, looking at me.

"For health, for the body to be restored." I said.

Peter added, "For strength in his leg and his arm so that he can go back to India."

"Yes of course." I said. "To recover and be well again; to go home."

Peter returned to the subject of God. "Human is the same everywhere—one God. But not everyone believes that. If everyone believed that, the world would be very different, I think. Now there is always fighting."

"Yes, it seems that our differences sometimes get in the way." Looking at Tarak, I asked, "Would it be all right if I say a prayer with you?"

Peter interpreted the question and then said, "That would be all right." He interpreted to Tarak as I prayed, line by line.

"O God who loves us all, thank you for the opportunity to talk with Peter and Tarak. As Tarak spends these days in the hospital, we pray that your healing will strengthen his body and that your spirit of peace would bless him. Thank you for the friendship that Tarak and Peter share. Thank you for the care of the medical staff here. Give the staff guidance and wisdom. We pray that Tarak will regain his strength day by day. We pray that he will soon be able to return home to India. May Tarak know your love and healing through the care of those around him. Amen."

After exchanging a few more words, I thanked them for the visit and we said good-bye.

One of the most obvious features of many intercultural and interfaith encounters is the difference in spoken language. Even the basics of everyday communication become a challenge. Nonverbal language communicates up to a point, but verbal language allows for the clarification of needs and confirmation of meaning.[17]

Tarak was in a vulnerable condition in the hospital of a foreign culture. According to my assumptions and our conversation, Tarak was counting on compassionate and competent medical care. He needed to experience respect for his cultural and religious preferences and to have a mediator between the Western culture of the hospital and his own context. Peter was a friend and caregiver in these and other respects.

For my part, I could have learned a little more about Tarak as a person rather than asking straight out about his being Hindu. I could have asked, "Do you have a place of worship here in Indiana?" or, "What gives you hope at a time like this?"[18]

My asking so brashly about their Hindu faith may have given the message that I was there to educate myself rather than to be attentive to their needs. I continue to remind myself that my own curiosity does not always have a place—I must learn to distinguish between "good" curiosity and simple nosiness.

Peter mentioned early on that he had been to a church. When I asked, somewhat puzzled, "to a Christian church?" he responded affirmatively. Much like Nasim conveyed his familiarity with Christianity, Peter's comments also seem to suggest a desire to minimize the differences between us. By *pointing* to the differences, I intended to communicate openness to learning about their culture and traditions, but I wonder if this rather had the effect of emphasizing the barriers between us. Whatever the case, they certainly extended hospitality to *me*.

Peter said, "There is one God—Krishna, Rama, Jesus—it is all the

---

[17] Had Peter not been present, I would have asked my colleague who was fluent in Hindi to accompany me on this visit. Resources such as an interpreter phone line are also available in some places. Such arrangements are fundamental to the communication of respect. They allow us to hear the patient's own expressed hopes and to build towards a therapeutic relationship.

[18] According to Mary M. Toole in *Handbook for Chaplains*, Hindu worship practices are not possible in the hospital. For this reason, the patient's family will conduct practices at home or at the temple. "As a greeting, Hindus join hands at the palms and bow from the waist saying *Namaskar* or *Namaste*, which means 'I bow to God in you; I love you and I respect you, as there is no one like you." Following is one example of a Vedic prayer: "O! All powerful God. You are the protector of the whole physical creation. May you protect my body. You art the source of all life. You art the source of all strength. Make thou me strong. O, omnipotent Lord, I live to thee to fill up all my wants and to give me perfection, physical, mental and spiritual." Toole, *Handbook for Chaplains*, 15–22. See also Kirkwood, *A Hospital Handbook on Multiculturalism and Religion*, 54–63.

same God." My reply to Peter's comment was an affirmative one: "Different names for one God." Why would I, as a Christian, make a response like this? My answer has two parts. First, I interpreted Peter's words as a statement about the dependence of human beings upon God and not as an invitation to a discussion about doctrine. Second and more to the point, while there are, of course, significant distinctions between Hindu faith and Christian faith, we know that Christianity cannot stop truth from existing outside of it. In fact, according to Peter Dula on Karl Barth, the church's constant temptation will be to insulate itself from the world when it is often the prophetic word from outside that promises to be the source of growth and transformation. Dula writes:

> To commit oneself to the practice of interfaith bridge building is to presume, with Barth, that there are true lights and words in other religions. The point of interfaith bridge building is to see and listen to these true lights and words .... Attending to other words and lights is, on Barth's grounds, the way to focus on Christ.[19]

In other words, for the Christian, any true word that is found "outside" of Christianity, will be a reflection and confirmation of the one Word. The *Confession of Faith in a Mennonite Perspective* states:

> We humbly recognize that God far surpasses human comprehension and understanding. We also gratefully acknowledge that God has spoken to humanity and related to us in many and various ways. We believe that God has spoken above all in the only Son, the Word who became flesh and revealed the divine being and character.[20]

In light of Biblical foundations, on the one hand, God is beyond all human description. On the other hand, God is truly knowable through revelation. In the Christian tradition God is revealed more fully than anywhere else in the person of Jesus Christ. If there are, then, any ways in which Rama or Krishna reflect the light of Jesus Christ, "it is all the same God."

I have a rudimentary awareness of the Hindu tradition—enough to

---

[19] Dula, "A Theology of Interfaith Bridge Building," 165.

[20] "Article 1: God," in *Confession of Faith in a Mennonite Perspective* (Scottdale: Herald Press, 1995), 10, 11. Scripture references upon which these statements are based: Exodus 3:13–14; Job 37; Isaiah 40:18–25; Romans 11:33–36; John 1:14, 18; Hebrews 1:1–4.

appreciate that there are similarities as well as significant distinctions between it and Christianity.[21] My commitment to the convictions of my own faith community does not give me license to make assumptions about the right-ness or wrong-ness of others' beliefs. Like the parable of the householder who did not trust the servants to preserve the wheat while pulling out the weeds, so too I must be careful about the judgments and assumptions I make about people from other traditions and their faith commitments.[22] What seems wrong to me in someone else may not necessarily be so. Peter Dula states it sharply when he writes:

> Barth is not saying that all we have to do is glance around and see what words are or are not reflecting the Word and then pay close patient attention to them. His whole point is that, given an awareness of our sinfulness, we will likely not be able to recognize, or will misrecognize, those words when we do see them.[23]

Our good intentions coupled with our human tendency to deceive ourselves can result in prejudice and discrimination of various kinds. We do, of course, make judgment calls based on our values and beliefs, and we must. We *should* act to promote what is life-giving and healing and work against oppression and violence. What the quote above highlights is the need to maintain a measure of humility in our judgments, recognizing that it is God in the end who is judge.

As Christian spiritual caregivers in health care settings, our role is to extend hospitality, to step into the borderlands between faith traditions and hospital culture, and to embody the love we believe in. While I did not fully understand what goes on within Peter and Tarak in regards to "the most profound things," I did learn that they have faith in a God upon whom they depend for life and well-being. In my prayer with them I addressed the "God who loves us all". May I continue to learn what it means to point to the God who is truly knowable and to humble myself

---

[21] Hindu deities represent different aspects of the one Supreme Being or God. The cosmic activity of the Supreme Being is characterized by three tasks: creation, preservation, and dissolution and recreation. Brahma represents the activity of creation, Vishnu represents preservation, and Shiva represents the work of dissolution and recreation. Rama and Krishna are the seventh and eighth incarnations of Vishnu. Rama represents an ideal man. Krishna, the flute player, is seen as the fullest representation of Vishnu. See C. J. Fuller, *The Camphor Flame: Popular Hinduism and Society in India* (Princeton: Princeton University Press, 1992), 29–56 and J. L. Brockington, *The Sacred Thread: A Short History of Hinduism* (Delhi: Oxford University Press, 1992).

[22] Matthew 13:24–30.

[23] Dula, "A Theology of Interfaith Bridge Building," 168.

before the same God who is truly mysterious.

Case #3: Megan Blomstein

While making rounds on cardiac telemetry, I stopped in the room of a 57-year-old woman named Megan. After introducing myself to Megan and three family members, I asked how she was feeling. She described what it was like to be recovering from a heart attack. Her husband also volunteered thoughts about his own recent experience of being hospitalized. After we had been conversing for awhile, I was about to offer a prayer, but before doing so, I asked:

"Are you part of a church community?"

"We're Jewish," Megan replied.

"Oh, you are."

"We go to synagogue, to one of the two synagogues here in town."

"Are they aware that you are in the hospital?"

"Yes, the Rabbi has been here."

"I don't encounter people from the Jewish tradition here very often. What is it like to be at a Lutheran hospital?"

"Oh, the staff have been wonderful. We have both received really good care here. The only thing I don't like is when people come to proselytize."

"Yes, that's not helpful."

"Something kind of funny happened the other day. A woman from dietary was here and I wanted to let her know that I did not want to be served anything with pork. There was no place to mark my request on her form, so she said, 'Well, we'll have to write it under food allergies!'"

We chuckled. "Hmm," I said, "It sounds like we need to revise those forms."[24]

Megan quickly responded, "We've been very happy with the care we've received here. My doctor is excellent."

"I am glad to hear that you feel you've been treated well. May that continue. I know Jews and Christians pray differently, but I …"

Before I could finish, Megan said, "If you would like to pray in the name of God, that would be wonderful."

---

[24] I pursued this matter with dietary staff who suggested that the best place for requests like this on the meal order forms would be in the "staff notes" section. While the hospital kitchen is not a kosher kitchen, I was told they do offer some kosher foods.

"Okay. I would be glad to." After a short pause for centering, I prayed: "God of grace and love, thank you for the opportunity to meet with Megan and her family. As she spends these days in the hospital, may she continue to know your loving care for her through the care of the medical staff and through the support of family and friends. May your healing touch restore her in body, soul, and spirit. Grant her your mercy and peace throughout the rest of this day and in the coming days. Amen."

"Thank you."

"You're welcome," I said and bid them farewell.

Megan and her family, even though they had experienced the irritation of having others attempt to proselytize in the past, were patient with me, a Christian chaplain who rather clumsily sought to communicate respect and care. This conversation seems to have had two notable features; Megan affirmed the good care she had received on the one hand, while expressing frustration, with humor, over experiences with religious insensitivity on the other hand.

After they shared with me that they were Jewish and were affiliated with a local synagogue, I sought to remain engaged, at least for a little while, instead of withdrawing and assuming this meant the termination of the visit. Withdrawal would have been easier. It would have been easier to act as if my task as a chaplain (to be a blessing and to address any spiritual needs) was irrelevant in the face of these discovered religious differences. As a spiritual caregiver, the fact that they were Jewish needed to *inform and guide* my role with them, not make my role irrelevant. It is possible, however, that my sense of being caught a little off guard hindered my ability to interact in a relaxed and non-threatening manner. For example, my response to Megan's statement about people coming to proselytize communicated a closing of my interest instead of an opening. Looking back, I wonder if Megan wasn't wary throughout our visit about where this conversation was going.

Earlier in the visit, I had stated that I don't encounter people of Jewish faith very often and could they tell me what the hospital experience was like for them. My intention in making this comment was to convey an interest in learning how we might be helpful. I wanted to communicate that I was not about to impose my "Christian services." My intentions were good. I'm not so sure that my words had the desired effect. First of all, as with Tarak, my statement accentuated their being different in a context where they deserved to be assured that they would be treated with the same respect and quality as everyone else. Second, by asking them to tell me what it is like to be Jewish in a "Christian" hospital, I may have sounded as if I was using them to educate myself instead of focusing on them and their needs. As spiritual caregivers we do have a responsibility to regard the care receiver as the expert on their own experience. The hope is to communicate respect and appreciation, not a self-interested agenda about my own learning.

Instead of saying, "I don't encounter people from the Jewish tradition very often; tell me what it's like for you here at the hospital," I could have said, "I'm glad to hear that you've been happy with the care you've received. Is there anything that has been frustrating or overlooked?" This would have been a better way to communicate a desire to be of service. After Megan spoke about her irritation when people come to proselytize, I could have said, "Tell me more about that." This might have created an opportunity to address the connection between her faith and her current experience.

Megan seemed to sense my offer to pray coming. I wonder whether she really felt okay with me praying, or if she felt exasperated and thought to herself, "If she's going to insist on praying, I will at least direct the terms." If Megan was irritated by my praying with her, then my actions were a misuse of my role and position in the hospital system. If she was truly extending the invitation, then my actions may have been a channel for the light and love of God. Instead of my comment, "I know Jews and Christians pray differently," perhaps I could have said, "I would like to offer a blessing for your recovery." Or perhaps I should not have prayed at all. Some would say it is inappropriate for a Jew and a Christian to pray together. Perhaps the most respect I could have shown would have been to *not* offer to pray. I might have said that I would pray *for* them. Or my parting words might have served as a sort of blessing. [25]

It is not necessary to include a prayer for a spiritual care visit to be of value, but *if the care receiver finds it meaningful,* it can be a powerful reminder of grace, connection, and hope, for both care receiver and

---

[25] See Chapter 5 in this book, "A Chaplain Reflects on Caring for a Jewish Family," by William H. Griffith. In this essay the chaplain forms his blessing by drawing upon texts that he and the family had in common, in this case, the Psalms and Deuteronomy.

There are four movements within Judaism. They are Orthodox, Reform, Conservative, and Reconstructionist. Most synagogues are affiliated with one of these. Kirkwood writes, "Jewish prayer embraces elements of petition, thanksgiving, praise, confession, sustaining and healing" (43). Toole includes this Jewish prayer: "Heal us, O Lord, and we shall be healed, save us and we shall be saved; for You are our glory. Grant complete healing for all our afflictions, faithful and merciful God of healing" (37). Mary M. Toole *Handbook for Chaplains,* 33–43. See also Neville A. Kirkwood, *A Hospital Handbook on Multiculturalism and Religion,* 41–53.

caregiver. The challenge is to determine whether or not the receiver would sincerely welcome prayer. We can say it is up to patients to refuse, but in their compromised position, will they feel free to say no? With Megan I have lingering uncertainty about that. By contrast, in the meetings with Nasim, Tarak, and Peter, the receivers clearly welcomed and, in Nasim's case, requested prayer.

Welcome of the stranger is a common theme throughout the Hebrew Bible and the Gospels of Jesus, as highlighted in several places in this book.[26] Megan and her family did show grace and hospitality throughout our interaction. I hope I showed hospitality by attempting to express respect and a desire to learn how to relate to them as a chaplain.

In conclusion, it was a privilege for me to spend time with each of these people—Nasim, Tarak, Peter, and Megan. I have learned much and will continue to learn from these encounters, these steps into the borderlands. As Christian spiritual caregivers in a multifaith milieu, it is not only our *professional* and *ethical* responsibility to engage people of other faiths with openness and respect, it is our *theological* and *pastoral* responsibility as well. In the words of Alain Epp Weaver, "we engage in interfaith bridge-building *because*, not in spite of, our Christological convictions."[27] While the subject of Christology requires another discussion, suffice it to say that Jesus' life and ministry, death and resurrection portray indiscriminate love in word and action. That is why our convictions free us for boundless compassion.

Engaging in interfaith spiritual caregiving, therefore, does not require that we give up our convictions, though they may be challenged. Neither is it an attempt to find merely a politically correct or "lowest common denominator" level of relating. It means that we open ourselves to the discomfort of interacting with people who present much to us that is unfamiliar. It means that we take the time to listen long and deeply. If appropriate and solicited, we may share about our own faith. If there is disagreement, we continue to maintain positive regard for the other person. If we detect that those we care for are somehow misguided we probe gently, directed by compassion, maintaining the possibility that we may be wrong or have something to learn. Interfaith bridge-building calls us to cultivate and deepen our own spiritual wellsprings. Again, it is pre-

---

[26] For example, see the Preface and Chapter 4, "Biblical Foundations: Challenges and Possibilities of Interfaith Caregiving," by Daniel Schipani.

[27] Alain Epp Weaver, "Interfaith Bridge Building in the Middle East," in *Mennonite Central Committee Peace Office Newsletter: Interfaith Bridge Building*, vol. 35, no. 4 (October–December 2005), 6, 7.

cisely by realizing the wideness of God's mercy, as demonstrated by Christ, that we are freed to extend hospitality to people we meet from other traditions.

From a clinical perspective, sharing prayer with someone of another faith tradition can be a meaningful bridge-building experience.[28] From a pastoral theological perspective, that practice is grounded in a Christian ethic of care. When patients and families remark that "there is one God," they are expressing, among other things, our common human dependence upon that which is beyond us. Death and loss are universally human experiences; we are not, ultimately, in control of the length of our days. We may, however, encourage one another as we glimpse, work towards, and wait for the full integration of justice and peace on earth.

As a Christian, my understanding of God and life is different in many ways from Islamic, Hindu, or Jewish understandings. On what basis, then, do I pray together with someone of another faith, once I've confirmed that that person desires prayer? First, Christians recognize that God is beyond comprehension. The God of mystery calls us to trust and to refrain from judgment. Second, Christians profess that God is knowable and revealed through Scripture and especially in Jesus. The God of incarnation calls us to compassion. Prayer is one way to give voice to pain, joy, fear, and hope. When making intercession for a patient or family in such a way that our words mirror their own expressed concerns, we communicate that we have heard them and that we want to be partners with them and the Holy Spirit in the healing process. As we step into the borderlands and open ourselves to each other, we discover the Divine is already there in our midst.

---

[28] For a thoughtful list on "Tips for praying with patients," see Johnston Taylor, *What Do I Say? Talking with Patients About Spirituality*, 98–100.

Biblical foundations
Challenges and possibilities of interfaith caregiving

Daniel S. Schipani

Pastoral theological reflection on the practice of caregiving must always include sound biblical-theological dimensions. As already noted in the previous chapters, interfaith spiritual care elicits a number of hermeneutical and theological questions that need to be addressed. This essay illustrates the responsibility pastoral caregivers have to carefully interpret and appropriate biblical material in light of the plurality of traditions represented in Scripture. This is, indeed, the case given the tension between exclusiveness and inclusiveness apparent in both Testaments, in Christian theology in general, and in denominational "confessions of faith" in particular. It is our assumption that interfaith spiritual care from a Christian theological perspective can and must be biblically grounded.

Our hermeneutical key is the normative testimony of Jesus' own faith, life, and ministry. The fundamental theological claim we make in light of that testimony consists in the affirmation of the unfathomable reach, inclusiveness, and availability of Grace. For that reason, we will focus on a window to Jesus' own existential and vocational struggle as a caregiver in a reported encounter with a stranger in the borderlands. The appendix presents a summary of selected Old and New Testament sources which can be considered to undergird spiritual care in interfaith situations from a pastoral theological perspective.

A study of Matthew 15:21–28 as paradigmatic story[1]

Throughout the centuries, Christians have interpreted and used the story

Daniel S. Schipani, Dr.Psy., Ph.D., is an ordained minister of the Mennonite Church. He is Professor of Pastoral Care and Counseling at the Associated Mennonite Biblical Seminary, Elkhart, Indiana.

[1] What follows is a revised and expanded version of my article, "Transformation in the Borderlands: A Study of Matthew 15:21–28," in *Vision: A Journal for Church and Theology*, vol. 2, no. 2 (Fall 2001), 13–24.

of Jesus' encounter with the Syrophoenician/Canaanite woman in many ways. In recent years writings from a variety of perspectives reflect renewed interest in this fascinating story.[2] Working with a practical theological perspective, I will address two interrelated questions: how might this biblical text become foundational for caregiving ministry?[3] How might this unique story further illumine the challenges and opportunities of intercultural and interfaith care for Christian caregivers?

I will follow the familiar movements of an inductive study process, in popularized Latin American terms: *seeing*, *judging*, and *acting*. First, we will take a close look at the biblical passage, trying to grasp its meaning afresh. Second, we will ponder its significance, keeping in mind the social and cultural context. Finally, we will draw implications for our embodiment of the message in truthful and fruitful ways.

The meaning of the text: *Seeing*

This story appears only in the Gospels according to Mark and Matthew. In fact, Mark chapter 7 and Matthew chapter 15 are remarkably parallel as far as narrative content and sequencing are concerned. Nevertheless, we note some significant differences between the two accounts of Jesus' encounter with a foreign woman.[4] These dissimilarities suggest that Matthew has an interest in underscoring and intensifying some features of the story. For this reason, I have chosen to focus on its narrative.

> Jesus left that place and went away to the district of Tyre and Sidon. Just then a Canaanite woman from that re-

---

[2] Elisabeth Schüssler Fiorenza took the title of her book, *But She Said: Feminist Practices of Biblical Interpretation* (Boston: Beacon Press, 1992), from the story of the Syrophoenician-Canaanite woman. In her view, the story "represents the biblical-theological voice of women, which has been excluded, repressed, or marginalized in Christian discourse" (11).

[3] As a practical theologian, I use the term "foundational" deliberately and precisely. For me, the Bible is foundational in at least four interrelated ways: (a) It informs my normative framework and perspective for practice and reflection, especially regarding wisdom (knowing how to live in the light of God); (b) it offers key content disclosed in the teachings, narratives, and other materials (poetic, prophetic, apocalyptic, etc.) which express the written Word in ways that illumine and address our human condition; (c) it calls for engagement in an interpretive process for the sake of discernment and wise living; and (d) it grounds my own spirituality as a man of faith and as a ministering person (pastoral counselor and pastoral care supervisor), theological educator, and theologian.

[4] One is inclined to think that the narrative would also fit well in Luke's Gospel, given what we know about Luke, a Gentile writing to Gentiles, who gives women a significant place in his telling of the gospel. According to Elisabeth Schüssler Fiorenza, Luke does not include the story because he puts Paul and Peter at the center of the debate about the mission to the Gentiles: "This Lukan historical model has no room for a story about an educated Greek woman, who as a religious and ethnic outsider argues with Jesus for the Gentiles' share in the power of well-being" (Fiorenza, *But She Said*, 97).

gion came out and started shouting, "Have mercy on me, Lord, Son of David; my daughter is tormented by a demon." But he did not answer her at all. And his disciples came and urged him, saying, "Send her away, for she keeps shouting after us." He answered, "I was sent only to the lost sheep of the house of Israel." But she came and knelt before him, saying, "Lord, help me." He answered, "It is not fair to take the children's food and throw it to the dogs." She said, "Yes, Lord, yet even the dogs eat the crumbs that fall from their masters' table." Then Jesus answered her, "Woman, great is your faith! Let it be done for you as you wish." And her daughter was healed instantly. (Matthew 15:21–28, NRSV)

Our story is placed in a particular context in both Matthew 15 and Mark 7. First, we learn about a serious controversy involving Pharisees and scribes concerning the "tradition of the elders" on the question of eating with defiled hands. Jesus responds by accusing them of breaking the commandment of God and making void the word of God for the sake of their tradition, including a damning quote from the prophet Isaiah (Mt 15:1–9, Mk 7:1–13). Then we are told that Jesus engages in authoritative teaching about the spiritual implications of his position. In fact, he does this by using both direct and indirect language, that is, parabolic communication that requires further explanation (Mt 15:10–20, Mk 7:14–23). Finally, after the story of the encounter with the Syrophoenician/Canaanite woman, the Gospel writers portray Jesus involved in ministry with admirable compassion and power (Mt 15:29–39, Mk 7:31–37).

It is significant that, before encountering the foreign woman, Jesus has been engaged in a very serious conflict situation. His adversaries put the controversy in terms of socio-religious, cultural adaptation, that is, the conventional wisdom of needing to follow the tradition of the elders. In other words, the Gospel accounts suggest that the nature of their argument betrays a two-dimensional vision: they understand holiness in terms of conformity to the precepts and practices handed down through religious teachings and socialization. Observance of the tradition, then, defines one's belonging to the chosen people of Israel. Jesus, on the other hand, views the struggle four-dimensionally:[5] for him, the real problem

---

[5] This is a direct allusion to James E. Loder's view of the "fourfold knowing event"—which involves the lived world, the self, the void, and the Holy. See *The Transforming Moment*, 2nd ed. (Colorado Springs: Helmers & Howard, 1989), chapter 3. Loder writes that "being human

lies in accommodating tradition while disobeying the will of God, as in the case of the commandment to honor father and mother. In that light, Jesus contends that the very worship of God has been compromised. So, for Jesus, the transformation of the tradition of the elders itself is a necessary outcome of radical trust in, and obedience to the living God of Israel. That is for him the way to life in lieu of those fruitless endeavors to gain divine acceptance and favor in the face of the threat of evil and condemnation.

It is also interesting to visualize Jesus speaking firmly, with certainty and authority, about the way of authentic spirituality right before he meets the woman in the borderlands and faces a seemingly different kind of conflict. Indeed, it may be argued that Jesus still needed to process more deeply, both existentially and theologically, the very meaning and implications of "tradition" being confronted by divine grace. Could it be that a difficult scanning process[6] requiring the collaboration of such a special stranger would eventually lead Jesus to further light, that is, a transformative learning that would translate into deeper caring and liberating power, and a clearer sense of vocation? With such a question in mind we now turn to that eventful encounter.

Focus on the encounter: Highlights of a stunning confrontation

A plain reading of the story presents a clear and unique instance in which Jesus yields. One could argue that here he is bested in an argument. The most striking and problematic part of the story is, of course, Jesus' initial response to the request of the woman: First a deafening silence, then an uncharacteristic affirmation of boundaries, followed by parabolic refusal. At that moment he appears to regard the woman's request as inappropriate, even as outrageously *out of place!* Only in this particular Gospel story does Jesus clearly ignore a supplicant, place the barrier of ethnicity before a plea for help, and then use offensive language to reiterate the barrier. Without question, "dog" is a disdainful metaphor, though Jesus uses a diminutive form ("puppy," "little bitch"). The implication, of course, is that the Gentiles/dogs have no place at the table. The woman, however, appears to play along with that harsh image and simply urges Jesus to take it one step further. She appeals to him as "Lord," asserts her

---

entails environment, selfhood, the possibilty of nonbeing [the Void], and the possibility of new being [the Holy]. All four dimensions are essential, and none of them can be ignored without decisive loss to our understanding of what is essentially human" (69).

[6] "Scanning" here denotes the conscious as well as unconscious process of seeking resolution to a given conflict situation, hopefully leading to new insight(s).

claim, and demonstrates her faith by arguing that at the very least both children (Jews) and dogs (Gentiles) are under the same caring, compassionate authority.

One need not infer that the woman agrees with the Gentile/dog analogy. Nor do we need to conclude that she considers herself unworthy and less than human, or that she identifies herself as a dog. On the contrary, we may assume that she is requesting that she and her daughter be included, that she hopes for a place at the table and challenges Israel's excluding ideology. When she says, "Yes, Lord …," she agrees with Jesus that it would be wrong to throw the children's bread to the dogs. But she also reminds Jesus that if even dogs may eat what their masters waste, she and her daughter should receive bread, too. The Canaanite woman understands the grave meaning and the implications of Jesus' initial response, but she proceeds wisely and daringly to reframe and recast it. Jesus' original challenge to the woman merely restates the status quo of gender, ethnic, cultural, religious, and political divisions. Her counter-challenge calls him to look to the place of new possibilities across and beyond the established boundaries. Instead of accepting the dichotomy of children (insiders/receive food) versus dogs (outsiders/no food), she imagines that both the children and the dogs can be graciously fed inside, within the same household and from the same table.[7] Stated in other terms, the foreign woman is facing the "Void"[8] as she tries to deal with the painful reality of her daughter's torment, and begs for mercy. Jesus, however, initially appears to cling to the very two-dimensionality that he had earlier rejected. He seems to be pushed to face the possibility of his own faithlessness and abandonment of God at this point and, thereby, to come face to face with the holiness of God "beyond the boundaries" at the prompting of the foreign woman.

The dramatic import of this encounter in the borderlands is heightened as we recall its historical and textual background. "Show them no mercy," Moses had said to the people of Israel (Deut. 7:2). "Have mercy on me, Lord, Son of David," the Canaanite woman implores the New Moses of Israel. This Canaanite woman thus shatters the lingering image of wicked Canaanites, who presumably offer their children in sacrifice to their gods; she pleads on behalf of her daughter, who cannot speak

---

[7] Elaine M. Wainwright lucidly argues this point in *Shall We Look for Another? A Feminist Rereading of the Matthean Jesus* (Maryknoll: Orbis Books, 1998), 86–92.

[8] In Loder's model, the Void ultimately denotes human existence "destined to annihilation … irrevocable drift toward utter emptiness and nothingness which accompanies human existence from the time of birth [and] has many faces—such as loneliness, depression, and death." (*The Transforming Moment*), 230.

for herself.[9] Well aware of his people's position and privilege as "chosen," Jesus initially reasserts the exclusiveness of his mission. But in the end, he welcomes the woman and she receives what she had sought with passion, courage, and determination.

Finally, this story parallels that of the Roman centurion in Mt 8:5–13. These are the only two healings in this Gospel explicitly involving Gentiles and accomplished from a distance. In both cases Jesus deems the people worthy of the gift of healing. In fascinating reversals, both Gentiles even become exemplar figures. Most commentators indicate that although Matthew's final word on mission to the Gentiles does not come until the last chapter of the Gospel (28:16–20), in these and related episodes the theme emerges that ethnicity does not define the people of God. Intertextual comparative studies indicate that Matthew's positive portrait of Jesus' response to the Gentiles constitutes a partial reversal of the Exodus tradition by focusing on the missional goal of bringing outsiders to the knowledge of the God of Israel.[10] God's purposes include Gentiles, and Jesus the Jew is the agent of divine grace on their behalf.[11] Transformation will happen in the borderlands.

The significance of the text: *Judging*

Above we raised the question whether Jesus, as a pastoral caregiver, needed to undergo a difficult "scanning" process requiring the collaboration of a foreign woman in the borderlands in order to further discern the nature and contours of divine grace. Earlier in the gospel text we saw him responding with clarity and certainty in the face of the challenge by Pharisees and scribes. Now he is treading unfamiliar territory and the

---

[9] For this way of restating the meaning of the encounter, I am indebted to my former student Leticia A. Guardiola-Sáenz, who shared with me a paper written during her doctoral work at Vanderbilt University (Summer 1998), "Jesus' Encounter with the Canaanite Woman: The 'Hybrid Moment' of the Matthean Community."

[10] Willard M. Swartley makes this point in *Israel's Scripture Traditions and the Synoptic Gospels: Story Shaping Story* (Peabody, Mass.: Hendrickson Pubs., Inc., 1994), 70.

[11] See, for instance, the fine commentary by Warren Carter, *Matthew and the Margins: A Sociopolitical and Religious Reading* (Maryknoll: Orbis Books, 2000), 320ff. Other recent biblical studies done with a "decolonizing" interest and perspective present a different picture as they attempt to unveil and deconstruct certain perceived biases in the biblical text. See, for example, Musa W. Dube, "A Postcolonial Feminist Reading of Matthew 15:21–28," pt. 3 of *Postcolonial Feminist Interpretation of the Bible* (St. Louis: Chalice Press, 2000). For this African scholar, "the divergent receptions accorded to the centurion and the Canaanite woman reflect the imperial and patriarchal currents at work in Matthew.... No doubt, the implied author, writing in the post-70 C.E. period, wishes to present the Matthean community as a nonsubversive community" (132–3). Dube's work includes serious critiques of the work of several white, western, middle-class feminist writers on this text (169–84). Her thesis and overall discussion are provocative; nevertheless, my appraisal is that she and other authors with similar perspectives often neglect to

"context of rapport" of his circle of disciples does not seem to be particularly helpful.

The text before us suggests and calls for several kinds of stretching. Geographic, ethnic, gender, religious, theological, socio-cultural, moral, and political dimensions are involved. No wonder, then, that the intrusion of the woman into his life and sense of vocation and ministry stunned Jesus. Because this narrative has much spatial and contextual import, it is fitting that our interpretation underscores that this marginal Canaanite woman emerges as the center of the story! In fact, the story is primarily her story. We observe a surprising, transforming reversal: Jesus comes to acknowledge that she has *great* faith. This Gospel uses that adjective to describe faith only once. The woman's faith encompasses her persistent demand for inclusion in the face of Jesus' resistance; her challenge to the gender, ethnic, religious, political, and economic barriers; her recognition of Jesus' authority over demons; and her reliance on his power.[12] Perhaps Jesus' praise includes a realization we can appreciate today as well: In that encounter in the borderlands, the Canaanite woman became a prophetic and wise teacher. Out of her desire for healing for her daughter, she acted and spoke counter-culturally and counter-politically as she reminded Jesus of the larger vision of the reign of God. And she did so in a way consistent with the converging prophetic and wisdom traditions with which Jesus/ Wisdom (Sophia) is interpreted in the Gospel of Matthew.[13]

Put in other words, the Syrophoenician/Canaanite woman had approached Jesus as a care seeker on behalf of her daughter; in the process of her encounter with Jesus, she also ministered to him by eventually focusing on *negating (or contradicting) the negation* inherent in the dog-Gentile analogy traditionally used by the Jews. In terms of transformational logic, her bisociating insight indeed amounted to a constructive act of the imagination[14] which eventually resonated with Jesus' own imagi-

---

acknowledge inherent tensions and dialectical import within biblical texts, and thus fail to appreciate one key aspect of their liberating and transformative potential.

[12] Carter, *Matthew and the Margins*, 324–5.

[13] Wainwright, *Shall We Look for Another?*, 88.

[14] According to James Loder's own definitions, "bisociation" denotes the surprising convergence of two incompatible frames of reference to compose an original and meaningful unity; bisociation is the basic unit of an insight, which may include several bisociations to form a complex new meaning. And "constructive acts of imagination" are those insights, intuitions, or visions that appear—usually with convincing force—in the borderline area between consciousness and unconsciousness; they convey, in a form readily available to consciousness, the essence of a conflict resolution. Loder, *The Transforming Moment*, 222.

nation work. The encounter itself—the unique relationality linking Jesus and the foreign woman—was transformed: confrontation became a kind of collaborative work. And while the disciples seemed to fade to the background, the foreign woman became spiritually closer to Jesus.[15]

The most vexing question for us as pastoral caregivers and theologians is, of course, why Jesus would act as he initially did in this encounter. An answer requires that we maintain the tension between two historical realities pertaining to his socio-cultural experience or lived world. On the one hand, we must assume that Jesus had been socialized into the conventional wisdom of his time and dominant culture. According to such socialization, prudence involved keeping clear boundaries; adhering to certain criteria of what is proper, clean, normal, and appropriate; and holding to right categories and patterns of perception, thought, and relationships. This socialization was undoubtedly part of Jesus' identity as a first-century Jew. From a human science perspective, we do not expect that Jesus would have been exempt from dealing with prejudice. Neither do we expect that he would have spontaneously developed the kind of understanding enabling him to readily appreciate and communicate with the woman across vast ethnic, social, cultural, and religious differences. On the other hand, we must also recognize that Jesus of Nazareth was himself a marginal person.[16] He was rejected by the dominant groups and became a friend of marginalized people such as tax-collectors, outcasts, women, the poor and oppressed, "sinners," and Gentiles. In other words, Jesus related abnormally well to those people and was accepted by them, because he was himself an outsider, a homeless person (Mt 8:20) living in two worlds without fully belonging to either.[17] In sum, from a theological perspective, whenever we look at Jesus the Christ we should see that the historical and existential reality of the incarnation is not only about "body" (sôma), but is also about "soul" (psyche) and "spirit" (pneuma). In other words, we propose to take seri-

---

[15] A formal definition of when it is appropriate to identify change as *transformation*, is in order. According to Loder, "transformation occurs whenever, within a given frame of reference or experience, hidden orders of coherence and meaning emerge to replace or alter the axioms of the given frame and reorder its elements accordingly." *The Transforming Moment*, p. 229.

[16] For a scholarly treatment of the marginality of Jesus, see John P. Meier, *A Marginal Jew: Rethinking the Historical Jesus* (New York: Doubleday, 1991).

[17] Jung Young Lee has insightfully discussed the question of Jesus and marginality in *Marginality: The Key to a Multicultural Theology* (Minneapolis: Fortress Press, 1995). Writing from an Asian (Korean) American perspective, Lee proposes "a new theology based on marginality, which serves not only as a hermeneutical paradigm but as a key to the substance of the Christian faith" (1).

ously the New Testament references which point to a holistic anthropology.

An outsider, a multiply marginal person, challenged Jesus to relate and minister across and beyond those boundaries. She gave him an opportunity to respond in tune with God's alternative wisdom expressed in an ethic and politic of compassion and radical inclusiveness. It is fitting to conclude that Jesus faced a major conflict and temptation, indeed a temptation from within, and that eventually he chose wisely, even as he was creatively challenged by the foreign woman. This conclusion need not compromise the christological conviction about the nature and work of Jesus as Christ. As Hebrews 4:15 puts it, "We do not have a high priest who is unable to sympathize with our weaknesses, but we have one who in every respect has been tested as we are, yet without sin." If we accept this interpretation, we must reject three other interpretations: (a) that Jesus was testing (that is, playing games with) the woman while knowing all along what he should and would do; (b) that he wanted to teach the disciples a dramatic lesson about loving enemies; or, as proposed by some radical feminists, (c) that Jesus had to be converted (repent from sin). The biblical text supports none of these interpretations. On the contrary, it is our view that the text implies the triumph of Jesus' (and the foreign woman's) spirit grounded and sustained by the Spirit of God. In fact, in addition to pertinent christological consideration, this gospel story illumines the question of how the spiritual life can become transcendent and at the same time preserve its immanent integrity in the context of human experience.

As Jesus appropriated the woman's insight significantly expanding the contours of compassion and care, energy was released (he praised the woman in unusual terms, her daughter was healed, and then more miracles took place), and Jesus further engaged in interpretation and ministry in the light of God's reign. The personal drama and the behavior of the Syrophoenician/Canaanite woman became a kind of catalyst of the multifaceted transforming encounter in the borderlands: many barriers were broken, temptation was overcome, understandings were deepened, faith was affirmed, and a child was healed.

The story as it unfolds makes clear that both the woman and Jesus became boundary walkers and boundary breakers. By eventually choosing to relate and to minister "out of place," Jesus and the woman pointed the way to God's utopia. "Utopia" means literally "no place," not in the sense of never-never land, illusion, or fantasy, but as the stuff of prophetic dreams. From a biblical perspective, utopias are places that are not yet, not because they are mere ideals beyond reach, but because evil and sinful structures and behaviors resist and contradict God's will for multidimensional (that is, ethnic, social, cultural, and religious) justice and reconciliation.

Finally, as we judge this text, we must realize its significance in light of the social and existential realities of the Matthean community. On the one hand, we recognize that the Gospel according to Matthew was written from the perspective of the chosen people of Israel, beginning with "Jesus the Messiah, the son of David, the son of Abraham" (Matt. 1:1). The author writes from the center of the tradition, and from a typically "centralist" point of view.[18] Within this framework Jesus instructs the disciples, "Go nowhere among the Gentiles …, but go rather to the lost sheep of the house of Israel" (Matt. 10:5–6). The latter expression is unique to Matthew and repeated in our text. The author leaves no doubt about Israel's priority in salvation history. On the other hand, the story of the Canaanite woman can help undermine and even dismantle—that is, dialectically speaking, negate the negation imposed by—chosenness as ideology, as justification for excluding and discriminating against the other, the stranger, the foreigner, the "pagan." A powerful paradox is at work here!

We surmise that the early readers of Matthew were Jewish Christians separated from the synagogue and relating both to a largely Gentile Christian movement and to the Jewish community. The story must have aided them to understand their new place and role in God's plan and reign. This story may also have helped free them from the ideology of chosenness so they could be transformed into a more liberating and inclusive faith community. Perhaps they were already beginning to experience such a community, but were unsure about how to cope with, legitimate, and reflect on it.[19] This transition and transformation of the Matthean community would have been crucial for their sense of identity as well as for the mission to the Gentiles. The new community—where there is no longer Jew or Greek, slave or free, male and female, for all are one in Christ (Gal. 3:28)—is thus called to celebrate, embody, and be an agent of the coming reign of God, the future in which God is making all things new. Transformation would indeed happen in the borderlands!

Embodying the text: Acting

In this final section we must focus on application. We will do that in

---

[18] Lee, Marginality, 116.

[19] See Leticia A. Guardiola-Sáenz's helpful discussion of this question in "Borderless Women and Borderless Texts: A Cultural Reading of Matthew 15:21–28," Semeia 78 (1997): 69–81.

light of the two questions presented at the beginning of this study: how may this biblical text become foundational for caregiving ministry? How may this unique story further illumine the challenges and possibilities of intercultural and interfaith spiritual care for Christian caregivers?

We may realize the creative and liberating potential of this story in many ways on personal and communal levels. The following interrelated guidelines illustrate how this text has become foundational for me and other pastoral caregivers or, in other words, how the text has ministered to us so that we can minister to others in intercultural and interfaith situations. Without trivializing the import of this wonderful story, I will briefly discuss three ways our text foundationally illumines specific and interrelated principles—that is, dependable guides to practice—for caregiving ministry.

Marginality, vulnerability, and *vision*

First, contrary to what dominant cultures hold, the borderlands can become privileged places for the blessings of creative and transformative caring and for personal and communal growth and healing. Conventional and pragmatic wisdom favors the safe havens of familiar territory, the shrewd and sensible stance of "playing it safe." The story of the Canaanite woman who confronts Jesus helps us realize that we can see reality better at places of marginality and vulnerability and from the vantage point available to us at the borders. Our vision may thus be transformed. Hence, we are called to creative "willful contextual dislocations."[20] This story asks us to move deliberately beyond our comfort zones, either by going out or by welcoming into our midst the stranger, the alien, or the different other. By moving from the center to the margins, we will find our perspectives significantly changed: we will become aware of the lenses through which we view the world, and our cultural and ideological captivities will be unveiled. We will be open to see better how God wants us to live and care for others in creative, redeeming, and empowering ways wherever we are.

Interfaith spiritual care situations present unique challenges and opportunities for pastoral caregivers to grow in *vision*, in the sense of perceiving care seekers and the very relationship of care with the eyes of

---

[20] I have described the notion of willful (or voluntary) dislocation in connection with transformative learning in Daniel S. Schipani, "Liberation Theology and Religious Education," in *Theologies of Religious Education*, ed. Randolph Crump Miller (Birmingham: Religious Education Press, Inc., 1995), 308–10; and "Educating for Social Transformation," in *Mapping Christian Education: Approaches to Congregational Learning*, ed. Jack L. Seymour (Nashville: Abingdon Press, 1997), 37–8.

God, as it were. That growth includes a number of dimensions and practices such as these: attentiveness, contemplation, and respectful and appreciative awareness of the uniqueness and value of the care receiver; critical thinking and creative imagination to deal with and transform barriers to communication and understanding and collaboration; spiritual discernment: (a) to recognize the care receivers' actual needs, hopes, and resourcefulness in their own terms; (b) to make available specific, pertinent care; and (c) to be intentionally open to receiving the spiritual gifts provided by those of other faiths. Finally, growth in *vision*, thus understood, must be considered together with growth in *virtue* and *vocation*, as defined below.

Conflict, suffering, and *virtue*

A second guideline suggested by our study is that situations of conflict and suffering can become opportunities for transformation, for renewal and healing, and for witnessing God's amazing grace. People who hunger and thirst for wholeness, justice, freedom, and peace are especially close to the heart of God because their desire reflects God's own longing for all people. For this reason they are blessed (Mt 5:3–11). For this reason the Canaanite woman was blessed. That is the meaning of the claim of liberation theologies, that God has a preferential option for the poor and oppressed, for the victim and the weak. According to the four Gospels, Jesus not only taught about this preference, he also showed concretely what it involves. In our story, the demonstration happened in a context of conflict and against Jesus' human inclinations! Christian pastoral caregivers are sent to continue his ministry and to embrace the ailing and suffering neighbor who longs for healing and hope. As we respond, our hearts will be nurtured and transformed.

Interfaith spiritual caregiving thus presents unique challenges and opportunities for pastoral caregivers to grow in *virtue*, in the sense of their hearts being formed in the light of Jesus Christ. In other words, the notion of "virtue" (singular) in this essay denotes the moral character of the caregiver. It can be described in terms of our innermost dispositions and attitudes, that is, the "habits of the heart" which help define the content of "Christian character." These are the deep affections and passions and, especially, the kinds of virtues (plural)[21] that, at their best,

---

[21] "Virtues" (in the plural) are those specific moral strengths, skills or capacities, and habits, which have particular moral significance. They are values that become character shaped by practice and discipline. Virtues are thus personal qualities constitutive of the moral character of pastoral caregivers, hopefully reflective of the character of the very faith communities they represent.

faith communities seek to foster and form in their members as genuine expressions of divine love and a way of life in the power of the Spirit. For pastoral caregivers, therefore, interfaith situations may become special places of grace as we are led and empowered to practice the values and the virtues essential for caring as representatives of Christ, such as humility, hospitality, love, compassion, patience, hope, generosity, and courage.

Mutuality, mission, and *vocation*

Third, as Jesus himself may have experienced, ministry at its best is a two-way street, a mutual practice and process. For us in North America, the center of the center in the ongoing globalization process, this kind of ministry poses special challenges. To become truly "missional," our faith communities will have to undergo a conversion to the margins. Many of us Christians need to shed our exclusivist ideology of chosenness to better attend to our deepest yearnings, limitations, and needs, as well as to the potential and resourcefulness of others. We bless and we are in turn blessed, sometimes the hard way, in spite of our blinders and shortcomings. Often we will unexpectedly find ourselves being ministered to. In fact, we cannot truly participate in other people's liberation and healing without allowing them to participate in our own liberation and healing.

Interfaith spiritual caregiving presents unique challenges and opportunities for pastoral caregivers to grow in *vocation*, in the sense of partnership with the Spirit as the essence of our ministerial practice. In the process of interfaith caregiving our common human vocation in the light of God can be reconfirmed and sustained. Furthermore, for us today the twofold blessing of mutuality and partnership may include an additional realization: caring and being cared for in the borderlands, across and against boundaries of culture and faith, again and again becomes the sacred experience of encountering and loving Christ anew. In due time it will be revealed to us, as in the eschatological parable of Mt 25:31–46:[22] "Truly I tell you, just as you did it to one of the least of these who are members of my family, you did it to me."

---

[22] Matthew's judgment scene in 25:31–46 is the culmination of a two-chapter eschatological discourse, and it has been interpreted in diverse ways. In any event, two things should be kept in mind. First, for Matthew, Jesus is identified with the (marginalized) community of disciples, and he is present with them as they engage in mission to communicate the gospel (18:20, 28:20). Second, in this text Jesus praises the actions of the righteous from "all the nations" (presumably Gentiles as well as Jews and Christians) because they have lived out the gospel by caring for the poor, oppressed, and marginalized; the actions of these "sheep" blessed by the Father are the practices of service expected of gospel bearers, followers of Jesus Christ.

Appendix

On the wideness of compassion in the witness of Scripture

An interpretive survey of Old and New Testament material allows us to highlight scriptural sources for an affirmation of the boundless reach of Grace in the face of diversity, including multifaith settings. In the words of W. Eugene March: "[We are] well aware and appreciative of an ex‑ plicit narrative in the Bible that focuses first on God's people, Israel, and then widens to include Christians and the church. The election of each of these peoples for specific service to God and on God's behalf in the world is clear. But there is another, implicit narrative … this has to do with God's ongoing relationship with others beyond Israel and the church. The service entrusted to Israel and the church assumes that all people are creatures of God and the objects of divine love."[23] Those biblical sources may, therefore, help us to undergird caregiving ministry in inter‑ faith situations. What follows is a selection of such foundational mate‑ rial in summary fashion.[24]

Old Testament background

- Genesis 1:26–27. All humans are created as spiritual beings "in [God's] image," "according to [God's] likeness."

- Genesis 3. All humans share the predicament of struggle and potential alienation resulting in the need for manifold care.

- Genesis 9:1–17. God's covenant with Noah is an all‑inclusive, fundamental, and universal "covenant of life," which is not can‑ celled by other covenants recorded in Scripture.

- Genesis 11:1–9. The story of the tower of Babel symbolizes the human will to concentrate and consolidate and the tendency to‑ wards power and domination. It represents disobedience to the divine mandate to "scatter and fill the earth"— which indicates that it is diversity, rather than homogeneity or uniformity, that is the outgrowth of God's design for human culture.

---

[23] W. Eugene March, *The Wide, Wide Circle of Divine Love: A Biblical Case for Religious Diversity* (Louisville: Westminster John Knox, 2004), x.

[24] See also, Cynthia M. Campbell, *A Multitude of Blessings: A Christian Approach to Religious Diversity* (Lousville: Westminster John Knox, 2007). In this book the author makes a compelling case: it is possible, indeed necessary, to paradoxically embrace the reality and value of religious diversity in terms of God's providential care for all of humankind, while also affirming the Christian confession that God has made Godself uniquely known to humankind in the life, death, and resurrection of Jesus.

- Genesis 12:3. Those who claim to be the chosen people of God are called to become a blessing "to all families," "to the nations." This is the key to the human vocation of partnership with Grace, which may be uniquely enacted in pastoral care ministry.

- Leviticus 19:24, Deuteronomy 10:17. "You shall love the alien as yourself ... the Lord ... loves the strangers." Welcoming and caring for the stranger: interfaith spiritual care can and must be a special case of hospitable compassion.

- Subversive stories (in addition to the role of "religious others"— Hagar, Asenath, Zipporah, Cyrus, and many others): Ruth the Moabite, the foreigner pagan becomes "one of us" and much more. Jonah, reluctant "missionary," reveals nagging divine compassion for the sake of strangers "lost."

- Wisdom books—Job, Proverbs, Ecclesiastes, parts of Psalms—and wisdom theology as a form of practical theology: they focus on human experience and predicament and draw from many wellsprings (including extra-biblical sources) for discernment of truthful knowledge and the way of the good life.

- Jeremiah 18:18. The gifts of priests/instruction, prophets/word, and sages/counsel summarize the biblical canon as well as the main "offices" for the formation and transformation of Israel as people of God. Those very gifts may be applied and bestowed especially in interfaith care situations.

New Testament guidelines

- John 1:14, 20:21. The key to an incarnation theology and ministry of presence: the Word (Logos=Wisdom) became flesh and lived among us. Pastoral caregivers may view themselves as sent by Jesus to embody good news (John 20:21).

- Story meets story: the narrative shape of the gospel encounters the narrative quality of human experience: the Jesus story and the stories Jesus told in light of our stories. Pastoral caregivers may view themselves as bearers of the Story, witnesses to the unfolding drama of care receivers' life stories, and mediators between and among stories.

- Luke 4:16–27. "The Spirit of the Lord is upon me ..." Pastoral caregivers committed to minister in the manner and with the spirit of Jesus may become radically inclusive instruments of liberation and healing empowered by the same Spirit.

- Mark 4:3–8. Parable of the sower: sent to sow generously and joyfully. Pastoral caregivers do not calculate beforehand if/how/when/where the seed will fall on "good soil" but go about the task with liberal, gracious freedom; they know that making things grow is not their concern because growth [formation and transformation] is in the hands of Another; they trust that, at the end of the day, there will be a surprisingly abundant harvest!

- Matthew 13:24–30. The parable of the wheat and the weeds. Suspend discrimination and judgment: Pastoral caregivers involved in interfaith situations must not dismiss, disregard, undervalue, the seemingly undeserving care receivers; they must care for everybody with equal diligence, competence, and generosity, regardless of religious affiliation, faith tradition, or type of spirituality; they must refrain from condemnation while trusting divine wisdom, mercy, and justice.

- Matthew 25:31–46. The parable of the judgment of the nations: Seeing and serving Jesus in interfaith situations. Pastoral caregivers may recognize and honor their daily walk into/within sacred places because visiting the sick strangers and their relatives (other-than-Christian) is an occasion to care for "one of the least of these …"; instead of trying to "bring Jesus" to the care receivers, they can confidently expect to encounter Christ in them and to care for Christ, as it were, through them: ("When did we see you …? I was a stranger and you welcomed me … I was sick and you took care of me."); they allow those strangers—"the least of these"—to become a blessing in turn.

- Luke. 10:25–37. Unexpected sources of revelation—encountering the (good) Samaritans: Pastoral caregivers engaged in interfaith situations may discover new dimensions of meaning and love through caring especially well for those who are different or a "minority"; re-discover gospel truth by being open to the faith of another (e.g. the gratitude of the Samaritan leper who was healed [Luke 17:16]); experience conversion again and again (becoming the Christian caregiver who looks more like the good Samaritan, the good Jew, Muslim, Hindu, Humanist…).

- John 4:1–41. Jesus and the Samaritan woman—interfaith encounters involve different kinds of dynamics. Pastoral caregivers may become aware of, and able to deal with, cross-cultural and inter-religious realities, and gender dynamics; willing to become vulnerable for the sake of care; and able to assess care receivers' spiritual needs as well as their resourcefulness.

- Mark 7:24–30. Jesus and the Syrophoenician or Cannanite woman: the risks, challenges and blessings of ministering at the margins. Wise pastoral caregivers ministering in the borderlands of interfaith situations will discover that: places of marginality, ambiguity, or paradox may become places of grace; tension and conflict connected with socio-cultural and spiritual-theological factors (e.g. temptation not to minister) can turn into occasions for new insight and other learnings, emotional and spiritual growth; and ministry, at its best, is always a two-way street.

- Luke 7, Acts 10. Other "outsiders" cared for: the possibility of recognizing the presence, goodness, and power of God is not limited to the "people of God," because "God shows no partiality…" Christian pastoral caregivers may become mediators of grace and not only recognize and affirm the spirituality of people of other faiths but delight in the interface of spiritual paths involving care seekers and caregivers.

- Acts 2:1–13. From confusion and alienation to communication and communion: Pentecost and the reversal of Babel (Genesis 11:1–9), without destroying diversity. Pastoral caregivers may partner with the Spirit as they become spiritually and theologically "multilingual," develop the skills of translating Good News through a variety of languages and cultural frameworks, and wisely practice spiritual assessment and specific caregiving work with discernment.

A Lutheran chaplain's nine theses on interfaith care ministry

John D. Peterson

One spring afternoon in 1971, I was sitting in the downstairs hallway of True Light Lutheran Church in New York City's Chinatown, when a Buddhist monk in saffron robes and sandals walked into the Missouri Synod church. The monk spoke in Chinese to the several young members of the church to whom I had been talking. "He wants a drink of water," one of the teenagers told me as another went to get a glass of water. His thirst satisfied, the monk went on his way. What makes this experience over 30 years ago memorable to me is the sense of anxiety and threat I felt as this very different man of a very different god entered what I considered to be Lutheran territory, and my relief when he left. The young folks thought it was neat and remarkable that they had had the opportunity to show kindness and care to a worthy stranger with a need that was easily satisfied. But to me, the Vicar [seminary intern], two very different theological planets had nearly collided.

   Almost thirty years of hospital ministry have caused my working theology to become deeper and broader. While traditional Lutheran theology takes a polemic stance toward other religions, insights central to Reformation theology are helpful for spiritual caregivers in relation to those of other faiths. I found many references in Luther's writings about Jewish or Muslim people; all have been polemic, and not understanding or compassionate in tone. However, I chalk this up to the context in those pre-Renaissance times—strikingly different than the present day in terms of the amount of diversity and pluralism expected and tolerated in the world.

   Coming into hospital ministry, I learned from the outset that the role

---

John D. Peterson, D.Min., is a supervisor of Clinical Pastoral Education and Director of the Pastoral Care Division at Lutheran Hospital of Indiana, Fort Wayne, Indiana.

of chaplain precludes an apologetic or competitive stance toward patients who present other (religious and non-religious) faiths. Patients and family members are in a dependent, 'one-down' position, and chaplains who used their access to patients to proselytize would be taking advantage of the patient's extreme vulnerability. There is a place for explicitly witnessing to one's faith or convictions, but it is when care seekers have control of their own environment, and can respond or engage with freedom and integrity.

Conversely, Christian chaplains have a rare opportunity to convey the power of the very grace that is the cornerstone of the Christian faith when they minister to the patient with respect and awareness of the patient's own belief system. In the movie, *The Shoes of the Fisherman*,[1] Russian Cardinal Kiril Lakota, newly made pope, escapes the confines of the Vatican and walks the streets, taking in the sounds and smells of Rome at dinnertime. A doctor approaches and asks him to hurry, fill a prescription. Father Kiril returns and enters the house. The family is Jewish and is shocked to see a priest, especially when he tries to give the dying man Last Rites. When a family member announces their Jewish faith, they respond with wonder and joy as Kiril begins to chant Kaddish. A similar joy is often evident when Christian chaplains are able to reach across religious boundaries and minister to patients on the care receivers' own terms.

Caring for Ahmet: A case study

The case study that follows is typical for interfaith pastoral visits that occur in the mid-western setting of the hospital in which I serve. The hospital itself was begun over 100 years ago by Lutherans, seeking to realize their understanding of Jesus' directive to care for the sick and injured. I direct a Clinical Pastoral Education (CPE) program within this hospital, and many of the visits made in our hospital are made by students. There are relatively few organized faith communities in the area that are not Christian, but, with increased immigration, there are now Muslim, Buddhist, Hindu as well as the more established Jewish communities in the area.

Preliminary data

The patient, whom I will call Ahmet, is of East European origin, aged 39, married. He is hospitalized with heart and kidney problems. Ahmet is an electrician and the visit is a random one, made one afternoon as the

---

[1] The film, *The Shoes of the Fisherman*, was directed by Michael Anderson and produced by Metro-Goldwyn-Mayer, in 1968.

student chaplain was making rounds on his assigned unit.

The Chaplain, whom I will call Douglas, is an ordained minister in an independent evangelical church. He is in part-time CPE and is also an assistant minister in an area congregation. He had had a difficult morning at the church and internally resisted coming to the hospital to make visits. "I asked God to prepare my heart for what I would encounter that afternoon." Douglas is learning to be more alert to the nonverbal communication that goes on in pastoral conversations, and especially strives to be alert to "the patient's attitudes as we talk and if there is anything that is especially bothering them." He also tries "to be a spiritual and emotional encourager to the person I am visiting," and to be sure that he doesn't allow "my 'emotional baggage' to get in the way of my ministry."

The Situation: The patient was sitting up on the side of the bed. He appeared to be a little fidgety. The television was on. Ahmet was a very polite gentleman who spoke with an accent. He appeared receptive to Douglas's visit and was willing to talk.

Content of verbatim

C = Chaplain

P = Patient

C1 (Chaplain knocks) Good afternoon, my name is Douglas and I am one of the chaplains here at the hospital. May I come in and visit with you for a few minutes?

P1 Sure come on in, I would love some company. (He spoke with an accent that I could not recognize at first).

C2 How do you pronounce your first name—Ahmet?

P2 That is correct. And you pronounce your first name—Douglas?

C3 That is correct, (laughter). I won't even try to pronounce your last name, but I am sure that I would mispronounce it.

P3 Oh it is easy. It is pronounced_____. See how simple that is! (He laughs, knowing that it is a hard name to pronounce).

C4 How long have you been here in the hospital?

P4 I have been here about a week, but I hope that I will get to go home tomorrow. Even so, I know that I am going to have to come back for some surgery at some time.

C5 What kind of surgery are you going to need to have?

P5 Well, I came into the hospital because I was having heart problems and while I was here they found I had kidney problems and now I am on dialysis. Sometime I am going to need a kidney transplant, but first they have to find a suitable donor for me.

C6 Is there someone in your family who is a good match, like a brother or sister?

P6 No, so far they have not been able to locate anyone, but perhaps I have some family in Europe who would make for a good match.

C7 What part of Europe are you originally from? I could not identify your accent.

P7 I am originally from Bosnia and I lived there until ten years ago when I came to the United States. I still have family back in Bosnia.

C8 What was it like living in Bosnia? All I really know about Bosnia is what I have seen on TV or have read in the newspaper.

P8 Bosnia was a very hard place to live with all of the fighting. I served in the Bosnian army for a number of years. It is very hard watching your friends being shot and killed. I was one of the lucky ones to get out alive. War is terrible and it benefits no one. All of the fighting is especially hard on the young who are left homeless and who have one or both of their parents killed in the fighting. It is also very hard on the old people of our land who are left with nothing.

C9 I have never been in the military or been involved in a war, so I can only imagine what it must have been like for you. You are right when you say that war benefits no one, and everyone pays a price of some kind for the fighting.

P9 I hope that you never have to go to war or serve in the army. Do you have children?

C10 Yes, my wife and I have two sons who are 23 and 26 years old.

P10 I hope that your sons never have to go to war either, or have to be in the army.

C11 What brought you to the United States?

P11 I have an older brother who was already living here and he was an electrician. I came to work with him and to help him start his own business. I did not know much about electricity when I came, but he has taught me much about what being an electrician means. So now I work on other people's wiring and I am here in the hospital because I need to have some of my own wiring worked on. That is a poor joke isn't it?

C12 At least you have been able to keep some sense of humor and laughter in the situation. Laughter is sometimes a good medicine for us when we are hurting and struggling with the problems of life. Another help during our times of struggle is our faith. Do you have any type of religious faith to lean on during this time?

P12 My religious background is Muslim. Do you know anything about the Muslim faith?

C13 I know a little bit about the Muslim faith, but I also know that there is more that I do not know. I do know that the Muslim faith and the Christian faith have the same roots originally in the person of Abraham.

P13 Tell me chaplain, why do we have so many different religions in the world and how did they come about?

C14 Wow, that is a big question. I suppose that I could try to give a short answer. We have so many different religions because we have so many different kinds of people with different religious viewpoints. Originally there was just one religion, the worship of Yahweh God, but then somebody had a different idea and a new religion grew up. And we see that same scenario happening down through the ages, until today we have hundreds of different religions.

[Douglas's opinion here is, of course, offered extemporaneously and is certainly incorrect in that there were a variety of religions in the world already in the time of Abraham.]

P14 That is kind of the way it was with Christianity and the Muslim faith.

C15 Yes, we all come from the same source. Abraham who is the father of the Hebrew nation believed in Yahweh God and he had two sons: Isaac and Ishmael. From the line of Isaac the Hebrew faith came about and from Ishmael came the Muslim faith.

P15 In the Muslim faith we believe in Jesus, but only as a good prophet, where you believe in him as the Son of God. We believe in a lot of the prophets and their teachings. A lot of what is written in the Koran is also written in your Bible. I think that we believe in the same God, but we use different names to describe Him. What bothers me is that there are so many Muslims who use their religion for other purposes, they do not even follow what the Koran is really saying, they change it to fit what they want to do. It bothers me when some Muslims use their faith as an excuse for killing other people simply to get what they want. The Koran does not teach us to do that. That is wrong. That is not religion.

C16 You know, Ahmet, people have been doing that same thing for years.

Look back in history at the time of the Crusades and the Holy Wars that were fought, all under the heading of religion. I think we will always have people who will use their religion as a means to accomplish what they want and who give no thought to what God really wants. It makes it harder to argue against someone's actions if they justify them for religious reasons.

P16 You are very right.

C17 Listen to us—we sound like a couple of philosophers who are trying to figure out how we can change the world and solve all the problems of the world. (We both laugh). I have enjoyed our conversation—it has been very stimulating. I sure do hope that they can find a match for you for a kidney replacement. If there is anything that I can do for you while you are here, please feel free to have one of the nurses page me, and if I am not here, one of our other chaplains will be happy to help you. Before I take my leave, may I pray for you in the name of Yahweh our God?

P17 I would appreciate that.

C18 Dear God, I want to thank you for this day and the blessings that you have provided for both Ahmet and me. I want to thank you that two people from different parts of the world could sit down and talk about life and religion the way we have this afternoon. I thank you for the opportunity to meet Ahmet and to hear a portion of his story. Dear God I want to thank you for the things that we have in common and the opportunity that we have had to be able to encourage each other this afternoon. I want to also pray that you would be with Ahmet as he prepares to go home in the next couple of days, that the problems with his heart have been corrected. And I also pray that you would be with him in the weeks ahead, that a suitable kidney donor might be found. I pray your care and your blessing might be upon him. These things I pray in the name of Yahweh, the God of Abraham and our God. Amen.

P18 Amen. Thank you Douglas for visiting me and praying with me.

C19 It was a privilege Ahmet. The best of luck to you.

Pastoral and spiritual assessment

Early in the visit, Chaplain Douglas was aware that he was visiting someone with a very different set of beliefs. The patient's welcoming attitude and openness facilitated the visit. Douglas tried to be respectful of the patient's belief system, which was made difficult by his awareness that he actually knew little about the patient's faith system. "I tried to find areas where we had common ground and to build off of those areas." Chaplain Douglas felt good that the dialogue included principles that he considers Christian, such as respect for persons despite differences, and demonstration of compassion for fellow humans.

Chaplain Douglas wished he had explored the call of Abram a little more in Genesis 12 and how that call related to each of them. "The story of Abraham is … a faith story of a man who knew the value of trusting in God, a concept that we could have developed more fully."

Chaplain Douglas assessed the relationship he developed with Ahmet as meaningful in that they both learned something new about each other and about their religious faiths. He appreciated both Ahmet's commitment to his faith system, as well as his disappointment with those who misuse that faith system for their own agendas. Douglas appreciated Ahmet's openness and the questions he asked, even though they moved the discussion away from Ahmet's hospitalization and immediate situation, to a more global discussion.

Nevertheless, Douglas saw the trust implicit in the patient's broad questions. I was uncertain whether Ahmet was eagerly taking advantage of an opportunity for a heartfelt discussion that would explore his faith with the chaplain for whom he felt some initial trust, and who represented the dominant religious paradigm of his adopted culture, or whether his questions represented a theological distraction that would keep the discussion global, and safely away from the intimacy of an existential discussion about his hospitalization.[2] My training and experience as a CPE supervisor leaves me with a bias toward the latter interpretation, that of an ambivalent patient and a student chaplain, colluding to avoid intimacy. Perhaps it was both!

Douglas was not aware of any desire to change Ahmet's belief system: "I felt like we were two sons of Abraham who were able to come together on some common ground. I believe that I was able to minister to him, and he certainly ministered to me."

Chaplain Douglas saw his role as that of emotional and spiritual "encourager" for this patient. He felt he was able to do this to the extent that they were able to establish "some common ground to work from." Douglas also thought that his presence and conversation were forces of encouragement for the patient. "Jesus taught us that we are to love one another and I believe that we were both able to demonstrate that principle in how we dialogued." Douglas saw the patient's permission for

---

[2] Similar to the sense I make of the comment in another interfaith discussion, that of the woman at Jacob's well in her encounter with Jesus. John 4:19–20.

prayer as evidence that some trust had been established.

Chaplain Douglas presented this verbatim with the following questions: (1) He was unsure if he should have (or could have?) gone further in discussing the divergent views of Jesus that surfaced in the dialogue. (2) He wanted feedback on his sensitivity "to the extreme difference in our faith systems." (3) Douglas wanted feedback on his attempts to balance his attention to the patient's physical needs, emotional needs and spiritual needs.

Summary of group and supervisory feedback

The supervisor realized that this was a first experience of ministry to a person of another faith system by this relative newcomer to hospital ministry. Douglas comes from a conservative, evangelical background, theologically, and his attempt to honor the inclusive approach to ministry that is part of CPE orientation in our hospital was evident.

The feedback given to Douglas was similar to his own ministry approach in that we tried to be encouraging—encouraging of his attempt to find common ground in his spiritual discussion with Ahmet, and his willingness to find ways to fully accept this man for being a fellow human. It was suggested to Douglas that he could have focused more attention on listening to the patient, for example, in the religious part of the discussion, asking Ahmet to teach him about the Muslim faith, especially those parts that were helpful in times of sickness and uncertainty. The group also encouraged Douglas to use the experience to find out more about ways of ministering to Muslims. There was doubt expressed about the "prayer to Yahweh" (the Hebrew name for "LORD") as being an appropriate way to minister to a Muslim. Finally, a seminar was scheduled for the group, featuring a hospital physician who is a practicing Muslim. My own curiosity was awakened by this visit about our widespread inclination to find "common ground" when confronted by a difference. Are there other, better ways to proceed?

Interfaith pastoral care and Lutheranism

When Luther posted 95 theses on the Castle Church door in the university town of Wittenburg in Germany 490 years ago, he was seeking to promote a theological discussion about the practice of indulgences. In a similar way, I would like to offer the following nine theses regarding ways in which Lutheran theology offers perspective on pastoral care to those of other faith traditions. My perspective draws on my experience as chaplain and supervisor of Clinical Pastoral Education in historically Lutheran institutions, as well as eight years in parish ministry.

Lutheran theology lifts up the importance of the individual

Martin Luther was at the forefront of leaders in both church and society of his day who gave new value to the interior and exterior human life. The human conscience and the individual human's behavior and goals suddenly became important. The Christian chaplain who ministers to persons of another faith can carry the value that 'every person's life is worth a novel,' that every person's experience, sense of right and wrong, is valuable.

The Christian caregiver is freed from anxiety of the law

Luther's own faith journey was initially fueled by a search for relief from anxiety; in his case, anxiety about a God whom he experienced as enraged about human sin. He constantly worried that his own actions and thoughts were not good enough, and acts of painful and damaging self-mortification in order to appease this wrathful God were of only temporary help.[3] In his great awakening, Luther discovered that the Gospel meant that Christ's merit interceded so that believers were set free from terror about God's righteous wrath. They were forgiven, for Christ's sake, freed from anxiety and freed to love and to serve. I draw great comfort from the Gospel as I minister to those of other faiths. I am set free from the anxiety that I feel in the presence of a different theological world. The Gospel means that I can be a non-anxious presence, reflecting, as best I can, God's love to fellow humans.

The Christian is called to live in trust that God's love is for the whole world

The eminent Swedish Lutheran theologian, Krister Stendahl, once stated that "God's agenda is the mending of creation."[4] Even though individuals are important to God, it is important for Christian caregivers to see the larger picture. Luther stressed that God's love is for all humans, and that humans are called to love neighbors whether they were seen as friend or foe.

Convinced of God's enduring love, the Christian is called into vocation

Some of Luther's most valuable insights have to do with his theology of vocation. To Luther, butchers, bakers, and candlestick makers have been called by God and have vocations that are just as valid as those held by pastors and teachers. All work to provide sustenance to humans and to a

---

[3] For a very readable and accurate study of Luther's life, including *Anfechtungen* [spiritual struggles] see Roland Bainton, *Here I Stand: A Life of Martin Luther*, Abington-Cokesbury, 1950.

[4] Krister Stendahl, as quoted by Roland E. Miller, "Christ the Healer," in Henry L. Lettermann, ed., *Health and Healing: Ministry of the Church*, (Chicago: Wheat Ridge Foundation Symposium Papers, 1980), 16.

world with many levels of needs. God chooses to accomplish many purposes on earth by calling humans to the ongoing job of care. In the hospital setting, this idea of vocation has been helpful in seeing nurses and physicians regardless of their faith traditions, as well as chaplains, as ministers.

Ministry to persons of other faiths needs to be more than just "evangelism"

No matter the Christian's specific vocation, the basic job description is to love our neighbor. As we are involved in service and ministry, addressing human needs, we are involved in what can be called the *penultimate.*[5] We feed the hungry, provide shelter for the homeless, encourage those who are sick and injured. As we do so, we trust that God is working through us, addressing the *ultimate* concerns. Luther was motivated to speak out about indulgences because he saw that the entire approach of the church toward individuals had been relegated to travelling salesmen. In our day and society it is sometimes a danger that we develop a similar tunnel vision, reducing 'outreach' to the point that it becomes synonymous with a kind of evangelism that is divorced from care and listening. When this happens the valid ministry of evangelism is reduced to a sales pitch, and the gospel is reduced to a 'product.' Our unavoidable and irreducible vocation is to love our neighbors, trusting that God will call whom God will call.

Pastoral care to those of other faiths is not extraneous, but central to the church's mission

A remarkable letter has recently been sent from an international group of eminent Muslim scholars to Jewish and Christian religious leaders.[6] The letter calls for solidarity and common advocacy for peace and witness to the world, an invitation to base this collaboration in the faiths' agreement that believers are called to love God and to love the neigh-

---

[5] Dietrich Bonhoeffer, *Ethics* (New York: MacMillan, 1955), 82. Cited in Edward E. Thornton, *Theology and Pastoral Counseling* (Englewood Cliffs: Prentice-Hall, Inc., 1964), 39: "No one has the last word, yet everyone may have the next-to-last word."

[6] "A Common Word Between Us and You." See the official website: http://www.acommonword.com: On October 13, 2006, one month to the day after Pope Benedict XVI's Regensburg address of September 13, 2006, 38 Islamic authorities and scholars from around the world, representing all denominations and schools of thought, joined together to deliver an answer to the Pope in the spirit of open intellectual exchange and mutual understanding. In their *Open Letter to the Pope,* for the first time in recent history, Muslim scholars from every branch of Islam spoke with one voice about the true teachings of Islam. Now, exactly one year after that letter, Muslims have expanded their message. In *A Common Word Between Us and You,* 138 Muslim scholars, clerics and intellectuals have unanimously come together for the first time since the days of the Prophet to declare the common ground between Christianity and Islam.

bor. This God-ordained hospitality is at its fullest when we are welcoming the stranger, when we show love to those who have been seen as enemy.

The Christian is always *simul iustus et peccator* (simultaneously just and sinner)

This phrase was used by Luther to describe a paradox of the Christian life: we are saints, trying to make God the center of our being, yet our vision always curves in on itself.[7] Our God is always too small, because we fashion our perceptions of the Divine in our own image and marginalize those whose image is different. Luther thought that it was always dangerous to anthropomorphize God. This, in a subtle way, puts us at center stage. If God is just like us, it's only reasonable to make others be like us as well. Luther had a healthy skepticism about councils and synods and the decisions they make. The Church always needs reforming. I experience myself as being called to care for those of other faiths, not because my God is small and needs my help, but because God is always larger than we can imagine.

As we minister to and relate to those of other faiths, we become more authentic and faithful Christians

If sin is, as Luther said, "cor curvatus in se," ('the heart curving in on itself'), our vocations should stretch our hearts. The Christian Scriptures offer many examples of people who were sent to love and serve those who were not only 'strange' and 'different,' but were the very ones despised and seen as problematic by the ones God sent. Jonah comes to mind.[8] The very act of hearts being stretched to where they would not formerly go makes that act a profound experience. In Clinical Pastoral Education, such stretching experiences happen often. An African-American student chaplain who grew up in the Deep South is called to minister to a dying white man, also from the south. A conservative Christian is asked to pray with a Jewish family. In the concreteness of the moment, we exercise our faith (or our faith exercises us); and we follow our human vocations. We give up trying to be God, and we let God be God.[9]

We are called to be ambassadors for Christ

We are always witnessing, whether we like it or not. As pastoral caregivers

---

[7] Luther wrote about *simul iustus et peccator* in many places. One such place is in his *Against Latomus: Luther's Works* (St. Louis: Concordia Publishing House, 1955), Volume 32, 190ff.

[8] For an excellent discussion of the book of Jonah that is relevant to this discussion, see Jacques Ellul, *The Judgment of Jonah* (Grand Rapids, MI: William B. Eerdmans, 1971).

[9] Philip S. Watson, *Let God Be God: An Interpretation of the Theology of Martin Luther* (Philadelphia: Fortress Press, 1966).

who will be easily identified as Christians by those to whom we minister, our vocation will be one of offering the quality of love that we have experienced in the Gospel to all those who struggle with illness, pain, and calamity. "See how they love one another," said Tertullian in the third Century about Christian communities.[10] In order to be effective, this love must contain tact and sensitivity, as well as respect for the other person and his or her faith. As ambassadors we must learn to live in a strange land in a respectful, peaceable way, trusting that there will be opportunities, when asked, to share about 'the hope that is within us, with gentleness and reverence.' (1 Peter 3:15).

In conclusion, Luther's words most dear to those who carry his name (a practice I doubt he would condone) are "pecca fortiter," or "sin boldly." In this brief essay, I have tried to "sin boldly" in the same sense that I imagine Luther did when composing his 95 theses, putting his convictions into the context of the accepted docrine of his day, so that current religious practice might be improved through the hoped-for dialogue within his faith community. I do so, knowing that, if I have erred, God will forgive me, and if I haven't, God will still forgive me.

---

[10] Tertullian, *Apology*, Chapter 39:7 Loeb Classical Library Series, volume 250, 1998.

A chaplain reflects on caring for a Jewish family

William H. Griffith

It was Saturday evening when my pager contact informed me of a need at one of our palliative care units. When I heard the name of the patient, I immediately suspected that he might be Jewish.

I wanted to be prepared to provide them the option of having a Rabbi so I checked my resource listings for that area and located the name of the Rabbi who was to be on-call for that weekend. As I drove to the facility my mind began to sort out the kind of spiritual support I might anticipate providing. This is a normal process whenever I am paged to the bedside of a dying patient, and as important as it is to be prepared I know that it is rare that what I anticipate is actually what I end up doing. I believe that each visit must be approached with an open mind and a flexibility that allows the caregiver to 'go with the flow' of the particular situation and appropriately improvise for the sake of timely and adequate care.

On this occasion I found myself hoping that they would be pleased that I had the name of a Rabbi that would be available on a Saturday night. Then, again, I thought they might be Jewish in name only and not even be interested in a Rabbi. What would I do if that were the situation? And if they were deeply religious Jews what would they expect from me as a hospice chaplain? What spiritual support would they expect from a non-Jewish, Protestant, Baptist chaplain?

I then realized that what I was really deeply concerned about was what I

William H. Griffith, D.Min., is a chaplain for the Hospice of South Central Indiana, Columbus, Indiana. Much of the content of this essay appeared in Griffith's book, *More Than a Parting Prayer: Lessons in Care Giving for the Dying* (Valley Forge: Judson Press, 2004), chapter 14—"Honor the Care Receiver's Faith"—pp. 56–58. Rev. Griffith graciously accepted our invitation to further document for us his reflective process on the ministry event involving a pastoral visit with a Jewish family. Griffith's comments *in italics* are meant to enable the readers to have some insight into his pastoral reflection as an interfaith chaplain providing care for that family. (The editors) had to offer this Jewish family. I knew that my Christian beliefs based on the teachings of Jesus' life, death, and resurrection, if verbalized, were helpful when providing spiritual care to a Christian, but would not be appropriate for caring for a Jewish family. I would need to use Old Testament scripture which was familiar and remind them of the healing truth they needed to affirm. I began to think about the many Old Testament verses that I used in officiating at Christian funerals and concluded many of them would be appropriate.

When I arrived at the patient's room, I found it to be filled with family members. The young men were wearing yarmulkes (skullcaps).

When I saw all of the yarmulkes I knew immediately that the family requesting me was not only Jewish, but were probably very religious. I thought they would surely want the Rabbi, and I was so pleased that I had thought to find his name and knew how to reach him.

A woman with gray hair who was standing by the bed looked at me as I entered the room; I concluded that she was the wife of the dying man. I introduced myself to her, and she said, "Pastor, thank you for coming. Jacob is not going to make it and we need you to be here."

I was a bit surprised in hearing her call me 'Pastor' but it did signal that she was aware of my role as a clergy of a different faith tradition. Her immediate comment that she knew her husband was dying and it was important for me, a non-Jewish clergy, to be there with them made me feel very welcome. It also signaled an expectation which I needed to clarify.

Not that there was much doubt, but I confirmed with them that they were Jewish and then asked if it would be helpful if I contacted a Rabbi for them.

I actually had the hope that they would be very pleased that I could do that and, if she said yes, then my support for this Jewish family would be successful.

The woman smiled and said, "No, our God is your God, and he hears our prayers."

Well, that meant she didn't expect me to call a Rabbi, and that she was content that I was there with them. Her statement 'our God', I believed, was also meant to signal to me that her belief in God was compatible with my belief in God, and the presence of a Rabbi would not be necessary for her to experience spiritual support. That of course was her way of informing me that she knew I would provide the pastoral care she needed. This is the moment in the visit when all the anticipation of what might happen and what one might do is left behind. It is the moment that specifically initiates the process of providing the spiritual care that is expected.

I affirmed her statement and, since Jacob was not responding, I asked her if he had the assurance of God's love and care in these dying days. She smiled again and said, "Oh, yes, he knew."

One of the common values that religious faiths share is the belief in a God of love, and knowing the Jewish teaching of the Old Testament, I felt it was a good place to start. This also gave me the opportunity to call the dying patient by name and therefore include him in our conversation. It is important not to ignore the non-responsive patient, because the medical profession informs us that hearing is the last sense to go and, in any case, a non-responsive patient needs to be treated with the same respect as any person who is able to respond in detectable ways.

I then was introduced to every person in the room, and the woman directed a grandson to get me a chair so that I could sit with her by the bed.

This gesture was another clear signal of the woman's expectation of the chaplain. She was not simply looking for a prayer to be offered by a religious clergy person as a ritual needed before the death occurs; she was expecting a person to provide some support by their presence. The offer of a chair meant this would be 'more than a parting prayer.' I knew that my sitting down by the bedside with the wife of the dying man would bring a direct focus on me, and they would all have some expectation of what would happen next. It was at such a time that I had to make a decision as to what spiritual care was expected and needed, and how I would provide it. Based on my assessment of expectation and need, I knew there were two basic directions that I could pursue. I could either start directly with the scripture, assuming I would choose those verses that would address their needs and expectations, or I could start with the present moment and listen for those needs to be clarified before drawing upon scriptural support. I don't believe there is simply a right or wrong way to proceed, but the personal assessment of the moment must determine the direction to be taken. It is much like preparing a sermon in that the preacher may start with a biblical text and amplify and apply it to life experience; or start with the latter and then shed light on the life experiences with the scriptures.

My choice in this situation was to start with the present moment of the people in the room who were all family and were all there to support one another while they all faced together the dying of someone they loved. They were all calm with no one showing any extreme emotion of grief, and the way they treated one another showed me their relationships were very caring.

I sat down, and I invited the people in the room to tell me about Jacob as they knew him. Different ones spoke up, telling me about their relationship with him and sharing some little remembrance of how special he was to them. There was laughter as they remembered things that had happened or lessons they had learned.

I have found that this exercise of remembering is important to all persons regardless of the faith that supports their spiritual journey. This life review exercise enables persons to celebrate the life of the dying as they desire to remember him. Inviting them to tell their stories is a way they support one another in affirming the relationship they have had with the person who is dying. This also enables them to introduce the one dying to the chaplain who does not know him. In that particular pastoral visit, it provided insights into his life of faith, his love for others, and his service to the community. These insights could then be woven into the content of a prayer of thanks offered on behalf of the family for the one who was dying. The chaplain facilitates this process by the questions that are asked to encourage people to share their stories. Their sharing also provides the chaplain with needed insights into what scriptures may be helpful for them as they continue their grief journey together. It is important for the chaplain to have knowledge of scriptures that can be identified as the stories are told, so that they may be shared at the appropriate time.

An hour passed so quickly, and when I felt the time was appropriate, I stood and told them how special it was for Jacob and his wife to have such a loving family present at such a time.

Knowing the opportune time to bring closure to a spiritual support visit is essential. The sense of the appropriate time must be based on what is happening in that room with those present for the occasion. All too often spiritual caregivers conclude a visit at a time that is more fitting to themselves, and often it is because they have become uncomfortable with the conversation among those who are present. Caregivers who feel inadequate and uncomfortable in dealing with death and dying issues need to examine their own feelings and know where their comfort or discomfort lies. Knowing when to offer a closing prayer is very important, and such a time should not be used as a way to exit an uncomfortable situation. It is also expected that the caregivers turn off cell phones or pagers so that their ministry to person or persons does not get interrupted making the ones being cared for feel disrespected or like someone else has a more important need than they do.

I knew the appropriate time had come because everyone in the room had spoken and all seemed content with the invitation given them to tell their stories. The wife who had requested the chaplain was also expressing thanks for the stories and what they meant to her.

I encouraged them to keep telling their stories and to tell Jacob how much he meant to them. I usually conclude my visits with a prayer, and I wanted to be sensitive to how I, a Baptist, could best minister to this Jewish family, so I asked them if I could leave them with a prayer and a blessing from the Old Testament.

The ministry I provided this family was essentially a ministry of spiritual presence. This is the kind of ministry that is often difficult for clergy who are so accustomed to 'doing' more than they are 'being.' I was very much aware that

I had been invited to be a presence with them, and I was not being looked to for answers to their spiritual questions. Spiritual caregivers need to be reminded that ninety percent of caregiving is just genuinely being there, and once there allow the next ten percent to be determined by those who are present.

All of the pre-visit anticipation I had about this visit was a good exercise in identifying the potential areas of need as well as resources available, but allowing the situation to shape the spiritual support offered was the key. The ministry of presence included selecting scripture verses that affirmed the importance of God's presence with us, and using only those scriptures that were grounded in their faith.

They agreed this would be very good, so I read to them the twenty-third Psalm, offered a prayer, and then blessed them with the benediction from Deuteronomy 31:8: "It is the Lord who goes before you. He will be with you; he will not fail you or forsake you. Do not fear or be dismayed."

One can hardly go wrong with this beautiful well-known scripture and I chose it because of the promise I wanted to affirm regarding God's spiritual presence. After reading the Psalm, I made a comment on the verse: "Even though I walk through the valley of the shadow of death I will fear no evil because you are WITH ME." I made the emphasis that I personally felt that this was one of the greatest truths in all of the scriptures, the truth that God is always trying to convince us that we do not face the uncertainties of life alone. God is with us. It is here that I knew it would not be appropriate to include my personal affirmation of this truth by telling them how wonderful it was that God even gave the name Emmanuel to Jesus! That is my belief and not theirs. What I intended to do was to affirm that truth from the perspective of their teachings, without raising controversy over my own convictions. At such a time I do not feel that I am compromising my convictions by affirming theirs, especially when those truths are woven into the fabric of my own faith, and are read from my own Bible.

When I offered the prayer I was able to verbalize gratitude to God for the man, Jacob. I was able to include specific words of praise that I had heard spoken during the time of story-telling. I was able to be very personal at a time when I did not even know the person about whom I was praying. The community of family was the community of faith in those moments of connecting us all with God. Knowing the life of the biblical Jacob I was able to make some positive comparisons with the Jacob who was dying, and by doing so, connect him to the one for whom he was named. I also concluded my prayer in a manner that would not be offensive to the Jewish family. I quoted the familiar words, "Hear our prayer O Lord, incline thy ear to us and grant us thy peace. Amen." As an interfaith chaplain, I do not feel it is necessary for me to end all prayers "*in Jesus name.*" *but in a manner that is appropriate both for me and also those with whom I am praying. This communicates something of respect for those who have invited me to care for them, and support them on their journey.*

The scripture I chose for a blessing and benediction for the family was from their Torah and it too carried the affirmation of the importance of spiritual presence, and of our God being with us. This is a verse that came to mind because I have often used it at the time of funerals when persons gather and are overcome with grief. Having available resources from a variety of spiritual experiences is very important. They do not always have to be memorized, but knowing where to find them is crucial when time is of the essence.

As I rode the elevator to the lobby, I was very much aware that I had just experienced a special moment unlike any I had ever experienced before. I was able to facilitate a meaningful closure with people whose religious experiences were in some ways similar and yet very different from mine. At the same time I had been blessed by that Jewish family. It was affirming to know that being sensitive to the belief system that has given people hope through the years makes it possible to connect with them in a very special way.

Further lessons for caregivers

Caregivers will discover that those people who have had a meaningful faith experience in life are most often the best prepared to accept death. The teaching and inspiration by which they have lived provides them with an inner confidence and trust at the time of death. They have lived a lifetime of values and beliefs that have provided them with assurance and the knowledge of God.

The interfaith caregiver has a unique opportunity to enter the lives of persons and provide them the opportunity to examine those spiritual values that have shaped a person's life. Chaplains are usually called upon when persons are confronted with some form of physical crisis. At such a time a person's beliefs and values can be a major source of spiritual support for their suffering.

"Voices of suffering—especially the voices of those who know they are dying and their families—become poignantly focused. Along with asking challenging questions regarding prognosis and other 'medical' inquiries, they become seekers and purveyors of 'spiritual' understanding and wisdom."[1] Chaplains have the unique challenge and opportunity to

---

[1] Keith G. Meador, "Spiritual Care at the End of Life," *North Carolina Medical Journal*, 65: 4 (July–August 2004), 226.

journey with such persons by becoming a pastoral presence and providing support for them.

Jacob and his family shared such a faith experience. Caregivers who participate in this kind of situation must recognize that their first priority is to invite the family to examine their beliefs and then to take the opportunity to affirm those beliefs as the family's needed hope and support. Caregivers need to remember that they are not there to change the family's beliefs if they differ from their own. Regardless of the label they put on their meaningful religious experiences, when people are able to articulate their beliefs with confidence and trust in a God who loves them, caregivers should affirm them by seeking a common ground where their faith traditions intersect. In my situation, my faith and the faith of the Jewish family was nurtured in the common ground of the Old Testament. From the Scriptures we both knew and valued, we were able to hear the Word of God for us in that moment.

I would remind all caregivers that what we do and say should be for the good of the dying patient and his or her family, and the attitude we bring to such a moment will shape the quality of our caring. It is an attitude that consciously remembers that whatever we do and say, it must be all about the mourning family and *their* personal faith values, not about us and our beliefs.

I cannot emphasize enough the importance of being open to those for whom we are called to care, and allowing them to share where they are so that they set the agenda for what we have to offer. A good biblical model for this approach to making available a spiritual presence is the New Testament story of the disciples on the road to Emmaus. It is a story that has a variety of meanings, but taken in its original setting it is a story of grief, and how someone cared for and enabled them to come to terms with their own faith beliefs. The one who cared for them joined them on their journey and asked questions that enabled them to open up and share how they felt, and what they believed. He used what they offered to assist them in clarifying their faith values and processing their grief. The end result of such caring was "their eyes were opened" and they became aware of a special spiritual presence that had cared for them. I believe a similar experience happened with the Jewish family, and happens often, as we join people where they are in their suffering, confusion, pain and sorrow and allow them to tell us their faith story.

Explorations I:
Applying an interpretive framework

Daniel S. Schipani and Leah Dawn Bueckert[1]

Our study of interfaith care situations has been enhanced by adopting and systematically applying a four-dimensional framework of analysis. We intentionally patterned the framework according to the structure of practical-pastoral theological reflection, and can describe it succinctly as follows:

- *Observe/describe*: what is going on in this situation? What are the key issues we can identify in this interfaith encounter, especially regarding the caregiver and her or his pastoral practice?

- *Interpret*: why do caregiver and care receiver behave and act the way they do? What is the psychological and theological significance of those actions? What is the caregiver seeking to accomplish?

- *Judge*: what are the ethical-theological and pastoral-clinical norms at work in the situation (or, to what extent is the caregiver's ministry truly effective and faithful?) Are there alternative norms that pertain in this situation?

- *Act*: what are some of the principles, in the sense of dependable guides for excellence in spiritual caregiving practice, which can be highlighted in light of this analysis?

In this chapter we illustrate one way of interpreting and judging a caregiving situation (steps 2 and 3 above) by applying a conceptual tool—the *grammar of transformation*[2]—that we have found to be particularly

---

[1] The case material in this chapter is based on one originally presented by chaplain Russ Dewell for our seminar group study. We are grateful to Rev. Dewell for granting us permission to use it in this chapter.

[2] The conceptualization of the "grammar of transformation" is one of the contributions of the late theologian James E. Loder as presented in his book *The Transforming Moment*. 2nd ed. (Colorado Springs: Helmers & Howard, 1989), chapters 2 and 4.

useful. The following case study was originally presented as an example of how chaplains often seek to "reconcile" their theological convictions with care receivers' different spirituality in sound ministry practice. The study of the case revealed that the situation may also be viewed as a case of reframing of the chaplain's initial assumptions coupled with his disposition to provide compassionate care (which actually facilitated the reframing). The next section presents the case as first brought to the seminar group followed by an appraisal of the case.

To bless and how to bless, Chaplain Jack's questions

The Child Birth Center rarely contacts the on-call chaplain with good news. This call was no exception: fetal demise, 28-week boy. "Would you come up to perform a blessing, chaplain?" the nurse asked. "Certainly. I'll be right there."

My sense of calling, theological education, and, most significantly, previous experiences with fetal demise automatically and naturally started informing and guiding me on how to proceed: what to watch for, issues to consider, what words might be caring, and so many words that would not be helpful. One thing I decided, we—the parents and I—needed to clarify was what "blessing" meant to them.

I wanted to be able to provide for them what they wanted (expected?) in this highly emotional and difficult circumstance so as to best give compassionate care and help them begin discovering meaning in the wake of their tragedy. So far so good. I was not forming an agenda of my own, except to frame the issue that was requested: "blessing."

However, theological education, doctrinal confession, and previous experience do not quietly lie around in my mind waiting for the first thing to come first (clarifying "blessing") before taking the next mental step, even though that step may not require education or, especially, doctrinal confession. This was no exception. Being a Lutheran, it was virtually instinctual that I wondered if "blessing" meant baptism to the parents, in even a remote sense. More than my being Lutheran, previous experience informed me that it is good to baptize deceased infants out of compassion for parents and respect for the mystery of sacramental ritual, even despite contrary doctrinal definitions about the necessity of such. I had never baptized a deceased baby before, but had been present when a Roman Catholic priest did so for parents and families in very similar circumstances. Did these parents want the same by asking for a "blessing?" I would have to wait and see. I was about to enter the holy place of the Child Birth Center room.

Alone in the room, sitting up in bed, was a late-30s-ish woman of oriental decent. I presumed Chinese.

C (chaplain) "Hello, I'm Jack, one of the hospital chaplains."

P (patient) "Hi Jack. I'm Jane."

C "I'm so sorry for your loss. I'm here to help you through this in any way I can."

P (Tearing up and weeping mildly.) "Thanks, I appreciate that."

C "The nurse told me you want a blessing for your baby."

P (quietly) "Yes, I do."

C "It's my privilege to help you with that. I want to help you as best I can."

P (quietly) "Thanks."

C "Can you share with me what it means to you to have your baby blessed?"

P (a little more strongly) "It's about the gesture."

C "Does the gesture come from any particular tradition?

P "No. I'm less religious than spiritual."

C "I understand. That helps me know how to care for you. Thank you."

Our conversation turned toward her general situation until I departed the room while a nurse tended to Jane.

I faced an interesting question. Jane did not even remotely refer to baptismal language or baptism. Could I, in good conscience, perform what she *wasn't* asking for? Part of my question came from the fact that I did not have "fetal demise blessing language" at my quick reference and use. Another source of my question was whether I fully understood what she meant by "gesture," and "spiritual." I was not going to grill and examine this nice woman in this heart-breaking tragedy so I could feel good about what support I provided. However, did I have enough information to feel confident that I could provide something to meet her need? It was not a question of whether or not I would do this for her, especially since I had already begun a pastoral relationship with her. I cherished the opportunity to provide compassionate care in the face of Jane's pain.

I was only uncertain how my automatic baptismal reflex was going to meet her desire for an other-than-baptismal spiritual gesture. Then, I realized my assumption. Even though, from a theological perspective, it is unnecessary for Lutherans to baptize deceased babies, the common practice of doing so out of compassion for parents and respect for sacramental mystery had become my reflexive response to fetal demise. Once I clarified my own theological convictions in my own mind, the clarity I experienced was as if the skies had cleared on a gloomy day. I knew that the *Lutheran Worship Agenda*[3] included blessings and dedications for civil marriages, churches, organs, schools, cemeteries, homes, and so on. Why not a deceased baby? Why not a deceased baby indeed?

Of course I could meet Jane's need as a by-the-book Lutheran with a non-specific other-than-baptism blessing. While this might seem like a blinding flash of the obvious to many (even to me after this event) the intense emotions of an event such as this, especially as an unannounced shock of an on-call shift, lead chaplains to refer to and rely on what they know and what they have experienced. For a Lutheran in this case, what I knew *and what I had experienced* was, specifically, baptism. However, Jane's request for a non-specific spiritual gesture has expanded what I know, and now, what I have experienced: to gladly provide something outside of my theological views and ecclesial practice *in good conscience*.[4] Thus, I avoided going through the motions just to fulfill Jane's request like some chaplain chore to get over with.

Having internally negotiated these doctrinal and spiritual hurdles, I was ready to provide Jane with compassionate and meaningful care.

A short time later, Jane's baby boy was returned to her. She, two of her friends, another chaplain, and I shared a meaningful and moving blessed gesture that included prayer for the boy, Jane, her absent husband (who was traveling and would join her soon), family, and friends. I had "reconciled" my doctrinal views, common practice, and Jane's spirituality. Praise God.

The case revisited

We will now present the case again by adding the interpretive framework proposed and several reflective comments. By focusing primarily on the spiritual caregiver and the internal conflict situation generated by the call to bless a deceased child, the ministry encounter can be viewed as analogous to the unfolding of a creative and transformative process.

---

[3] The *Lutheran Worship Agenda* includes a "Burial of the Stillborn" service. It has prayers and language that are easily adaptable to a blessing for a stillborn baby in a hospital setting without imposing Lutheranism on parents and families. I had forgotten about this service at the time of the call to Jane's care. I re-discovered the service in writing this vignette. It would have been very helpful to keep in mind in the midst of the emotions of the moment.

[4] Chaplain Jack emphasizes "in good conscience" as crucially important in all of his pastoral care ministry.

Conflict/Struggle in a context of rapport[5]

My sense of calling, theological education, and, most significantly, previous experiences with fetal demise automatically and naturally started informing and guiding me on how to proceed: what to watch for, issues to consider, what words might be caring, and so many words that would not be helpful. One thing I decided, we—the parents and I— needed to clarify was what "blessing" meant to them.

[*Perhaps the chaplain started with the assumption that his need to clarify what "blessing" meant, so that he could be helpful, was also the care receivers' first need.*]

I wanted to be able to provide for them what they wanted (expected?) in this highly emotional and difficult circumstance so as to best give compassionate care and help them begin discovering meaning in the wake of their tragedy. So far so good. I was not forming an agenda of my own, except to frame the issue that was requested: "blessing."

[*It seems the chaplain assumed that the care receiver needed to somehow "discover meaning"—a primarily cognitive activity—as, perhaps, their main need?*]

Scanning[6] in search of resolution

However, theological education, doctrinal confession, and previous experience do not quietly lie around in my mind waiting for the first thing to come first (clarifying "blessing") before taking the next mental step, even though that step may not require education, or especially doctrinal confession. This was no exception. Being a Lutheran, it was virtually instinctual that I wondered if "blessing" meant baptism to the parents, in even a remote sense. More than my being Lutheran, previous experience informed me that it is good to baptize deceased infants out of compassion for parents and respect for the mystery of sacramental ritual, even despite contrary doctrinal guidelines about the necessity of such. I had never baptized a deceased baby before, but had been present when a

---

[5] The supplied subtitles beginning with "conflict in a context of rapport" highlight the phases of what Loder calls the *logic or grammar of transformation*, the structure and dynamics of which are analogous to those of the *creative process*. Not unlike scientific discoveries and creation of works of art, such process potentially leads to transformation. It is our view that, indeed, a kind of transformation process took place during the ministry work described and analyzed in this chapter.

[6] Interlude for "scanning" defines the second step in the logic of transformation. "During this phase the conflict is for a time put out of one's conscious attention; the creative unconscious then has opportunity to search beneath the surface of awareness for … patterns that allow the reenvisioning and resolution of the conflict." Loder, *The Transforming Moment*, 225.

Roman Catholic priest did so for parents and families in very similar circumstances. Did these parents want the same by asking for a "blessing"? I would have to wait and see. I was about to enter the holy place of the Child Birth Center room.

Alone in the room, sitting up in bed, was a late-30s-ish woman of oriental decent. I presumed Chinese.

C (chaplain) "Hello, I'm Jack, one of the hospital chaplains."

P (patient) "Hi Jack. I'm Jane."

C "I'm so sorry for your loss. I'm here to help you through this in any way I can."

P (Tearing up and weeping mildly.) "Thanks, I appreciate that."

C "The nurse told me you want a blessing for your baby."

P (quietly) "Yes, I do."

C "It's my privilege to help you with that. I want to help you as best I can."

P (quietly) "Thanks."

C "Can you share with me what it means to you to have your baby blessed?"

P (a little more strongly) "It's about the gesture."

C "Does the gesture come from any particular tradition?

P "No. I'm less religious than spiritual."

C "I understand. That helps me know how to care for you. Thank you."

[*Alternative responses by the chaplain might have been: "I see. I wonder, what do you wish for your child as I bless him?"; or "What would you like to happen because of the blessing?"*]

Our conversation turned toward her general situation until I departed the room while a nurse tended to Jane.

[*Here the chaplain could have engaged more the spirituality of the patient as a step towards nurturing her own healing and well-being. From the conversation provided, we don't know what her sense of need was, her hopes and her resources; neither do we know what kind of sense of the Holy or transcendence she had, sense of meaning, community and so on. Without that kind of information, it is difficult for chaplains to effectively visualize desired outcomes with or for the patient. It is also difficult to visualize pertinent pastoral interventions or to (eventually) evaluate to what extent pastoral care was effective.]*[7]

I faced an interesting question. Jane did not even remotely refer to baptismal language or baptism. Could I, in good conscience, perform what she *wasn't* asking for? Part of my question came from the fact that I did not have "fetal demise blessing language" at my quick reference and use. Another source of my question was whether I fully understood what she meant by "gesture," and "spiritual." I was not going to grill and examine this nice woman in this heart-breaking tragedy so I could feel good about what support I provided. However, did I have enough information to feel confident that I could provide something to meet her need? It was not a question of whether or not I would do this for her, especially since I had already begun a pastoral relationship with her. I cherished the opportunity to provide compassionate care in the face of Jane's pain.

[The ministerial impulse and desire expressed by the chaplain was certainly key!]

Moment of insight (Bisociation[8])

I was only uncertain how my automatic baptismal reflex was going to meet her desire for an other-than-baptismal spiritual gesture. Then, I realized my assumption. Even though, from a theological perspective, it is unnecessary for Lutherans to baptize deceased babies, the common practice of doing so out of compassion for parents and respect for sacramental mystery had become my reflexive response to fetal demise. Once I clarified my own theological convictions in my own mind for myself, the clarity I experienced was if the skies had cleared on a gloomy day. I knew that the *Lutheran Worship Agenda*[9] included blessings and dedications for civil marriages, churches, organs, schools, cemeteries, homes, and so on. Why not a deceased baby? Why not a deceased baby indeed?

Of course I could meet Jane's need as a by-the-book Lutheran with a

---

[7] One of the best resources to strategize spiritual care (in terms of both "assessment" and "intervention") is found in Larry VandeCreek and Arthur M. Lucas, eds. *The Discipline for Pastoral Care Giving: Foundations for Outcome Oriented Chaplaincy* (New York: Haworth Pastoral Press, 2001).

[8] Bisociation is the basic unit of an insight. The terms refers to the "surprising convergence of two incompatible frames of reference to compose an original and meaningful unity." Loder, *The Transforming Moment*, 222.

[9] The *Lutheran Worship Agenda* includes a "Burial of the Stillborn" service. It has prayers and language that are easily adaptable to a blessing for a stillborn baby in a hospital setting without imposing Lutheranism on parents and families. I had forgotten about this service at the time of the call to Jane's care. I re-discovered the service in writing this vignette. It would have been very helpful to keep in mind in the midst of the emotions of the moment.

non-specific other-than-baptism blessing. While this might seem like a blinding flash of the obvious to many (even to me after this event) the intense emotions of an event such as this, especially as an unannounced shock of an on-call shift, lead chaplains to refer to and rely on what they know and what they have experienced. For a Lutheran in this case, what I knew *and what I had experienced* was, specifically, baptism. However, Jane's request for a non-specific spiritual gesture has expanded what I know, and now, what I have experienced: to gladly provide something outside of my theological views and ecclesial practice *in good conscience*. Thus, I avoided going through the motions just to fulfill Jane's request like some chaplain chore to get over with.

Release of energy[10]—Interpretation and verification[11]

Having internally negotiated these doctrinal and spiritual hurdles, I was ready to provide Jane with compassionate and meaningful care.

[There seems to be an implication or assumption here that, if the chaplain had not resolved certain "doctrinal and spiritual hurdles" he could not have provided compassionate and meaningful care. Could the reverse also have been the case: the disposition to provide compassionate and meaningful care facilitated such internal negotiation and resolution?]

A short time later, Jane's baby boy was returned to her. She, two of her friends, another chaplain, and I shared a meaningful and moving blessed gesture that included prayer for the boy, Jane, her absent husband (who was traveling but would soon join her), family, and friends. I had "reconciled" my doctrinal views, common practice, and Jane's spirituality. Praise God.

[Jane's main need was for support to cope with the loss of her child; the pastoral-priestly acts of blessing/praying undoubtedly served: (a) to validate the mother's wishes for her child (and for herself) and (b) to contribute to the necessary grieving process she needed to go through.]

Some time after this pastoral care event, chaplain Jack received a

---

[10] Release of energy and new openness is the fourth step in the logic of transformation in which the energy bound up with the conflict is released, and a new openness to the surrounding environment ensues.

[11] In order for the process to be completed, interpretation and verification are necessary. The chaplain needed to experience *congruence* as a subjective test of truth or good resolution of the internal conflict (that is, to what extent his sense of resolution was actually fitting in light of his initial dilemma). Further, the chaplain needed to experience *correspondence* in the sense of a public test of truth: his colleagues would judge whether a satisfactory resolution had indeed been achieved.

thank you card from the couple who lost their baby. They had named him Wayne as a way to connect them and him to their experience at the hospital. They wrote in appreciation of Jack's care ministry and his help in their decision to name the child, which had been significant in their healing process.

Further discussion

In a real sense, the group analysis of the case became a significant part of the final step in the *logic of transformation*, namely interpretation. We critically re-examined the whole caring event in order to help establish whether the chaplain's insights and actions had been appropriate. The seminar discussion of the case included consideration of the questions indicated below together with summary responses articulated as a result of our work together.

1. What assumptions, of their own and those of others, about sacraments, rituals, and/or practices do chaplains have to sort through to provide meaningful care when doctrine meets spirituality? That is, meaningful for the patient and the chaplain so neither is reduced to "going through the motions" of a rite contrived to fill the space of a pastoral visit.

   - On the one hand, it is not helpful to juxtapose or otherwise compare and contrast "doctrine" and "spirituality" because they belong to different categories (therefore, one cannot actually "reconcile" them as such either)

   - It is, on the other hand, helpful to seek "common ground" as much as possible, as implied in the statement "meaningful for the patient and the chaplain…." The vignette actually illustrates this point nicely because a real blessing[12] was experienced by care receiver and caregivers alike.

2. How do chaplains and patient(s)/families negotiate the best way to shape the requested and available sacrament, ritual, or practice?

   - Seeking the clarity provided by adequate spiritual assessment, and timely permission from the care receivers (patients and/or family members) are essential.

   - It is often possible to include the care receivers' input which in

---

[12] "Blessing" is here understood as the (mediated) bestowal of well-being or good upon the persons involved, including in this case the child's body. According to the vignette, the chaplains ministered authoritatively as mediators of Grace. They offered the blessing as a special expression of the shared hope that, indeed, child and mother would receive the wished-for gifts of well-being and peace through and beyond the experience of death and loss.

itself can be validating and empowering. For example, as suggested as an alternative response on the verbatim, the chaplain could have asked Jane what she wished for her child (and for herself, spouse, etc.) and make that a part of the prayer/blessing as appropriate.

3. What authority does a chaplain have, exercise, or abdicate to reconcile doctrine, practice, and spirituality? There are various sources and kinds of authority at play, such as:

• The authority that comes from the ecclesial body which either commissions, ordains, or otherwise authorizes pastoral care ministry in the hospital setting. The chaplain has therefore delegated authority, and she/he ministers as a representative of the church and/or denomination whether explicitly or implicitly. As such, the chaplain discerns and makes judgments, sometimes including consultation with either chaplains (or other caregivers) of different denominations or faith traditions, or with colleagues, supervisors or otherwise "authorities" of her/his church.

• The authority that stems from being authorized (and therefore also expected) by the hospital to provide competent and effective pastoral care service as a chaplain, whether employee, volunteer, or CPE student.

• The professional authority that stems from an integration of the above in terms of vocational commitment, personal character, and ministerial competence.

• The authority conferred by the care receiver (patient and/or family member) who welcomes or otherwise expects to be cared for adequately by the chaplain.

Explorations II:
Hawaiian chaplains reflect on interfaith care

A group contribution[1]

The following paragraphs present a sample of responses to a question-naire that served as an introductory tool to the study of interfaith spiritual care. The questions have been shared with many colleagues who in turn reported on their consideration. Readers too may find these questions helpful for self-reflection and discussion.

1. What are the biggest challenges and opportunities you encounter in interfaith situations?

Martin Buber, in his seminal work on the "I–Thou" relationship, reflects a tension that can be of significance in the area of interfaith dialogue. Too often, the interchange that takes place in efforts to engage other belief systems reflects an "I–It" relationship. There are nuances of "being tolerant" which often diminish the personhood of persons and of the power of their faith. Too often "tolerance" is an easy way out of becoming engaged in a respectful process of "give and take." Tolerance has a way of placing a person or a "religion" on the fringe of our existence, to some extent, "out of sight, out of mind." There is no need to engage, to understand, to accept, and to love.

---

[1] The material in this chapter consists of excerpts from a discussion of interfaith care involving Christian caregivers and Buddhist care receivers in Hawaii. These are the names of the chaplains whose responses are included: Charles Card, Anke Flohr, Glenn Harada, Al Miles, Pearl Misa-Lau, and Kim Noble; all are ordained ministers. We gratefully acknowledge the contribution of Rev. Anke Flohr, for having led the discussion of these questions with several colleagues, and having sent us available written records. She also secured permission from the participants to include a selection of responses for publication. Anke Flohr, M.Div., is Director of Clinical Pastoral Education at Pacific Health Ministry, Honolulu, Hawaii. She is also a CPE supervisor and a chaplain serving at the Good Samaritan Retirement Community at Pohai Nani, Kaneohe, Hawaii.

The biggest ongoing challenge I face is to resist the temptation to either "Christian-ize" or "Westernize" the spiritual care situations in which I have the privilege of serving. Having been indoctrinated in American cultural and fundamental Protestant Judeo-Christian values, there is still a tendency on my part to assess and judge people through this very narrow lens.

Unfortunately, within most faith traditions, there are built-in doctrines, perspectives, values that automatically build barriers. The danger can be seen in the ministry in hospitals, where persons are in crisis and are most vulnerable, and we justify our "doing of ministry" in order that we can have access of "sharing Christ" with the person. Because Christianity claims to be "the way, the truth and the life" we feel justified in ignoring or even more pernicious, denigrating the person's personal faith, especially if the person is not a Christian.

One challenge in interfaith situations is working with patients of another faith who have perceptions and stereotypes of chaplains. They may feel that we cannot help them because we come from another faith background. They prefer to be ministered to by someone of their own faith. The opportunity for chaplains trained in interfaith ministry is that we know where to find resources to assist this person in need. Another challenge is ministering to those who have had negative experiences with religion. They tend to close themselves off from effective religious coping mechanisms in handling the struggles of life. Those with negative religious experiences tend to categorize good religious people they encounter as bad and who cannot be trusted. On initial pastoral visits, they may have a difficult time trusting the chaplain. It may take time to develop trust with the patient.

Often I feel uneasy and cautious. I am my biggest challenge. I am concerned about reading and understanding non-verbal messages and about being able to read between the lines.

The biggest opportunity I have encountered in interfaith situations is the receiving of many blessings when I allow myself to remain open to the mysteries and sacredness of teachings from people who embrace religious and spiritual traditions other than my own.

The most powerful modality of interfaith dialogue is through talking story … that is also true of how we engage cultures. If we start with our doctrine, we hinder the free give-and-take of true dialogue. It is important to find our common ground, the place where our humanity merges with the other and then we can begin the discussion of those issues that are critical to each faith and culture. There is great power in acceptance and in the art of listening. True dialogue happens in the minute events of the I–Thou relationships that are not based on knowledge and tolerance but in engagement and the risk of being true friends with persons of other cultures and faith perspectives.

2. What kind(s) of "spiritual assessment" do you practice?

I am most helpful to others as a faith leader when I allow those I'm called to serve to determine their spiritual course of action. I invite people to tell me what gives them hope, meaning and purpose; provide brief reflections or utterances on what they share; and then ask these individuals how they think I can best serve them. If prayer, readings, referrals, or other resources are determined or requested, I provide this information. But, I shy away from advice-giving.

I work with several models:

(a) The 7x7 Model for Spiritual Assessment developed by George Fitchett (*Assessing Spiritual Needs: A Guide for Caregivers* [Minneapolis: Augsburg, 1993]). He notes seven dimensions of "holistic assessment" (biological, psychological, family systems, psycho-social, ethnic, racial and cultural, social issues, and spiritual) and seven dimensions of "spiritual assessment" (belief and meaning, vocation and obligation, experience and emotions, courage and growth, ritual and growth, community, and authority and guidance).

(b) A shorter assessment model is "HOPE" (including, source of Hope, meaning, comfort, strength, peace, love and connection; Organized religion; Personal spirituality and practices; and Effects on medical care and end of life issues.

(c) The ADDRESSING model, especially applied with the staff and CPE students, developed by Pamela A. Hays (*Addressing Cultural Complexities in Practice* [Washington, DC: American Psychological Association, 2004]).

3. What kinds of "care interventions" do you consider most appropriate and why?

Ministry of presence works the best: empathetic and compassionate care with active listening. I need to be authentic, genuine, warm, real.

One of my spiritual tools is my ears which I use by listening to patients. I provide opportunities for religious worship. I pray for those who desire prayer. If they desire religious literature, I provide religious literature that is interdenominational. I have provided Mormon patients with the Book of Mormon. I ask Buddhist patients if they would like a Buddhist priest to visit them. Catholic patients receive visits by the priest and are offered sacraments and communion. If they desire, I make myself available to those with "no faith" and provide ministry of presence for them.

It is also essential that I work in partnership with a team of individuals from a wide field of professional disciplines: advocates, batterers' intervention specialists, child protective services providers, crisis intervention counselors, law enforcement officers, legal professionals, shelter workers, victim and witness assistance personnel, and other health care and spiritual care providers, to name just a few.

I have discovered over my four years of being a chaplain that in the beginning, I do not approach each person too differently. I listen and try to be respectful of his or her belief system. Establishing a relationship through listening, and consistency for those I visit over a longer period of time, are my key strengths in providing spiritual care for my patients, residents and family members.

Chaplains must ensure that the spiritual values of the patient are affirmed in a nonjudgmental way. We must respect the culture, ethnicity and religious preference of each patient. As chaplain, I am the primary spiritual caregiver to the patient and function in that capacity until the patient requests a change. At that time I inquire if the patient has a connection with local clergy and if he/she would like for me to contact anyone specifically. Then a referral is made to the spiritual caregiver of their choice.

4. What kinds of "good news" do Buddhist care receivers especially welcome or wish to receive?

I experience Buddhist residents and patients as very welcoming. Kindness and gentleness, open ears and mind, a listening heart, creating a space to share, have been appreciated. Respect without judgment.

The greatest assistance I can usually provide to people in need centers not so much on the words I offer, but instead on my ability to listen in silence to their sacred stories.

In my experience, Buddhist care receivers are among the most accepting and open group of individuals. I am often called to visit Buddhist patients and families at the medical center where I serve, even though the requesters know that I am a Christian pastor. This is especially true of health care colleagues who are Buddhist. The needs vary, but these requests commonly center on my offering a few compassionate words at or near the time of death, or during a funeral or memorial service.

Simple prayers are often appreciated, such as these [from the verbatim of a pastoral visit to a patient in the process of dying, with the husband and sons at her side]: "O God, we ask your help at this time. We especially ask that you would be with Mrs. N during her last moments. We pray that she is not in pain and that her transition from this life be gentle and peaceful. We pray that anything that may be burdening her would be released. We thank you for her family that is present ... for their love and support of her. We pray that you would comfort them in their time of need and give them grace and strength for the moments and days ahead. We pray all of this in your name. Amen." In the same situation, a prayer after the death of Mrs. N (requested by her husband): "Dear God, we thank you that Mrs. N is no longer suffering and she has transitioned from this life into the next. Watch and care for her. God, we thank you for what she was to those who love her and we ask for your comfort for them as they grieve the loss of their wife, their mother, and their friend. May you grant all of us peace. Amen."

5. As a Christian spiritual caregiver, how do you evaluate theologically the interfaith situation as such and your interaction with the patient (and/or relatives) in particular?

The core value of my theological belief system centers on a God and Christ who love equally humankind from both genders, and from all cultures, races, religions, sexual orientations, socio-economic levels, and spiritual disciplines. Therefore, my spiritual care practice must model these same essential qualities.

Jesus is my teacher and model for healing relationship, love, dialogue, respect, and forgiveness. Through Christ we know that God reaches out in love to all. I am called to walk the path of holiness that Jesus showed me. He reached out to the Samaritans, "lepers," bleeding women, sinners, the poor. God shows the face of mercy and love. We must be subject to all human beings, servants, God's willing instrument. Jesus healed the ones in need, the marginalized. He loved them, ate with them, touched them, comforted them, blessed them, served them, encouraged them, taught them, and liberated them by his own suffering, death, and resurrection. Finally, Jesus breathed on them to infuse them with the power of the Holy Spirit. Jesus journeyed with people full of compassion.

I have no hidden agendas. No theological argument but about human sharing. Dialogue strives to eliminate defensiveness.

6. How do you characterize a fruitful (both effective and "faithful") practice of interfaith pastoral care?

From one's own spiritual tradition, we must assist or help patients and relatives engage their spirituality or religiosity in order to face their life and death struggles. Staff members must be educated on the importance of spirituality as a resource in handling the difficulties of life.

A fruitful practice of interfaith pastoral care must have at its core acceptance of and respect for all religious and spiritual traditions. I firmly believe that any religious beliefs, doctrines, and practices which espouse bigotry, hatred, male domination and female subjugation, violence, and any other beliefs that add to the oppression of other human beings or animals, need to be condemned. At the same time, all religious and spiritual traditions that practice and teach love, respect, and the equal value and worth of all humanity need to be embraced.

I look for "connection" in pastoral care. My caregiving is grounded in building relationships. I look for a sense of "meeting" each other. The "between" is the essential dimension.

Also important are knowing spiritual and religious resources available and knowing how to access these resources whenever needed for patients or staff. Interface with your staff and see if they are aware of spiritual issues of patients. Meet with Pacific Health Ministry chaplains and staff monthly to discuss interfaith ministry.

Over the years, I have become more adept at being short on speaking and long on listening to and learning from the experiences of people who espouse religious and spiritual traditions other than my own. In turn, colleagues from other religious and spiritual traditions have shared that they too have found it helpful to learn more about my religious upbringing and spiritual practices.

Explorations III:
An exercise in pastoral-theological imagination
Daniel S. Schipani and Leah Dawn Bueckert

This is the third and final chapter on alternative explorations in pastoral theological reflection that were considered in the seminar group we led at Lutheran Hospital of Indiana. It refers to an unusual activity that we devised after John Peterson[1] shared with us an excellent article from *The New York Times* on the ministry of Chaplain Peggy Muncie in New York City. The article is reprinted below with permission from the publisher.[2]

Offering comfort to the sick and blessings to their healers
By Jan Hoffman

At 1 p.m. on a weekday, the emergency department at St. Luke's-Roosevelt Hospital in Upper Manhattan is in full cry, with bays crowded, patients on stretchers lining the hallways, and paramedics bringing in more sick people. Time for the Rev. Margaret A. Muncie to work the floor.

Not shy, this pastor with the clerical collar, the Ann Taylor blazer and the cheerful insistence of one whose own mother called her a steam-roller. Among the first women ordained an Episcopal priest and a self-described "Caucasian minority," she's an odd bird among the ethnically diverse staff and especially the patients, most of them black or Latino. But she keeps pecking her head behind curtains, parting gatherings of worried family members, impervious to startled looks of suspicion.

"Hi, I'm Peggy Muncie, a hospital chaplain," she says. "Would you

---

[1] As previously indicated, Rev. John D. Peterson is Pastoral Care Division Director at Lutheran Hospital of Indiana in Fort Wayne. He is also a CPE supervisor.

[2] The article was originally published in *The New York Times* on July 17, 2007.

like a visit?"

She's not there to thump. Deftly, she asks people how they're feeling, then lets them vent their pain and fear, their anxiety and frustration. She nods, a little pushy with her probing. She flags a nurse. "Can you direct a doctor toward that patient?" she whispers.

And always, at the end of a visit: "Would it be all right if I prayed with you?" The health care chaplain will touch a forehead, hold a hand and quietly pray worries to the Divine, speaking with inflections that, as needed, may be Pentecostal, Roman Catholic, Hindu, Jewish, Muslim. For the Baptist woman in Bed 7 whose anxieties are making her chest pain worse, the chaplain prays for calm to allow the medicine to work. Gradually, the patient's breathing slows.

"My job is to be present to patients without judgment," Chaplain Muncie says as she pumps a hand sanitizer, "and to help them find out what is meaningful to guide them through the stress of illness."

Most health care facilities around the country work with clergy members. But their involvement varies widely. Some hospitals merely have a list of on-call pastors; others retain professionally trained, board-certified health care chaplains, like Ms. Muncie, who is the only full-time cleric at St. Luke's. (The hospital also has a rabbi and an imam part-time, and a supervisory program for theological students.)

These varying levels of commitment have less to do with differing philosophies about spirituality and healing than with the bottom line. Insurance carriers do not reimburse for a chaplain's salary.

"We're a non-revenue-producing service, and in the economics of modern health care, that's not a good place to be," said the Rev. George F. Handzo, a vice president at the HealthCare Chaplaincy, a New York City organization that trains and places many chaplains.

"But there is a lot of indirect contribution to the mission of a hospital," he added, "as well as to its margin: customer satisfaction, customer retention and goodwill in the community. From a revenue standpoint, that's crucial."

The chaplain is also expected to minister to the hospital staff. As Chaplain Muncie, 59, makes her way throughout St. Luke's with a painstaking limp, she chats easily with doctors and nurses. She has sat with an intern who sobbed uncontrollably after pronouncing her first death and prayed with a ward clerk whose mother was in intensive care.

Every year, the chaplain performs a "Blessing of the Hands." She wheels a cart adorned with a tablecloth, flowers, a bowl and an MP3 player. Surgeons, nurses, aides crowd around as she dips their hands in water, blessing their healing work.

Although intercessory praying for the sick has existed since the time of ancient shamans, the chaplain's role now reflects the impact of modern technology on medicine. In her nearly five years at St. Luke's, Ms. Muncie has helped mediate "do not resuscitate" decisions, organ donations and bioethics disputes. After a visit, she puts the details in a patient's chart.

Now she's off to the intensive care unit, where many patients are intubated or comatose. Undeterred, Chaplain Muncie goes room by room, soul-searching. From one bed, eyes watch drowsily but intently; from another, a gurgle: "Ahhh," then, faintly, "mennnn."

"They say the last sense to leave is a person's hearing," she says. "Well, I was a cheerleader and I can belt it out as loud as anyone."

Spotting the chaplain, a woman jumps up from a bedside and embraces her. "Her husband is semicomatose," Ms. Muncie explains later. "She is going to be a widow soon and she knows it. She trusts me now, so I can begin to ask the difficult questions: 'Have you started to plan for your future?'"

One of Chaplain Muncie's signature responsibilities is to stand with a patient's family in the bleak early hours of death. The St. Luke's chaplains are paged when a child or a staff member dies; if a death is traumatic; or in the event of a calamity like a fire. But though raw, savage grief has no vocabulary, Chaplain Muncie must give it voice, in a multitude of languages.

Recently, a woman from Mexico who spoke no English had to be told that her eldest son, 16, had been stabbed, and died just after surgery. As Chaplain Muncie helped deliver the news, she realized that the shocked woman was Pentecostal. So the chaplain held her, praying in the name of Jesus that Jesus would take her son to Heaven, that Jesus would give her strength to bear this.

A few weeks ago, the chaplain had to prepare a Jewish family for a morgue viewing of their father. "I know that in Judaism, you don't say that the deceased goes to heaven," she says now. "You talk about memory and legacy. This family was having a hard time getting closure. So I said: 'What would your father be saying to help you get through this? What memory will you hold of him?' And their mood changed."

Her core belief about healing, says Chaplain Muncie, is animated by Psalm 121: "My help cometh from the Lord, who made heaven and earth"—spirit and body; faith and medicine. In 1996, doctors found a benign tumor in her brain the size of a tennis ball. The day after it was removed, she had a stroke. Her right side became paralyzed.

"I was frightened and mad," she says, over a hasty salad. "But mostly

I worried about my husband and daughters: What about them?"

So many people prayed for her. She was not allowed to abandon hope, not through the years of pain and physical therapy that reduced the paralysis to a lurching limp, thanks to a device she was recently fitted for—"an electronic doohickey, my own little miracle."

She hitches up a pants-leg to show off the gadget, a neurostimulator. "I walk faster now," she says. "I'm the kick-butt chaplain." The experience deeply informs her ministry. "In Scripture it says, 'Get up from your bed and walk, your faith has made you well,'" she continues.

"'Well' doesn't mean perfect. But wholeness and healing can happen, even when there is still brokenness on the outside," she adds, tears spilling. "I'm more whole now than 12 years ago. But I still walk a little funny."

After lunch she visits the acute-care floor, sitting at the bedside of an 87-year-old glaucoma patient.

"The hospital can be a busy, lonely place," Chaplain Muncie says. "Who is there to walk this journey with you?"

The patient doesn't hold back. Brittle-thin, blind, she lives in public housing with her grandson, 19. But he's in serious trouble with the law. If she doesn't kick him out in three days, she says, she'll be evicted. The grandmother is heartsick about ejecting her grandson, yet terrified by looming homelessness.

The chaplain promises to alert a social worker. Immediately.

The patient pleads: "Would you call my grandson and ask him to visit? He hasn't been by."

The chaplain agrees. She gently mentions the parable of the Prodigal Son, of letting a profligate young man go so that he may one day return, mature and penitent.

Hands clasped, the women pray.

Chaplain Muncie stands to leave. "Oh, you lifted my spirit!" the patient calls out. "Will you visit me again?"

All seminar group participants read the article. We then discussed it in depth by focusing on the question, "How might Chaplain Peggy Muncie justify pastorally and theologically her spiritual care practices (especially prayers, blessings) with patients and staff of different faiths?" The activity was called an exercise in pastoral theological imagination. What follows is a summary of our response to the question.[3]

---

[3] We were able to get in touch with Chaplain Peggy Muncie, first by e-mail and then by phone in order to share with her about the seminar group experience and the use of the article as a

- First of all, Peggy Muncie is clear about her personal and pastoral identity: a 59-year-old, "Caucasian minority" woman, spouse and mother of two daughters; an ordained Episcopal priest who serves as pastoral caregiver at a hospital in Upper Manhattan. As a full-time chaplain, she is a member of the health care team which includes two part-time spiritual care colleagues, a rabbi and an imam. Her own experience of illness, hospitalization, suffering and loss, and recovery has been a transformative process that deeply informs her ministry.

- She is committed to always care *Christianly*, especially in the multifaith world of a health care center.[4] "Caring Christianly" is the kind of spiritual caregiving that stems from three key dimensions of the Christian faith: a particular vision of reality and the good life; a disposition to care as a form of love of neighbor-stranger inspired by Jesus Christ; and a sense of vocation to serve in partnership with the Spirit of God.

- Because of her faith and ministerial identity and vocation, this chaplain's prayers may be assumed to be implicitly offered "in the name of Jesus" even though she will not mention Jesus in her prayers and blessings for other-than-Christian care receivers and colleagues.

- We assume that Chaplain Muncie always offers to pray with and/ or for people for several reasons: (a) prayer is a universal, cross-cultural spiritual practice and faith language (although, for people of non-religious faiths, prayer may be neither significant nor desirable); (b) prayer is potentially good for spirit, soul, and body; (c) when she prays with and/or for people, she has an opportunity to give voice to the care receiver's heart, their hopes and desires; (d) when she prays, she can exercise multilingual competency by using spiritual or religious language familiar to the care receiver (while realizing that common language does not necessarily connote theological commonality, a realization that also pertains, of

---

testimony of her work in New York City. We also shared with her the responses to the question, "How might [you] justify pastorally and theologically [your] spiritual care practices (especially prayers, blessing) with patients and staff of different faiths?" She graciously and enthusiastically engaged us in conversation, affirming much of what we shared and offering clarification and expansion on some points. We are grateful for having become acquainted with Peggy Muncie and her fruitful and inspiring ministry of spiritual care in a multifaith setting.

[4] In our phone conversation, Chaplain Muncie stated being deeply committed to Jesus Christ and ministering, in her words, as an "incarnationalist."

course, when she prays with Christian care receivers!); (e) by offering prayer she seeks to communicate compassionate concern; by telling people that she will pray for them she communicates that she will remember them (and remembering is actually a key dimension of care).

- Praying can be emotionally and spiritually helpful. Chaplain Muncie always prays for herself and also regularly for patients and their families and colleagues, whether they know it or not. So the question for this caregiver is not, "should I pray for so and so …?" Rather, the question is, "when and how will I pray well for so and so …?"

- Performing a blessing (e.g. the yearly "Blessing of the Hands") is not only a *pastoral* act but a *priestly* one as well. When Chaplain Muncie blesses people she bestows grace on them as a representative of Divine Grace. She communicates affirmation of the care receivers and of their deepest longings for healing and wholeness. She seeks to be a blessing to those around her as she embodies the good news ("gospel") of healing and hope. She also thanks staff for the blessing they are to others.

- We might say that Peggy Muncie seeks to keep growing in pastoral wisdom in three dimensions: *being* (key to *presence*: "My job is to be present to patients without judgment …"; "standing with a patient's family in the bleak early hours of death"); *doing* (key to *guidance*: "and to help them find out what is meaningful to guide them through the stress of illness"; "she trusts me now, so I can begin to ask the difficult questions: 'Have you started to plan for your future?'"); and *knowing* (key to understanding in context: "My help comes from the Lord, who made heaven and earth," "… spirit and body, faith and medicine …").

- Chaplain Muncie knows that Christian pastoral caregivers must cultivate a theological understanding that is born out of their religious tradition. What sets pastoral or spiritual practice apart from other clinical and psychological practices is that very theological and ministerial identity.

- Chaplain Muncie does not see that her job as a Christian spiritual caregiver is to try to save people's souls so they may go to heaven. Her job is to minister according to the model of Jesus, so that people may suffer well, may heal as well as possible, and may also die well.

Further reflection and dialogue prompted by this exploration led us to design the following diagram. It is meant to represent the triangle assumed to be always present in interfaith pastoral care situations viewed from a pastoral theological perspective:

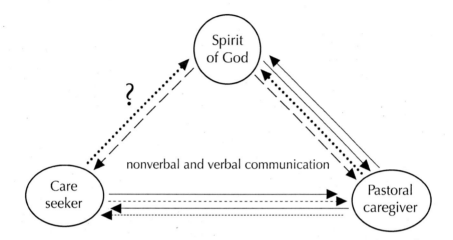

The arrows between care seeker and caregiver indicate the dynamics of nonverbal and verbal communication between us. The arrows linking Christian pastoral caregivers and the Spirit of God symbolize the communion that sustains and orients us as ministering persons. Such communion is experienced consciously as well as unconsciously (hence the arrows with broken lines).

The arrows between care receiver and God's Spirit indicate a fundamental theological claim we make: the Spirit's creating, liberating, healing and empowering work is already present in people's lives regardless of the shape and content of their (religious or nonreligious) spirituality, whether or not they would speak of a relationship with the Spirit of God.[5] In any event, from the perspective of the Christian pastoral caregiver, the relationship between care receiver and God's Spirit is assumed not as a problem to resolve but as a mystery to behold.

---

[5] In simpler terms, such a theological-anthropological claim is consistent, for example, with the Quakers' call to recognize the Light in any human being: "Do you respect that of God in everyone though it may be expressed in unfamiliar ways or be difficult to discern? Each of us has a particular experience of God and each must find the way to be true to it." *Quaker Faith and Practice* (Warwick, England: The Yearly Meeting of the Religious Society of Friends [Quakers] in Britain, 1999), Advices and Queries, chap. 1, no. 17.

Spiritual care in public and faith-based hospitals

Cornel G. Rempel

This essay starts with a characterization of chaplaincy as a special relationship, a service, and a discipline. The following sections consider professional standards, the place of chaplains within the health care institution, five operative dimensions of accountability, and the chaplain's image within the health care system. The final two sections, on the use of authority and power and the integration of the chaplain's role, include vignettes of interfaith spiritual caregiving in the hospital.

Relationship, service, and discipline

As a special *relationship*, spiritual care is a response to the spiritual need of another involving caring gestures such as a reassuring presence in the time of loss, a gentle touch in a time of pain, a prayer in time of need, a listening ear in time of confusion, the validation of another's emotions or cry of distress, or the celebration of new-found meaning. As such, acts of spiritual care may be planned or spontaneous and can be received from certified chaplains, volunteers, hospital staff and virtually any caring person.

As a *service*, spiritual care is the provision of support through structured activities such as initial visits, pre-op visits, communion, baptism, a smudging ceremony or an anointing. Such deliberate services are provided by persons who have been granted the authority to do so.

In the health care system spiritual care also functions as a *discipline* with defined ecclesiastical, professional and administrative accountability so that it is professionally recognized and organizationally connected to other professional disciplines. To do so with integrity it must be:

Cornel G. Rempel, M.Div., is a retired chaplain currently living in Winnipeg, Manitoba, Canada. He most recently served as Director of Pastoral Services and CPE Supervisor at Philhaven Behavioral Healthcare Services, Mount Gretna, Pennsylvania.

- Endorsed by and be accountable to the interfaith community.
- Recognized by the health care industry.
- Responsible to the administration of the institution.
- Accountable to a professional association through professional certification, adherence to its code of ethics and standards of practice.

In this chapter I will deal primarily with chaplaincy as a discipline, comparing and contrasting chaplaincy as a discipline in public and faith-based institutions. The term public institutions will refer to the broad range of government-operated facilities, university teaching hospitals, for-profit hospitals, and community-based not-for-profit hospitals. Faith-based will refer to institutions with religious affiliation. My intent is not to contrast the character of the institution but to focus on how public versus religious sponsorship may affect the position and function of chaplaincy.

The difference between chaplaincy in institutions with religious affiliation and public institutions is more subtle than obvious. The similarities are greater than the differences, for several reasons:

- The same professional standards apply to chaplaincy in public and faith-based institutions even though some services may differ.
- Public hospitals are not devoid of spiritual awareness, and faith-based hospitals deal with fiscal, ethical, and management issues that are similar to those of public hospitals.
- The significance of spiritual factors in healing is broadly recognized today apart from specific religious affiliation.
- Many staff members in public institutions are people of faith who are concerned about patients' spiritual well-being.
- The provision of spiritual care is mandated for all health care institutions by hospital accrediting bodies, so the provision of religious services is by no means exclusive to institutions with religious affiliation.

In this essay I will reflect on how public versus religious sponsorship may affect chaplaincy in regard to application of professional standards, the chaplain's place in the system, levels of accountability, the chaplain's image, the chaplain's use of authority, and integration of the chaplain's role in the institution. Similarities as well as differences will be touched on.

Professional standards

Professionals in most fields are certified by a professional body and, as such, are accountable not only to their employer but also to their professional association. The same cannot be said for clergy in general. Most pastors are accountable to their denominations. Some are accountable only to their congregations. Some ministers are self-appointed.

Because of the absence of common standards of practice among clergy, health care institutions for too long were reluctant to call on clergy because they did not know what they could expect from them. Consequently, the spiritual needs of patients were sorely neglected. The Association of Professional Chaplains (APC) in the United States and the Canadian Association for Pastoral Practice and Education (CAPPE) in Canada are the major professional associations that promote and grant board certification for chaplains in order to assure a common standard of practice even though their religious affiliations and roles will differ from institution to institution. Certification requirements include:

- A Master of Divinity (M. Div.) or equivalent.
- Ordination or endorsement for specialized ministry from a religious body.
- A minimum of four units of Clinical Pastoral Education.
- Demonstration of ministerial and professional competence through a certification process.
- Adherence to the professional code of ethics and engaging in ongoing professional development.

Specialized ministry to the spiritual needs of people who come from a wide range of religious backgrounds, or with no religious background, at a vulnerable time in their lives requires specialized preparation, ongoing professional development, and appropriate accountability in both public and faith-based health care institutions. For health care institutions, whether public or faith-based, to employ chaplains as directors of spiritual care who are professionally certified and have received interfaith endorsement, assures that the candidate is acceptable to the interfaith community and is professionally prepared. For an institution to disregard certification places it in the position of having to make judgments in an interview process that it is ill equipped to make. Can you imagine a hospital determining in an interview process whether a prospective surgeon is qualified to do surgery? The medical profession determines that issue.

Certification is also in the best interest of the larger faith community because it assures that the chaplain is prepared to function appropriately in a multicultural and multifaith context. Major public medical centers are almost certain to hire only board-certified chaplains in order to avoid the need to establish their own standards for chaplaincy, and in order to offer a level of service in spiritual care that is consistent with the standards of other disciplines in their institutions. Prisons, nursing homes, and retirement centers often opt to hire part-time chaplains without requiring certification for economic reasons. Faith-based facilities may also place greater emphasis on the chaplain's character and religious affiliation without regard for certification. Hiring uncertified chaplains, however, perpetuates a lack of clarity of what to expect from a chaplain.

Having said that, to demand that all spiritual care personnel be fully certified is unrealistic at this time. Persons with a variety of qualifications can provide a variety of valuable services very effectively. But for the service to be recognized as an authentic discipline, it must at least be directed by a fully certified chaplain.

Place in the system

Public institutions, whether for-profit or not-for-profit, are established to provide a service in the community. Faith-based health care and social service organizations are driven by a moral imperative that flows from the sponsoring body's identity and may be expressed through added value or by providing for the underserved who would otherwise be neglected. Religious motivation and history shape medical and spiritual care in faith-based institutions. This, in turn, affects chaplaincy in terms of the chain of command, the allocation of space, the integration of spiritual care in the system, and the scope of expected services.

Roman Catholic sisters, driven by a clear mission to care for the indigent and people with disabilities or addictions, have a long history of providing a broad range of health care services across the United States and Canada. These health care initiatives as well as those sponsored by the Lutheran church, the Salvation Army, Seventh Day Adventists, United Methodists and others unquestionably originated to provide for the underserved and included generous provision of spiritual care on a salaried and volunteer basis.

Mennonites established mental health centers after World War II in response to the compelling case made by Mennonite young men who served as conscientious objectors in the overcrowded and understaffed state hospitals. These men came back to their home communities saying, "There must be a better way." Their persistence and motivation resulted in the establishment of seven community mental health centers across the United States and one in Manitoba, Canada. Services were characterized by competence, compassion and respect. Chaplaincy in these centers focuses not only on providing spiritual care for clients but also on resourcing staff to promote best practice in behavioral sciences in the spirit of Jesus' nondiscriminatory, compassionate ministry.

The mission of hospitals with religious affiliation is driven by the moral and spiritual vision of their founders. Therefore spiritual care will be more central to the institution's mission; reporting to the chief executive officer is more likely; the chaplain and administration are more likely to speak a common language, making chaplaincy less subject to the vagaries of administrative changes.

The mission of public hospitals at best is driven by humanitarian values. In a public hospital, the chaplain is more likely to report to someone lower in the chain of command whose responsibility for a variety of departments may place the spiritual care budget at greater risk when resources are limited. Transitions in administrative leadership also pose a risk if spiritual care as a service and as a budget item has to be justified each time administrative leadership changes.

In public hospitals the primary link of spiritual care as a department is with other disciplines whereas in faith-based institutions the primary link may be with administration. Public hospitals are more likely to view spiritual care as a profession and faith-based hospitals are more likely to view chaplaincy as a calling. About twenty years ago, when chaplains in a university teaching hospital in Winnipeg were negotiating work schedules, salary, and benefits, hospital administration encouraged them to join an existing union in order to standardize negotiations, because virtually all other staff were unionized. By doing so, the chaplains gained negotiating power. In a hospital with religious affiliation unionizing would undoubtedly be seen as secularization. Adding volunteer on-call time to regular work hours would be the more likely expectation, by virtue of the chaplain's calling.

Faith-based institutions typically have the added expectation that the chaplain will represent the mission of the sponsoring faith group and help to keep the institution's mission consistent with the religious values of the sponsoring constituency.

Accountability

Because chaplains serve in multifaith contexts in both public and faith-based institutions, it could be assumed that chaplains in public hospitals must compromise personal conviction to ensure the provision of nondiscriminatory service, and that chaplains in faith-based institutions are prone to impose a religious bias. Chaplains themselves may at times be unclear on these matters. Indeed, chaplains do serve people of all faiths and those who claim no religious faith. The question is whether preserving the integrity of faith of the patient can compromise the integrity of faith of the chaplain. Put another way, how can the spiritual tradition of patient and chaplain and sponsoring institution be fully respected in an act of spiritual care? Does the provision of spiritual care on an interfaith basis necessitate compromise? The answer, in part, lies in an examination of the issue of accountability.

Most professions exercise authority and maintain accountability based on their professional credentials and their employment contract. For the chaplain, regardless of the type of institution being served, several additional dimensions of accountability apply. If properly adhered to, they can minimize misgivings on the part of the public and confusion on the part of the chaplain. The operative dimensions of accountability for the chaplain should be:

- **Personal** authority derived from the chaplain's sense of call.
- **Ecclesiastical** authority granted by the chaplain's faith community.
- **Interfaith** endorsement.
- **Professional** authority through credentialing from a professional association.
- **Administrative** authority based on the chaplain's job description.

Personal authority, based on a sense of call, must be exercised cautiously to guard against imposing self. Ecclesiastic accountability calls for appropriate faithfulness to the chaplain's religious tradition without imposing it on others. Endorsement granted by an interfaith body permits the chaplain to serve the full spectrum of clientele without apology. Professional accountability assures oversight in reference to standards of practice. Administrative accountability pertains to fulfilling the employment contract.

Proper accountability in each of the above areas in both secular and faith-based institutions serves to assure competent professional practice while avoiding compromise. Let me illustrate.

Suppose a chaplain scheduled for on-call duty is paged to neonatal care because a newborn is at risk, but the chaplain does not show up as promised. The failure to respond is a breach of agreement and therefore an issue to be dealt with by the administration.

If, on the other hand, the chaplain shows up but gets into an argument with medical staff about the treatment plan, this is an issue to be taken up in professional supervision because the matter pertains to professional practice.

If the chaplain comes and is asked to baptize the infant but declares that offering the sacrament is not appropriate, then the religious affiliation of the chaplain and that of the infant's family come into play. If the chaplain lacks the authority to baptize because of difference in religious affiliation, then the chaplain is professionally obliged to refer to someone who is able to provide the service. If, however, the chaplain and the family are of the same denomination and the chaplain determines that the circumstances prevailing in this situation do not permit providing baptism, then neither hospital staff nor professional peers can insist that the service must be provided. This is an ecclesiastical issue that must be handled by the chaplain's ecclesiastical authority.

Proper differentiation of authority in both public and faith-based hospitals assures that provision of nondiscriminatory spiritual services will happen while preserving the patient's and chaplain's integrity.

In a faith-based institution, there is an additional, albeit subtle, level of accountability to the faith community that sponsors the institution. At times this adds weight to the services that are offered. At times it may impose expectation to preserve the moral code of the founders in a way that compromises the chaplain's objectivity in patient counseling. For example, in a hospital where abortions are not provided on moral grounds, the patient may not trust the chaplain to offer an unbiased hearing on a personal dilemma regarding her pregnancy.

The chaplain's image

In a public hospital the chaplain's identity may actually be kept in sharper focus than in a faith-based institution because the chaplain is seen more exclusively as the keeper of the spiritual keys. When an invocation is needed, the chaplain is called on to offer it. When a patient's religious beliefs conflict with medical treatment the chaplain is likely to be consulted. In an institution that is deeply rooted in a religious tradition the chaplain's role in reference to such services is less exclusive. Other staff may be just as likely to offer the invocation. They may claim equal authority in spiritual matters and feel less need to consult. As a result, the chaplain's education and expertise may inadvertently be underutilized. In public hospitals chaplaincy may be underutilized due to lack of recognition. In faith-based hospitals chaplaincy may be underutilized when staff claims equal authority to deal with spiritual matters.

As already stated, in a faith-based hospital the chaplain is more clearly linked to the founding mission of the institution than in a public institution. This may affect the patient's view of the chaplain. In my experience in Catholic hospitals, patients expected the sisters to make initial visits without a prior request for spiritual care. The visits were seen as hospitality calls with the intent of welcoming the patient into their care. In a public hospital the patient may initially contribute the motive of an unsolicited visit to evangelization or bearing bad news. The chaplain in a public institution may be seen as having a personal mission, and the chaplain in a faith-based hospital may be seen as representing the mission of the sponsoring faith community. The patient's willingness to accept the chaplain would then depend on the patient's image of the institution's sponsoring body.

Use of authority and power

Chaplains must pay attention to the use of authority and power. In any institution chaplains function on the basis of authority that is granted as well as trust that is earned through relationships. Formal authority is derived from the chaplain's position in the system. In a faith-based facility the chaplain may derive additional authority from the sponsoring faith group. On the one hand, if the chaplain exploits this conferred authority by converting it to personal power, that can raise resistance in staff, particularly when clinical decisions outside the realm of the chaplain's expertise are involved. Over-spiritualizing a psychiatric diagnosis in a behavioral health care setting would be a case in point. Arbitrarily interfering with medical treatment without due process would be another.

On the other hand, positive use of authority contributes to healing. The chaplain in a general hospital was called to the psych unit to see a middle-aged woman who had refused to eat for several days. Nursing staff observed that she had religious items on her night table so they decided to involve the chaplain in a last ditch attempt to avoid intravenous feeding. The chaplain found the woman rigidly stretched out on her bed with a blanket securely tucked under her chin and having a blank look. He introduced himself as the chaplain and gave her time to decide whether she would relate to this stranger. After a few moments she began to offer brief responses. When it seemed that some trust had been built the conversation proceded as follows:

Chaplain: I understand that you have not been eating your meals. I'm interested to know why you are choosing not to eat.

Patient: I want to die.

Chaplain: I'm sad to hear that. Could you tell me why you would want to die?

Patient: I want to die for Jesus.

Chaplain: And why would that be?

Patient: I want to die for Jesus because Jesus died for me. And by dying for him I will prove my faith.

Chaplain: Tell me, Agnes, why did Jesus die for you?

Patient: To save me from sin.

Chaplain: (In a quiet tone) And why would Jesus want you to die for him?

Does he need to be saved?

Patient: (That question seemed to startle her. After a moment of reflection,) No, Jesus does not need to be saved.

(Agnes had been clutching a crucifix at her chest all the while and had claimed affiliation with the Ukrainian Orthodox church so the chaplain surmised that she would hold in high regard the authority of the clergy.)

Chaplain: (with a tone of authority) Agnes, I am a chaplain in the Protestant tradition and I want to assure you that Jesus does not want you to die for him. When Jesus died he counted on us to carry on the good work that he did for people. Jesus does not want you to die for him. He wants you to live for him.

Patient: (Agnes looked into space and pondered what she had heard. Then she slowly sat up and drank the glass of juice that was on her nightstand. The chaplain waited in silence.) I would like to have my supper now.

Chaplain: (Suppressing his gratification) I will ask the nurse to bring you a tray.

Patient: I would like to go to the lunchroom. (So chaplain and patient walked arm in arm to the lunchroom at the end of the hall where she was served.)

The next evening the chaplain was paged again because Agnes was refusing to eat. After brief encouragement she decided to have supper and abandoned her fasting after that. This encounter is an example of positive use of authority because the patient's change of heart resulted from the authority she granted the chaplain as a member of the clergy.

Authority and power,[1] whether derived formally or informally, must be exercised with discretion. The chaplain, in best practice, is actively engaged in the system, yet separate enough from the system to be a safe listener, a support, an advisor, and a confidant not only for patients and their families but also for staff. I often marvel at the depth of trust that can be earned and the range of influence a chaplain can exercise at all levels in the system. In the course of a day, the chaplain may offer spiritual support to the critically ill; comfort to families in grief; connect with staff, patient and family members in the dilemmas of difficult treatment decisions; participate in clinical care conferences; offer consultation to parish pastors; encourage members of staff; participate in bioethical decision making; conduct a memorial service; and respond to emergency codes. Acceptance and effectiveness develop from wise use of professional authority.

Integration of the chaplain's role

Spiritual care functions most effectively when it is integrated in the system, whether in public or faith-based institutions. Such integration is achieved first by a well-defined referral system in which the profession of chaplaincy is recognized and utilized as a discipline among disciplines. A second dimension of integration derives from the involvement of community clergy in the care of their parishioners while in the hospital and in follow-up care. A third dimension of integration goes beyond viewing spiritual care as a support service, to the intentional integration of spiritual care in the treatment process itself. The following case studies illustrate several dimensions of integration.

The first example comes from the medical unit of a general hospital. Bob was a 45-year-old male. His diabetes had reached a critical stage. Infection in his toes had set in to the extent that amputation might become necessary. Bob, however, refused all medication and treatment. He rebuffed attempts of persuasion from the physician and nurse, who were unable to treat him without consent. Recognizing that Bob was a

---

[1] "Authority" and "power" are used in this chapter as very closely related but not as synonyms. *Authority*—whether conferred, earned, or taken—denotes the right or the "empowerment" to make certain decisions and to influence behavior in certain ways. *Power* means the actual ability to cause or prevent change. To use categories proposed by Rollo May, therefore, chaplains are "authorized" to use *nutrient power* (power "for") and *integrative power* (power "with") in dealing with care-receivers, as illustrated above. They must avoid using *manipulative or exploitative* (power "over"), and *competitive* (power "against") forms of power. Rollo May, *Power and Innocence: A Search for the Sources of Violence.* New York: Norton, 1972), 99–120.

religious person, the physician consulted the chaplain.

The patient's record indicated that Bob's religious affiliation was with a Protestant charismatic group. The chaplain offered to visit Bob without identifying the visit as a referral in order to avoid being dismissed on suspicion of collusion with medical staff. The chaplain focused on Bob's need for healing rather than the physician's need for Bob's compliance. Bob welcomed the chaplain and declared that he was an itinerant minister in aboriginal communities in northern Canada. When the reason for Bob's admission to the hospital came up in conversation, the chaplain discerned that Bob was dealing with a crisis of faith.

The doctor is trying to convince me that I have diabetes, but I don't believe that.

You find it hard to accept what the doctor is saying.

I don't think it is serious. Besides, I have no need for a doctor. God can heal me without a physician.

So you want to entrust yourself to God for healing.

Yes. And if my faith is unwavering, it will happen.

Are you saying that accepting medical treatment would represent lack of faith on your part?

God has promised to do whatever we ask in faith. That is what I preach every Sunday.

And now you want to practice what you preach as a testimony to your faith.

Yes, and I count on God to keep his promise.

Bob, you go from one community to another in the north to preach the gospel. Why do you do that?

God has called me so that the people can hear the gospel message and be saved.

Why doesn't God save them without you?

[emphatically] God called me to proclaim his word. That is how God works. If I didn't preach, they would stay in their lost condition.

You believe that God won't save the people without your preaching but expect God to heal you without the physician. Do you suppose the physician could represent the hand of God in your healing just like God's message of salvation comes to the people through your preaching?

The chaplain left Bob to contemplate the question. On his visit the next day, the chaplain found that Bob was accepting treatment.

Another example is from a behavioral health context. Troubled by guilt, Jan sought help from a therapist in a mental health center. She was twenty-four years of age and engaged to be married. Now that she antici-pated marriage and a family, she was deeply troubled by a decision she had made at the age of eighteen to terminate a pregnancy. It was evident to the therapist that Jan was dealing not just with psychological issues but also with a crisis of faith. The therapist dealt with spiritual and psy-chological dynamics in helping Jan come to terms with her guilt, but it appeared that Jan needed to seal in her heart what she had come to terms with in her mind.

The therapist was a man of faith who could have initiated a religious ritual of closure, but he recognized that involving a chaplain at this point would introduce an added dimension of spiritual authority. With Jan's permission, the therapist discussed her situation with the chaplain. The chaplain then arranged for Jan and her fiancé to come to the meditation chapel and bring an object that would represent the lost fetus. He also suggested that she prepare a written statement or a prayer to express what she felt she needed to say. The chaplain invited the therapist to be present for her support and as a sign that the therapy sessions and reli-gious ritual were components of the same therapeutic process, rather than separate events.

The ritual included carefully selected scripture readings and prayers. At a given point, Jan approached the altar and addressed God and her terminated fetus with a tearful confession. Then she placed the rose she had brought at the foot of the cross and left it there as a sign of leaving her lost fetus in the care of a loving God. This act was followed by the chaplain's words of absolution and assurance of forgiveness.

To regard Jan's burden only as a spiritual issue would have been inef-fective, because a premature ritual of closure would not have resolved her conflict. The psychological issues also needed to be addressed. How-ever, cognitive therapy alone was not enough to assure healing either. The therapist's recognition that the issue was both psychological and spiritual made Jan's healing more complete. This event represented whole-some integration in that neither the therapist nor the chaplain acted in isolation.

In the first example, separation between the chaplain and the physi-cian was needed to neutralize Bob's resistance. In Jan's case, the presence of the therapist in the ritual of closure was important to symbolize the integration of the psychological and the spiritual in the healing process. Such integration may happen more naturally in a facility with religious affiliation where it is likely to fit with the culture of the institution. But it can be done in a public institution as well, based on relationships built between chaplains and the clinical staff.

The previous examples represent integration at the professional level. The following examples represent integration at the systemic level. A middle-aged woman escaped from the psych unit of a general hospital and walked into the nearby river to commit suicide by drowning. Staff members felt devastated and asked the chaplain to place the call to the family. The chaplain met the family when they arrived and joined them in their meeting with staff and provided follow-up care for the family. Several days later staff engaged in a clinical review of this tragic event. Among other things, the review resulted in drafting a new policy on steps to be taken in the event of a suicide. The policy included a clear definition of the chaplain's role in relation to family and to staff in the event of a suicide.

A final example comes from the intensive care unit where it was determined that a male patient showed no brain activity after repeated tests. Family was in agreement that life support be discontinued but the timing of that was not specifically discussed. The chaplain was called when the man's son arrived forty-five minutes after life support had been discontinued. The chaplain learned that the respirator had been turned off at about the time the son arrived at the airport from across the country. With a delay of only forty five minutes the son would have experienced his father's death in a very different way than he did now. He had come a long distance only to miss an opportunity to sit with him and speak words of affection even if his father could no longer respond.

Determined that this should not happen again, the chaplain arranged with medical staff that whenever a decision was made to remove life support a chaplain should be called prior to carrying it out because at that point they were no longer dealing with a medical situation but with a family situation. The chaplain would meet with family to assess their readiness to let their loved one go, and determine if anyone else should be there before it was carried out. The chaplain would then offer the family the opportunity to gather around the bed for their final farewells and for a prayer of release. When all family members had drifted back into the family room and felt sad but satisfied, then the chaplain would notify staff that they could proceed to turn off the respirator.

Discontinuing life support is not pleasant for anyone. By following this protocol, not only would the family be helped to achieve closure but medical staff would be helped as well by being assured that the family was at peace and that the removal of life support was a completion of what the family had already done in the ritual of release.

In the case of the suicide by drowning, the chaplain's role was written into the psych unit's policy and procedure manual. In the intensive care unit the agreement was verbally made and maintained through regular practice. In both cases the chaplain's defined role in the treatment team was based on chaplaincy being recognized as a discipline rather than as only a random act of care.

Conclusion

Spiritual care is provided through caring relationships as well as established services and, in its fullest dimension, functions as an integrated profession within the system. In both public and faith-based hospitals chaplaincy focuses on providing spiritual care, not in reference to a particular tradition, but in reference to people's need. Nondiscriminatory spiritual care requires that we draw on our own spiritual resources as we help people access theirs. But in specific needs that pertain to the patient's religious tradition we don't have to be all things to all people. In fact we violate them when we try. For the chaplain to refer specific needs to the most appropriate spiritual caregiver is as important as it is for medical staff to refer to the chaplain.

Common standards of training and common standards of professional practice minimize differences in the delivery of spiritual care between public hospitals and faith-based institutions. However, the religious and cultural orientation of an institution affects the way spiritual care is recognized and supported.

In the future, increased attention to cultural diversity may make differences more noticeable between institutions of different types. Some public hospitals have chapels that feature specific worship centers appropriate for various religious traditions. Some provide a suitable space where a smudging service can be provided without setting off the fire alarm. Chapels in hospitals with religious affiliation will more likely continue to reflect the tradition that sponsors the institution without denying others the opportunity to worship. Public hospitals will tend to focus on *spiritual* care more generically, while hospitals with religious affiliation will likely retain a more specific focus on *pastoral* care. Nevertheless, with growing public interest in alternative medicine, a general shift away from a narrow focus on religious doctrine, and a greater interest in spirituality, chaplaincy in institutions of both kinds will continue to have a significant role in the healing arts in the years to come.

Part 2

Interfaith spiritual care
in diverse cultural contexts

*The expanding field of interfaith spiritual care
and the commonalities and differences
encountered in a variety of
culturally-specific settings in diverse countries*

Different lyrics but the same tune
Multifaith spiritual care in a Canadian context

Patricia (Pam) Morrison Driedger

Many years ago a friend and I were engaged in a conversation about hospital chaplaincy. In the course of this conversation, he told me about a chaplain in a large hospital in Canada who was herself a practitioner of Wicca. At the time I wondered how such a person could be an effective chaplain. My comments, I am sorry to say, went something like this: "I rather doubt that there are enough practitioners of Wicca to keep a chaplain busy, and I think the differences between Wicca and most of the mainstream faiths are too great for a Wicca chaplain to be of much service to anyone else." I went on to say, "I am a fairly open-minded, multifaith oriented person, but I would be uncomfortable with the idea of someone who identified herself as a "white witch" offering me spiritual care. I would feel that this person's god was not my God, and I would wonder about what they were inviting into the conversation. If I feel that way, how would it be for someone from a "more conservative" background?

At the time of this conversation I thought that the role of hospital chaplain was to offer people the hope and the strength of faith during a difficult time. The chaplain would, I thought, speak the words of faith that would shore up a patient's lagging spirits and give him or her the courage to face whatever was coming. In my way of thinking, the effectiveness of the chaplain with any given patient would be somewhat dependent upon how closely aligned the chaplain's faith was to that of the patient. When I reflect upon my comments about the great distance between Wicca and more mainstream religions, I realize that I assumed that a Christian chaplain would be able to offer the best support to a

Pam Driedger, M.Div., is Director of Spiritual Care at Eden Mental Health Centre, Winkler, Manitoba, Canada.

person of their own denomination because they would know how to interpret and explain things in a way that fit with what the patient had been taught. The chaplain would be able to offer significant support to other Christians who held a large number of beliefs in common and some encouragement and insight to all who practice a monotheistic faith. I assumed a person from a pagan tradition would not be able to reflect any of my own beliefs back to me with enough conviction to make a difference. Even if she were able to recite the proper words, she wouldn't really know what they meant and so she wouldn't be of much support if my faith was at all shaky.

Today as I provide spiritual care for people from a wide variety of religious traditions, including earth-based traditions, and for people with no religious tradition whatsoever, I am somewhat embarrassed by my long-ago comments. Over the years I have learned to think differently not only about the role of a spiritual care provider in a multifaith setting, but also about what it means to have a multifaith orientation. I have come to believe that a multifaith outlook is not rooted in finding the common content or common beliefs in different religious traditions, but rather in recognizing the common process of faith and of orienting one's life around one's faith. While I used to think that the spiritual care provider had to share the specifics of a patient's faith, I now realize that the primary role of the spiritual care provider is to understand the way that faith permeates everything else in life and to engage patients from within the paradigm of faith.[1]

What is the Canadian context?

My thinking about what it means to provide spiritual care across religious traditions has been significantly influenced by the Canadian approach to diversity. Throughout Canadian society a high value is placed upon cultural diversity and cultural distinctiveness. Canadians regularly distinguish themselves from their neighbours in the United States by saying that Canada is a "mosaic" while the US is a "melting pot." One of the clearest examples of what this means is found in the Canadian ap-

---

[1] A paradigm is a philosophical and theoretical framework. There are many different paradigms which shape the day-to-day choices and the long term goals of individuals and communities. Not only individuals but also professions operate from within particular paradigms; within each profession practitioners observe, analyze and respond to the problems they encounter according to a specific set of criteria with a specific set of goals. When spiritual care providers interact with patients/clients their focus is on the meaning and value system which the care receivers have identified as their own. Spiritual care providers strive to understand and respond to issues of illness and health, hope and despair from the perspective of the patient/client rather than from some external, "objective" perspective.

proach to the national anthem.

Talk to any Olympic athlete who has won a gold medal and they will speak about the moment when they stood on the podium and their national anthem began to play. Watch the faces of athletes when their national anthem is played at the opening of an international game. A national anthem is one of the central signs of communal identity and belonging. When an anthem is played it connects athletes to millions of people they have never met but who care about them and about what they will do. A national anthem is one of the central symbols and forces of unity.

Now consider Canada's national anthem.

"Oh Canada!
Our home and native land!
True patriot love in all thy sons command.
With glowing hearts
We see thee rise,
The true north, strong and free"

"Ô Canada! Terre de nos aïeux,
Ton front est ceint de fleurons glorieux!

Car ton bras sait porter l'épée,
Il sait porter la croix!

Ton histoire est une épopée
Des plus brillants exploits.

"O Canada! Land of our forefathers
Thy brow is wreathed with a glorious garland of flowers.
As in thy arm ready to wield the sword,
So also is it ready to carry the cross.
Thy history is an epic of the most brilliant exploits."

"Uu Kanata!
Nangmini nunavut!
Piqujatii nalattiaqpavut."

"Oh, Canada
Snow falling from the sky. Snow on the ground.
Snow dissolving into the sea. Snow building up on sea ice."

These are the opening stanzas of Canada's National Anthem as it is sung in English-speaking Canada, in French-speaking Canada, and in the territory of Nunavut: three distinct languages, three distinct meanings, but only one country, and only one tune. The music connects Canadians to one another and to their country even though different groups may have different understandings of what it means to be Canadian and what it means to be connected. The music influences the phrasing and sentence structure of the lyrics. It shapes the overall tone and atmosphere of the anthem and the way it is likely to touch and move the "soul," but the music does not influence the intellectual content. The music shapes the way the meaning will be heard and interpreted but it does not influence the basic meaning of the lyrics. The music links the hearts of people from different cultures without requiring that they link all of their thoughts.

The idea that the national anthem should be sung with different words in different places to reflect the distinct cultural perspectives and emphases of those places, rather than sung with one set of words which would highlight what all the cultures and regions hold in common, epitomizes the Canadian approach to diversity. This multicultural approach to the national anthem in Canada provides a window into understanding the multifaith approach to spiritual care in the Canadian context. Canadian spiritual care providers build upon the well-established tradition of playing a melody to which everyone can sing their own song even if everyone's lyrics are completely different.

Changing the thinking: Manitoba's experience

The recognition that it is a common melody (paradigm of faith) rather than common lyrics (the specific tenets of faith themselves) which creates a foundation for multifaith spiritual care did not spring up overnight. In Canada as in many other places, interfaith dialogue began with efforts to understand each other in a way that would allow for a deemphasizing of differences and an emphasizing of commonalities. There was an effort to find an essential transcendent truth on which people of different faiths could agree. There was a sense that multifaith spirituality and multifaith care would find and attend to the common denominator in beliefs. It would not be ideal for anyone, but it would be better than nothing. Imagine everyone singing "O Canada ... ." (the first words of the Canadian anthem and the only words which all three languages share) and then humming the rest of the song.

In the past the importance of faith groups within the fabric of society was taken as a given. The primary threat to any particular religious group came from people who practiced religion in a different way. Faith communities worked together to improve their relationships with each other and to find the common denominator in their beliefs so that they would not use their influence to pull in opposite directions when in fact they shared a common goal.[2] In recent years the primary threat to faith communities has come from the secular community that sought to discredit or sideline all religious groups and concerns. Faith groups have begun working together not so much to find the commonalities in their beliefs but more to find the commonalities in their goals and in the paradigm out of which they operate. Now groups work together to help the secular world understand the place and value of faith and spirituality in the world, in whatever form they take.

The Province of Manitoba, where I live and work, has a very active interfaith community that has worked together for many years advocating for the importance of spiritual care for people in health care and correctional institutions. Initially, spiritual care was understood primarily as *pastoral* care and the primary concern of the Manitoba Interfaith Council[3] was that neither hospitalization nor incarceration be allowed to separate people from the supports of the faith community which might be instrumental in their recovery. In more recent years the Council has shifted its focus away from the shared interests of faith groups in caring for their own, to the shared belief of faith groups that the perspective of faith has a place in health care decisions and that attention to the concepts and constructs of faith affects health outcomes. While in the past the council advocated for the rights of faith groups to provide a type of care that is particularly appropriate for those of their tradition, today it advocates for the rights of patients to receive care that is attentive to their personal faith story whether that is in lock step with their inherited tradition, at odds with their tradition or somewhere in between. In the past the focus was on the rights of faith groups to practice their faith regardless of what others thought. Today the focus is on the spiritual nature of all people, those within and those outside of faith groups, and the importance of giving attention to that spiritual nature in any quest for health or rehabilitation.

One of the catalysts for this change in focus was the introduction of

---

[2] Consider the ecumenical movement which resulted in the formation of the World Council of Churches in the 1960s. Consider too the series of dialogues and subsequent accords between the Catholic Church and various other Christian denominations.

[3] The Manitoba Interfaith Council works to ensure the provision of spiritual care in provincial healthcare and correction institutions. MIC is particularly concerned that spiritual care be provided in a manner that honours the faith perspective of the client.

new privacy laws which raised questions about if and how spiritual caregivers could be informed of a person's hospital admission or condition. There was concern that some of the prevailing interpretations of privacy laws would result in an artificial division between those providing spiritual care and those providing other forms of care to hospital patients and care home residents. This in turn might impair communication that might otherwise facilitate healing. Leaders from the various faith communities began by discussing their concerns that they would no longer be able to adequately serve those people who were on the fringes of their community, those whose health condition might be unknown to them, but who would need and want care at times of crisis.

As the discussions progressed, those involved became increasingly aware of the fact that although they might disagree about the specifics of faith, and the specifics regarding what it is that gives meaning and purpose to life, they all agreed that attention to the questions is essential to a person's well-being. They began to realize that their concern was not simply that people from their own tradition receive "religious care," but that all people receive a form of care that is attentive to the spirit. Conversations began to focus less on religious or faith needs and more on understanding the place of these needs in the overall understanding of health.

The Manitoba Interfaith Council, the Interfaith Health Care Association of Manitoba[4] and the Manitoba branch of the Canadian Association for Pastoral Practice and Education (CAPPE)[5] worked together and met many times with government to enhance the understanding of spiritual well being as an integral component of overall well-being. Much of the discussion was built around the modern understanding of health as more than just the absence of disease. The World Health Organization defines health as "a state of complete physical, mental and social well-being." The Manitoba Interfaith Council and the Interfaith Health Care Association of Manitoba and CAPPE stressed that both mental and social well-being depend upon a person's ability to find meaning and purpose in the midst of whatever is happening. Individuals are likely to be thrown into turmoil if they are unable to respond to the present circumstances within the meaning and decision-making framework which they have chosen for their lives. Physical or mental illness can result in

---

[4] The Manitoba Interfaith Council has representatives from almost all of the faith groups which meet for worship in Manitoba. The Interfaith Healthcare Association of Manitoba's members include all of the healthcare organizations in the province which are owned and governed by faith groups. For more information on IHCAM see http://www.cham.mb.ca/IHCAM/index.

[5] For more information on CAPPE see www.cappe.org.

significant spiritual distress and create a need for spiritual care. Spiritual care is intended to help people maintain or recover their sense of meaning and purpose when it is threatened or has been undermined by illness. When spiritual care is made available, health outcomes improve.

In 2004 health was officially defined in Manitoba law as "the condition of being sound in mind, body, and spirit."[6] The decision to make "sound in spirit" part of the definition of health reflected the consensus that an integral relationship exists between a person's spirituality and a person's response to illness and treatment plans. People inside and outside traditional faith structures wanted to ensure that in the pursuit of physical or mental health the impact of treatment on the patient's spiritual well-being was not overlooked. Furthermore, there was broad-based support for the concept of enabling patients to draw upon the strengths of their spiritual traditions to aid them in maximizing their well-being during illness and/or in the movement toward recovery.

Applying the Canadian approach to diversity to a clinical setting

The naming of spiritual well-being as a component of health resulted in the recognition of spiritual care as a distinct component of health care and not merely a service offered in support of "real" health care. This in turn has created a need to describe spiritual care outside of systems of faith, and to establish standards of spiritual care that can be understood within the context of the secular, without reference to any particular religious tradition or belief system. There is an increasing pressure to ensure that spiritual care is truly multifaith care, and that spiritual care providers are able to offer the highest standard of care to *all* people who have spiritual needs.

Spiritual caregivers in many places have learned to step outside of their own faith traditions in order to reach out to others who are in need or in pain and who are not being served by someone from their own tradition. In many settings, spiritual caregivers have learned to do this because of their own drive toward compassion. They have wanted to help and so have found a way to help. Multifaith care has been learned and is being learned by necessity more than by design. In Canada, the push toward multifaith care comes not just from individual care providers who see it as something which they must do out of compassion; the push comes even more strongly from the health care system itself. In order to understand the systemic drive toward multifaith spiritual care, it is necessary to reflect upon the Canadian approach to health care in

---

[6] Bill 43, 2nd Session, 38th Legislature, The Personal Health Information Amendment Act.

general and the ongoing shift in the understanding of the place of spiritual care in health care.

The Canadian Health Care system is driven by a set of five principles which impact every aspect of health care. These five principles are: public administration, comprehensiveness, universality, portability and accessibility.[7] All five of these principles influence Canadian thinking around spiritual care.

Because health is publicly administered, decisions with respect to the place of spiritual care within the health system are open to public discussion and debate and policy. In the past, pastoral care was primarily viewed as something which various faith groups offered to patients in hospitals and residents in care homes. Pastoral care was something that patients carried from their home lives to the hospital or care home; it was not an integral part of the health care plan. Pastoral care was most commonly found in facilities which were owned and governed by faith communities. This was because these communities established health care facilities as a means of ensuring that illness would not isolate a person from community supports, and pastoral care was recognized as one of the important community supports. From a public policy perspective, pastoral care was seen as one of the things which a caring community had the right to offer as a part of their self-expression. If a community chose to offer pastoral care, they had the right to do so as long as such care was not imposed on those who did not want it, or made a condition for the reception of other care.

In recent years, there has been a mounting body of evidence measuring the positive impact of spiritual care on health outcomes.[8] As health care decision-makers reflected upon this evidence they began to think of spiritual care not as something that the community brings into the hospital but as something the hospital offers the community. As soon as spiritual care became a service of the hospital to the community and not the other way around, it became necessary to apply the principles of comprehensiveness, universality, and accessibility. This in turn led to a shift in the way spiritual care is understood and offered.

If Canada's health care system were driven primarily by market forces, spiritual care would be provided when those who were paying indicated a strong desire for the care or when the hospital administration believed

[7] See The Canada Health Act: Overview and Options: www.parl.gc.ca/information/library.

[8] See Levin J. God, Faith and Health: Exploring the Spirituality-Healing Connection. New York, NY: John Wiley and Sons; 2001. See also Culliford, Larry, "Spiritual care and psychiatric treatment: an introduction," Advances in Psychiatric Treatment (2002) 8: 249-258, The Royal College of Psychiatrists.

that spiritual care had a positive effect on the bottom line. In a market driven system, the hospital must make sure that it does not interfere with a patient's right to receive spiritual care from those who choose to make it available, but the hospital does not have a responsibility for providing that care for any given faith group unless that group's market share dictates such a responsibility. Canada's health care system, however, is not primarily driven by market forces (although it is influenced by them); it is driven by principles. And these principles necessitate that a change in the understanding of the impact of spiritual care will require a change in the way spiritual care is provided. This is because a change in the understanding of the impact of spiritual care creates a change in the responsibilities resting with the care provider.

Based on the principles of comprehensiveness, universality, and accessibility, if spiritual care has been demonstrated to have a significant positive and cost effective effect on health outcomes, it should be included in the service provided to all patients. It is not sufficient to say that the majority of patients in this organization are Catholic or Protestant therefore we will have Catholic and Protestant chaplains who will serve people in their respective groups and provide for others "to the extent that they are able." Nor is it sufficient to say that pastoral caregivers from Jewish, Christian, and Protestant communities are willing to come and offer services, but there is no one from the Islamic community so we will be unable to offer spiritual care to Moslems. In keeping with the Canadian philosophy of care, if the organization is going to provide spiritual care for some patients it has a responsibility to provide comparable care for every patient, even those who come from very small minorities. Since it is not possible to provide a chaplain for every religious group or every type of spirituality that is represented among hospital patients, it has become necessary to think about spiritual care in new ways.

This change in thinking can be seen in a change in language from speaking about _pastoral care_ in clinical settings to speaking about _spiritual_ care. The words, "pastor" and "pastoral" conjure up images of a shepherd with a flock. The shepherd guides the flock from where they are to a better place, carefully skirting dangers and pulling those who would wander back from precipices or out of ditches. The flock follows because they know the shepherd's voice and have learned to trust it. Within a faith context, the pastor shepherds the flock on its journey toward God or toward ultimate reality, and helps individuals find the things which will nourish them on the journey and avoid the things which will harm them. The flock follows because they recognize the pastor's voice, words, and tone. Any who are not comfortable with the voice, words, and tone will not follow. They will know that they must wait for another shep-herd—a different pastor.

The presumption in the shift of language from "pastoral care" to "spiri-tual care" is that even if no pastor arrives to lead a person, it is possible to support their spiritual journey in a way that fosters health. Looking at the various studies around spiritual care, it would appear that it is not the end goal of a particular spiritual path that is the primary determinant of health, but rather the process of spiritual discernment. To return to the opening musical analogy, it is not the lyrics but the melody which makes the song of the spirit what it is.

Becoming a spiritual caregiver instead of a pastor

The traditional role of the pastor is to lead the spiritual song; as with the national anthem of Canada, the meaning of the song will depend upon the language (in this case the spiritual language) which the leader knows and chooses. It is difficult to imagine a Christian pastor knowing and choosing a spiritual song that did not call people into relationship with the God revealed in Jesus. A Buddhist would be inclined to choose a song that encouraged the patient to let go of their strong sense of "self" and their belief that there is anyone or anything that is truly "other." The Native American song would emphasize the permanent connected-ness of all things and the influence of each upon the others. It would be difficult, if not impossible, to lead people and serve as pastor for people from very different traditions without losing one's own authenticity. It would be difficult if not impossible to sing one song that would have deep meaning for people from all three of these traditions, but it would be possible to play a melody that was recognizable and significant within each tradition.

The shared melody of all spiritual traditions is heard in the questions of meaning and purpose that are the same for everyone.[9] The music of the spirit is expressed in the universal quest for love, inner peace, be-longing, and hope. This quest is the same whether one is Christian or Muslim, Jewish or Buddhist or agnostic. All people have a need to ask questions about the meaning, purpose, and value of life; and each person needs to find answers that enable him or her to respond to the unique experiences of his or her own life. Some people will be conscious of the fact that they have asked and answered these questions. Others will be

---

[9] The spiritual nature of human beings can be understood from an anthropological perspective as well as from a theological perspective. A widely cited definition of spirituality which refers to these common questions can be found in Murray, R.B. and Zentner, J.P. , *Nursing Concepts for Health Promotion*, (London: Prentice Hall, 1989), p. 259.

content with the answers provided to them by their families and communities and may be unaware that there are questions to be asked. Nevertheless the questions and the answers still exist and create the framework for each person's existence, and the basis for every decision. The role of the spiritual caregiver is to recognize the importance of the spiritual process in shaping every aspect of life and to provide accompaniment for people as they engage in the process.

The role of a spiritual care provider in a multifaith health care environment is not to help people find a particular set of answers to their questions, but instead to help them become more aware of the ways in which their own framework of questions and answers impacts their health and their health-related choices. The spiritual care provider is also expected to be attentive to the impact and/or significance of decisions made by the treatment team when viewed through the patient's particular worldview or lens of faith. When necessary the spiritual caregiver can help present treatment decisions in a manner that makes sense within the context of the patient's faith, and/or present the patient's faith concerns in a manner that makes sense within the paradigms used by the treatment team.

Each member of the treatment team within a health care facility has a particular expertise and a particular perspective from which he or she views the well-being of patients and advocates for a transformation from illness to wellness. The spiritual caregiver is the member of the treatment team whose expertise is the realm of faith and spirituality. The significant tasks of the spiritual caregiver in a multifaith environment include: 1) understanding how individual belief systems and communal belief systems impact a person's health and a person's response to treatment; 2) entering into the faith paradigm of the patient, as it is presented by the patient, in order to hear the cry of the spirit; 3) being a listening presence accompanying the patient through illness from within their own worldview/understanding of illness; 4) enabling the patient to use the resources which he or she can see in his or her own faith as sources of strength, hope, meaning and purpose; 5) helping the health care team recognize the conflicts that arise because the faith paradigms of the team and the faith paradigms of the patient are not the same and 6) helping the patient and the care team to address any conflicts which exist between the patient's spiritual goals and the patient's other health goals.

Providing multifaith care as a Christian caregiver

In the normal course of events, individuals choose their own paradigm of belief, find their own sense of meaning and purpose, and walk their own spiritual path. Some walk that path in the company of a faith community, following the map of an established religious tradition. Others develop a meaning system that is uniquely their own, drawing on inputs from a variety of religious, philosophical, and secular sources. Traditional Christian teaching holds that any path that is not directed toward the One God, who became human in the person of Jesus and remains in the world through the presence of the Holy Spirit, is a dead end. Different Christian denominations have different understandings of what it means to walk a path oriented toward God, but all accept the individual's right to choose his or her own path.

This acceptance of the right of individuals to choose their own spiritual path can become more complicated during periods of significant illness. This is because significant illness often throws people off their chosen paths or brings to light significant hazards along those paths. When any of us see other people who are finding it difficult to follow the path which they have chosen, it can be very tempting for us to encourage them to try a new path. Many Christians watching non-Christians struggle with feelings such as hopelessness, despair, doubt, anxiety or guilt, honestly believe that if the non-Christian would come to know Christ, his or her journey would not be as hard. It can be tempting for the Christian spiritual caregiver to suggest Christian faith as the support that will make a difference to a patient who is struggling. This temptation is not unique to spiritual caregivers. It can also be tempting for a Christian doctor, a Christian nurse or a Christian social worker to suggest their faith as a part of the best treatment plan. Like the others, spiritual caregivers need to remember that their task is not to evangelize but to offer health care, and in fact using their position of power as a health care provider to evangelize would be wrong.

Doctors, nurses, and social workers often avoid the temptation of imposing their faith on patients and clients by avoiding spiritual issues altogether. Spiritual caregivers cannot do that; instead they have to hone their skills in enabling the spiritual process without prescribing the spiritual content. The multifaith nature of our health care facilities is forcing spiritual care providers and others to recognize that spiritual health care is not about providing a set of answers but about helping people identify and wrestle with a set of questions.

Jesus said, "Ask, and it will be given to you; seek, and you will find; knock, and the door will be opened." (Matthew 7:7) The Christian spiritual caregiver, the Jewish spiritual caregiver and the Wiccan spiritual caregiver all can help patients ask, seek, and knock. It is important that the caregiver be rooted in his or her own faith tradition because that rootedness enables the caregiver to truly understand the significance of the spiritual process. As with any health care practitioner, the specific faith of the caregiver may motivate the caregiver and may give meaning and purpose to his or her work, but the terms of the caregiver's faith are not the focus of a spiritual care visit. This is because the spiritual caregiver plays the melody, but the care receiver provides the words.

Competencies for pastoral work in multicultural and multifaith societies

Anke Flohr

In my many years of ministry away from my mother church, the Northelbian Evangelical Lutheran Church, I have discovered that the academic training and encouragement I received provided a solid base for my work.[1] To my surprise I found out that my upbringing as a farm girl—born and raised in a small farming community fifty kilometers east of Hamburg—became more and more an asset. In my early years on the farm, I learned something about the importance and interdependence of community with each other and with the land. I had to travel to the other side of the world to appreciate the simple truth of the importance of family and community and the value of nurturing relationships with people and nature. My Samoan friends say it boldly: "Family is our life insurance." Coming from North-European, Protestant roots I have always put individualism and independence as my top guidelines. The rediscovery of the simple truth of the importance of interdependent communities has been a major learning, or shall I say "relearning," for me in the last decade. I am therefore also grateful to my parents and family for having given me a firm foundation for my life; it is a foundation that sustains the professional work partially reflected in the following pages.

In the first part of this essay—"Context, challenge, and guidelines"—

Anke Flohr, M.Div., an ordained minister in the Evangelical Lutheran Church in America, is a supervisor and Director of Clinical Pastoral Education at Pacific Health Ministry, Honolulu, Hawaii. She is also a board certified chaplain serving at the Good Samaritan Retirement Community at Pohai Nani, Kaneohe.

[1] My special thanks goes to Professor Theo Ahrens. It was my honor to have studied under him at the Institute for Missiology, Ecumenics and Religious Studies (Department of Protestant Theology at the University of Hamburg). It was Professor Ahrens, in the early eighties, who opened the doors for me to embrace cultural diversity and follow my calling to specialize in research, pastoral care and counseling in multicultural societies, especially the communities in the region of Oceania, such as in Papua New Guinea.

I will introduce the context, "Hawaii," from which I speak and I will describe the need for new competencies for pastoral work in multicultural and multifaith communities. I will explore seven areas of competency: passion, personal awareness, knowledge, skills, action, embracing ambiguity and patience. In summary I use Pacific Health Ministry as an example of how to teach multicultural competencies in pastoral care. In the second part—"A window to reflective practice"—I will present an interfaith care situation including verbatim material and a comprehensive analysis.

Part 1
Context, challenge, and guidelines

Context: Pacific Health Ministry in Hawaii

I joined Pacific Health Ministry[2] in Hawaii in 1994 to specialize in Clinical Pastoral Education (CPE) and to become a CPE supervisor. The pastoral care agency then was eight years old, founded and sponsored by local churches, temples, and communities of all faiths expressing a need for spiritual care in the major hospitals of the island of Oahu.[3] Pacific Health Ministry (then called Interfaith Ministries of Hawaii) was asked to provide spiritual care and education for a community that had become a "mosaic" of about fifty diverse (immigrant) cultures and traditions in the last two hundred years. The first immigrants were the Hawaiian people themselves (700–900 CE). The Native Hawaiians established their monarchy with about 300,000 people. They had a single, understood lifestyle, religion, and culture. Change came with the arrival of James Cook from England in 1778.

American and European businessmen were followed by three large waves of immigrants from China, Japan, and the Philippines until the early 1900s. Smaller immigrant groups came from Korea, Portugal, and a few other European countries. The need for cheap, compliant agricultural workers was great on the many sugar plantations. American missionaries (Congregationalists) from New England arrived in 1820. The State of Hawaii Data Book 2004[4] estimates that about 33 percent of the current population is European/American, 23 percent Japanese, 19 percent Filipino, nine percent Native Hawaiian, six percent Chinese and

---

[2] http://www.pacifichealthministry.org

[3] Hawaii consists of eight islands with a population of about 1,275,000. Eighty per cent of all people live on the island of Oahu It's capitol is Honolulu.

[4] http://hawaii.gov/dbedt/info/economic/databook/

other mainly Asian and Pacific Island groups (see chart). The widely accepted practice of intermarriage has left many individuals with complex ethnic backgrounds. For example, it is very common for a person to say, "I am Hawaiian, Chinese, German, and Korean." People in Hawaii often define their identity as a "local identity" which consists of their own ethnic roots blended together in Hawaii to a rather unique lifestyle which expresses its love for diversity and living on the islands. Living the "Aloha Spirit" is one expression of that. The Native Hawaiians claim their Hawaiian identity and resent the overthrow of their last Queen, Queen Liliuokalani, in 1893, and the fact that Hawaii became the 50th state of the US in 1959. There are constant tensions between those who embrace the new "local identity/local culture" and those who want the sovereignty and their "aina" (land) back which was lost to more recent immigrant people.

Hawaii has many cultures and ethnic groups living closely together with as many languages spoken as there are different ethnic groups. Each group has brought its culture and religion with them. Each has developed unique ways of understanding life and death. Each practices healing and gives care to people in special ways. In Hawaii approximately 50 percent of the population is Christian with more than two dozen denominations. These include the Roman Catholic Church, which is the largest, the Southern Baptist, United Methodist, Episcopalian, United Church of Christ, the Church of Jesus Christ of Latter-Day Saints and, in the last 10 years, several fast-growing Foursquare churches. Buddhists comprise 35 percent with seven major sects. The Honpa Hongwanji is the largest and most influential group. The rest is a combination of Jewish, Islamic, and native Hawaiian beliefs, and other religions and people who have no particular religious affiliation. Many people living in Hawaii would say that they are "spiritual" and that their "local culture" has a lot to do with their spirituality. Learning to minister to all people as they face a crisis in life is a central focus of Clinical Pastoral Education. In Hawaii being able to engage in "interfaith dialogue" is a necessity for chaplains which creates interesting learning opportunities: "Can I fully serve others who are different from me?"

In the ten major hospitals and health care facilities on Oahu in which Pacific Health Ministry chaplains serve, we encounter patients, families, and staff from all backgrounds. Chaplains with Pacific Health Ministry make well over sixty thousand pastoral contacts a year. The essence of the mission of Pacific Health Ministry is to be Kukulu Kumuhana. "Kukulu Kumuhana" has a special significance in the Hawaiian culture. It is the process of "pooling together" in unity the spiritual, emotional, and psychological strengths of the individual who is ill or in a special circumstance with that of family, friends, and other concerned individuals to achieve a positive outcome.

A more commonly used clinical word for "pooling together" is the word *assessing*: To be a professional spiritual care provider in this multicultural and multifaith setting we need to be competent in assessing those we serve and "pooling together" information and people. We always seek to look at the *whole person*—mind/body/spirit—in her or his context and are concerned with how a person finds meaning and purpose in life, including a sense of belonging and connectedness. We gather insight about their lives considering spiritual, psycho-social/interpersonal, emotional, intellectual, vocational, ethnic/racial/cultural and physical dimensions. Following that data, the health care chaplains develop care plans together with the interdisciplinary care team. This assessment process, the "Kukulu Kumuhana" is supported by a *ministry of presence*, which builds relationship by creating a non-judgmental environment of compassion and care. The spiritual care provider comes from a place of humility in conjunction with the ability to think critically. Pamela A. Hays says it well: "People with genuine humility are effective helpers, because they are realistic about what they have to offer, aware of their own limitations and accepting of the contribution of others."[5]

The need for multicultural and multifaith competencies in pastoral work

Hawaii is unique because it is culturally so diverse and so isolated by the Pacific Ocean. By most peoples' descriptions, Hawaii is called "Paradise." It truly is a "Paradise" for multicultural learning and teaching and offers its "manao" (knowledge) to the world. Beyond, Hawaii's cultural diversity is part of the fabric of North American social life. One third of the U.S. population comes from other cultural traditions than the still predominant European-American. By the year 2050 this number is estimated to have increased to more than 50 percent of the US population. Over 2,000 identifiable expressions of religion and spiritual paths were found in the USA.[6] We are involved in a multicultural and multifaith revolution. We live in a world that has many points of view about what "reality" is. Mary A Fukuyama and Todd D. Sevig define multiculturalism as "many cultures, many worldviews, many languages, many values, and

[5] Pamela A. Hays. *Addressing Cultural Complexities in Practice* (Washington, D.C.: American Psychological Association, 2004), p. 25.

[6] J. Creedon. "God with a Million Faces," *Utne Reader* (July–August 1998), 42–48.

many customs, existing and serving to form human communities. Secondly, it means seeking common ground, respecting differences, and working for social justice in a system that historically has kept various groups from access to resources and power."[7] This means that "multiculturalism" is more than a descriptor of a social situation; it also denotes certain values. In a multicultural society, cross-cultural and intercultural engagements are the norm.

The new context of our times is a globalized community with international relations. The complexity of our multicultural and globalized world with its new spiritual demands is challenging for pastoral/spiritual care providers. Multicultural competencies are now required for chaplains in U.S. and Canadian hospitals. My Korean American colleague Samuel Lee from the Claremont School of Theology—who was raised in Hawaii—compares the multicultural interactions in pastoral care with the movements of dance partners.[8] For three years we served together on the Multicultural Taskforce of the Association for Clinical Pastoral Education. In those years the task force members tried to learn together "multicultural dance steps" to become multicultural dancers who open up to meaningful encounters across and beyond differences in order to be mutually enriched and transformed by meeting the other. Having attempted to learn the Hula after moving to Hawaii, I understand Lee's dance metaphor and all the discipline, practice, good attitude, resiliency, physical strength and endurance it takes before the dance with the group starts becoming harmonious.

Seven multicultural-multifaith dance steps

To the question of what makes a competent pastoral/spiritual care provider in our multicultural and multifaith society, therefore, we respond with a choreography including the following steps.

Passion

Passion is the first essential competency. It is energy, curiosity, a calling for the process and often the hard work of encountering the unknown,

---

[7] Mary A. Fukuyama and Todd D. Sevig. "Cultural Diversity in Pastoral Care," in Robert G. Anderson and Mary A. Fukuyama, eds. *Ministry in the Spiritual and Cultural Diversity of Health Care* (New York: The Haworth Pastoral Press, 2004), p. 28.

[8] K. Samuel Lee. "Becoming Multicultural Dancers: The Pastoral Practitioner in a Multicultural Society." *Journal of Pastoral Care*, 33 (2001), 389–396. For the use of the dance metaphor in pastoral theology, see also Luis Elier Rodríguez, "Intercultural Awareness in Spiritual Caregiving: An Invitation to Dance with God," in Leah Dawn Bueckert and Daniel S. Schipani, eds., *Spiritual Caregiving in the Hospital: Windows to Chaplaincy Ministry* (Kitchener: Pandora Press, 2006), p. 93–104.

engaging "otherness" and leaving one's comfort zone. It is the ability to deeply care for multicultural encounters and to articulate this care to others.[9] It is the ability to connect head and heart, express compassion and truly value difference and unfamiliar territory. It means taking risks, making oneself vulnerable, unlearning and learning. It goes far beyond the initial excitement, interest or thrill in "different faces, accents, foods, and ways of looking at life."[10] Without a passion for these types of encounters, little will be learned.

Personal awareness

Self awareness as cultural beings and an understanding of one's own personal and cultural values and beliefs is an important second step in becoming more competent as pastoral and spiritual caregivers. The ability to know and explain one's own spiritual and cultural background is crucial.[11] To examine one's cultural background the Pacific Health Ministry CPE team found the ADDRESSING model of cultural assessment developed by our colleague Pamela Hays from Anchorage, Alaska, especially helpful.[12] We apply it with the staff and Clinical Pastoral Care students. ADDRESSING is an acronym that identifies a framework for understanding the personal and cultural development of individuals. Each letter represents a word that is a component of one's life and experience:

A stands for age and generational influences (describing my generation, how it has shaped me and continues to shape me in accordance to or in rebellion to it)

D stands for developmental (my experiences of growth and maturation)

D stands for acquired disabilities (my physical condition and my relation with my body seen through the lens of my culture)

R stands for religion and spiritual orientation (my relationship with the Transcendent, as well as my inner self and neighbor, seen through received teachings, cultural influences and personal experiences)

---

[9] A. Cavina, "Multicultural Competencies in Clinical Pastoral Education: Clinical Issues in Cultural Competencies." Unpublished presentation at the annual ACPE conference, Portland, Oregon, October 2004.

[10] A. M. Van Beek, *Cross-Cultural Counseling* (Minneapolis: Fortress Press, 1996), p. 101.

[11] Robert G. Anderson, "The Search for Spiritual/Cultural Competency in Chaplaincy Practice: Five Steps that Mark the Path," in Anderson and Fukuyama, Ministry in the Spiritual and Cultural Diversity of Health Care, p. 13.

[12] Pamela A. Hays, *Addressing Cultural Complexities in Practice* (Washington, DC: American Psychological Association, 2004).

E stands for ethnicity (common ancestry through which I have evolved shared values and customs)

S stands for socio-economic status (the influence of class and economy in my development as an individual)

S stands for sexual orientation (how it has been influenced by my own culture of origin; how it has shaped my relationship with my cultural groups, and with others and their worldviews)

I stands for indigenous heritage (cultural heritage within my ethnicity)

N stands for national origin (my political status and citizenship)

G stands for gender (the constructed gender identity that I received and my gender identity development).

As the reader can see, with each letter Pamela Hays signifies assessment of the impact of power or the lack of it for people. The awareness of cultural privilege, unearned advantages, unintentional racism, assumptions, and biases can come to the forefront. Experiences of being discriminated against by age, disability, ethnicity, socio-economic status and gender orientation can be named. In using the ADDRESSING model as a personal cultural history framework one will hopefully recognize that one's own cultural heritage "did not constitute the world, but a world, and that embracing cultural diversity would both expand and destabilize a person's understanding of his or her world."[13]

The ADDRESSING model has become my preferred tool in working with Clinical Pastoral Care participants. I invite people to write about each letter and then share with the CPE group what they choose. A Hawaiian student told me that this method allowed her to share her "na'au." The "na'au" are literally the intestines but in Hawaiian understanding the seat of speaking one's heart and mind. The ADDRESSING model allowed her to speak of her pain in searching for her identity as a Hawaiian woman; she suggested that we always look for the "na'au" when inquiring about a person's culture. Her Korean peer was not familiar with the "na'au" but with "han." "Han" is the Korean concept of psychological and spiritual hurt caused by unjust oppression and suffering. "Han" is central to the Korean cultural and personal identity. Like "na'au" it forms people's self awareness. The self-knowledge that comes with such learning as described above is essential to understanding the dynamics in cross-cultural pastoral relationships with the clients we serve.

---

[13] T. Breisford & C.R. Foster, *We are the Church Together: Cultural Diversity in Congregational Life* (Valley Forge: Trinity Press International, 1996), p. 11.

Knowledge and training

Once engaged in this ongoing self-assessment process, the third step for pastoral/spiritual caregivers is to learn about diverse identities. This step addresses the ability to be sensitive, to identify and to learn from experience and about information that is outside of one's own cultural reference. The pastoral/spiritual care provider needs to have multicultural knowledge and training and needs to continue to expand and develop specialized knowledge about history, traditions, faith practices, lifestyle, and family systems—in short the worldviews of various ethnic groups and cultures. This includes familiarity with cultural identity development theories and conceptual frameworks. The ADDRESSING model used for assessment of others may help as a source of information. The care provider needs to be knowledgeable about issues around identity, power (history of dominance and oppression), social location, and connection/isolation. Other areas of knowledge are the use of time and space, the relation of individual and community, the focus on content or context, values, and beliefs connected to life and death and life cycle, and distinctions between sacred and profane, personal and public.[14]

This learning process is not always a clear-cut book learning and gathering of facts, but rather a process that pushes the learner beyond her/his comfort zone. Also, diversity brings multiple perspectives, and multiple perspectives often lead to conflict. For example, a CPE student from Mexico explained the traditional role men have in his culture. He often said "it is a guy thing," such as hanging out with other men and joking together. One of his female North American peers in the group who was raised in California was offended by his joking, laughing, and his assumed—as she called it—"sense of entitlement." She found disrespectful what he found totally "normal." Both explained their cultural reasons. And both did not like what they learned about each other. Yet, they continued to dialogue and found a "meeting place/space of exchange" in this process. "The between" became an essential dimension in the meeting of these two students without reinforcing *dominant power structures but rather by showing respect for each other.*

Skills

The saying attributed to Abraham Maslow puts it well, "If the only tool you have is a hammer, everything looks like a nail." The task for chap-

---

[14] Derald Wing Sue and David Sue, *Counseling the Culturally Diverse: Theory and Practice*, 5th ed. (Hoboken: John Wiley & Sons, 2007), Section I, "The Multiple Dimensions of Multicultural Counseling and Therapy," pp. 1–311.

lains working in a multicultural environment is to gain a broad spectrum of skills that will help them to encounter the culturally different client and establish effective communication and connection across cultures. The qualities of a culturally competent pastoral/spiritual care provider reflect cultural humility, an acceptance of and openness to differences among people, genuineness, warmth, and empathy. To provide accurate empathy, the spiritual care provider needs to enter the "cultural border-land,"[15] the area where differences and similarities overlap and then develop a tolerance for ambiguity and create a space for not knowing. Further, the pastoral care provider needs to have good communication skills. They must be attending and responding; they must have language skills; they must be able to receive both verbal and nonverbal messages in response to direct and non-direct communication styles; they must pay attention to body language, voice, emotional expressions, and relational dynamics. And, they must be able to establish a connection across differences. When faced with barriers and limitations—both situational and interpersonal—the spiritual care provider needs to be able to access resources to assist her/him and make appropriate referrals.

A CPE student from Myanmar used to sit in our CPE classes with crossed arms resting on his upper body. My "quick judgment" was that he was probably not really interested, sleepy or somehow protective. Being aware of the danger of "quick judgments" in multicultural work I clarified my assumption with him. I learned that in his culture this body posture shows respect for the teacher and peers and shows full attention.

Action

Step five describes the ability to behave or act in a manner consistent with the above steps. It brings together passion, awareness, knowledge, and skills and goes into action.[16] It asks pastoral care providers to be watchful of their pastoral practice, to be faithful to the many lived realities and, in the words of Samuel Lee, to "keep the dance floor open for all persons."[17] They are asked to look at the larger picture and larger issues in the community, to reflect a global consciousness and to invite transformation and change. Pastoral caregivers need to be able to move beyond individual dialogue to broader actions and community involvement. The practice being called for is a constant process of working on a

[15] Cavina, "Multicultural Competencies in Clinical Pastoral Education."

[16] Mary A. Fukuyama and Todd D. Sevig, *Integrating Spirituality into Multicultural Counseling* (Thousand Oaks: Sage Publications, 1999), p. 71.

[17] Lee, "Becoming Multicultural Dancers," p. 386.

personal, institutional, and systemic level. For example, in hospitals chaplains are involved in Ethics Committees, Palliative Care Committees, End-of-Life support and other groups that attempt to improve patient care and monitor the health care system. Chaplains usually have teaching responsibilities in the broader health care system.

Pacific Health Ministry (PHM) began six years ago to expand its services from the hospitals to low-income housing areas and areas where the many homeless live. PHM nurses offer free basic health check-ups and consultation. PHM chaplains accompany them and offer spiritual support. Together with other community groups and churches they try to make a difference in the lives of people who are least supported and most marginalized in Hawaii.

Embracing ambiguity

I mentioned this step earlier as part of the needed skill-building. Learning to live with ambiguity is a key step. The pastoral and spiritual work in multicultural communities is not a place for experts. Working in pastoral care means learning to live in a dilemma and in a "grey zone." The multicultural pastoral care provider is asked to embrace a "both/and" perspective and, for instance, to be able to say with integrity, "I can be a Christian and value someone else's experience and faith." What the multiculturally-skilled chaplain knows to do is to be in a constant interfaith/intercultural dialogue—a two-way street of meeting each other. There is not just one truth in pastoral/spiritual work in multicultural communities. The All Believers Network Hawaii under the co-leadership of St. Joan Chatfield—one of the founding members of Pacific Health Ministry—held an island-wide conference in the fall of 2006 on the theme: "Moving from Exclusion to Inclusion in My Faith." A similar conference was held the year before and it caused tensions for some Clinical Pastoral Education students who wanted to speak their faith and proselytize. To learn to live with these tensions is part of the sixth dance step. Diana Eck says it this way, "The diversity of communities, traditions, understandings of truth, and visions of God is not an obstacle for us to overcome, but an opportunity for our energetic engagement and dialogue with one another. It does not mean giving up our commitments but rather opening up those commitments to the give-and-take of mutual discovery, understanding, and indeed, transformation."[18] In my own personal life I realized that the many years of sharing meeting places

---

[18] Diana Eck, *Encountering God: A Spiritual Journey from Bozeman to Banaras*. (Boston: Beacon Press, 1993), p. 168.

with people from other cultures and religions led me to a deepening of my own faith.

Patience

Living and working in a multicultural world takes a lot of patience. The "dance steps" mentioned earlier require lots of practice and constant learning and reflection.

Two years ago a group of about one hundred Lutheran women from various Lutheran parishes in California came to Hawaii to hold a conference about women in the Lutheran church. This felt so easy for me, a refreshing breather because we all claimed Lutheran roots, were all women (mainly of Scandinavian/German descent) with similar goals, wanted to be change-agents for justice, peace, and integrity of creation, and prayed and worshipped in the same ways. In all these years in Hawaii I had almost forgotten how easy it is to be in a group of people who are more similar to me than different.

There is comfort in being alike, feeling a sense of belonging, participating in family and group rituals, and speaking a particular language. I think it is much easier to "dance" with German Lutherans than in a Hawaiian Hula Halau (dance group) or on the multicultural dance floor. But with enough patience and deep breath the new steps can be learned.

Teaching and learning multicultural competencies

The most effective way to grow professionally as intercultural and interfaith caregivers is by exposure and direct experience. The CPE environment, its experiential form of education, and its "action-reflection-action" model deal with—as the founding father Anton Boisen said—"living human documents."[19] This process learning allows the CPE participant to reflect on cultural encounters as they happen. Learning emerges out of pastoral encounters. CPE by nature creates meeting spaces; they are spaces of exchange where trust grows through relationships. CPE with Pacific Health Ministry is like a multicultural interactive laboratory. Not only do the patients, families, and hospital staff come from diverse ethnic backgrounds, but so also does the CPE group itself. We purposefully bring together chaplaincy students from a variety of countries with different ethnic, cultural, and faith backgrounds. At the time of this writing, the group has students from Indonesia, the Philippines, Korea, Hawaii, and North-America. The facilitators and teaching chaplains are equally diverse. I am German, and others have Japanese, Chi-

---

[19] See Anton Boisen's essay, "Clinical training in theological education: The period of beginnings." *Chicago Theological Seminary Register* (1953).

nese, Indian, Filipino, African American, and other North American cultural roots. The guest speakers represent a variety of community leaders from different faith traditions as well. Excursions to and immersion into Hawaii's diverse faith groups are part of the CPE curriculum.

On the CPE journey of discovery the participants leave their comfort zones. In the CPE group everyone is a teacher and everyone is a student. Much time is spent with understanding each other and the meaning behind the words spoken and unspoken—many CPE participants do this in their second language which often brings major challenges, especially when it comes to the use of humor and idioms.

The group reality cannot be defined by one set of cultural assumptions; there is no right way. The participants step away from their assumptions and see other ways of looking at questions and issues. We also look at the simultaneous conversations that are going on at any time, the external verbal exchanges and the many other internal dialogues in people's heads.

Sometimes students—probably many of us once in a while—"hide" behind their culture. For example a student from Puerto Rico had issues with professional boundaries when visiting patients. He spent an enormous amount of time with each patient and their loved ones and got overinvolved. He explained that in his cultural understanding a pastoral visitation meant limitless care and concern for those who suffer. He did not see that his own needs and neediness were leading him in his work as chaplain. Culture in this case was used as an "excuse" to not change and learn. Sometimes when I am tired I get impatient. Then, I can get very directive, want things done right away, my way and I express it clearly. In those times I am lucky that I have good colleagues who check with me: "What's the matter with you?," they ask. Then I hear myself saying, "I am German. I like things done a certain way. I can't help it." The truth is, I can help it, of course, and so can anyone else. But it requires intentional effort to stay in dialogue as spiritual and cultural beings so as to dismantle the walls against others and one's personal and professional growth. Unfortunately, there are many cultural, religious, and other walls in our world. My hope is that conferences and books like this and the widespread multicultural movement will inspire many to become multicultural and multifaith dancers.

In the CPE environment, by design, the participants are encouraged to take dance steps. Stepping on each other's toes is part of the experience. In the CPE laboratory we learn how to embrace the complexity of multiculturally lived realities and how to be the best pastoral caregiver we can be, equipped with helpful multicultural and interfaith skills and knowledge.[20]

Part 2
A window to reflective practice

Introduction and verbatim

Ms. N. is a 94-year-old female Japanese American living in a nursing home. I have known her since she moved to the nursing home eight years ago. Due to strokes her speech is very slow and reduced to words and short sentences. She speaks English and Japanese. The charge nurse asked me to see Ms. N. because she was "upset because she experienced spirits in her room." I found Ms. N. in the dining room at her table, much earlier than lunch time. Her table mates had not arrived yet. I asked her whether I could sit down with her. She smiled and invited me to sit down. The visit lasted 40 minutes.

C = Chaplain

N = Ms. N.

Italic ( ) = Chaplain's feelings, thoughts, internal conversation

Non-italic ( ) = description of what is happening

---

[20] At the conclusion of CPE Level II (ACPE *Standards Manual* [2005], pp. 12–13) students are able to:

Pastoral Formation

312.1 articulate an understanding of the pastoral role that is congruent with their personal values, basic assumptions and personhood.

Pastoral Competence

312.2 provide pastoral ministry to diverse people, taking into consideration multiple elements of cultural and ethnic differences, social conditions, systems, and justice issues without imposing their own perspectives.

312.3 demonstrate a range of pastoral skills, including listening/attending, empathic reflection, conflict resolution/confrontation, crisis management, and appropriate use of religious/spiritual resources.

312.4 assess the strengths and needs of those served, grounded in theology and using an understanding of the behavioral sciences.

312.5 manage ministry and administrative function in terms of accountability, productivity, self-direction, and clear, accurate professional communication.

312.6 demonstrate competent use of self in ministry and administrative function which includes: emotional availability, cultural humility, appropriate self-disclosure, positive use of power and authority, a non-anxious and non-judgmental presence, and clear and responsible boundaries.

Pastoral Reflection

312.7 establish collaboration and dialogue with peers, authorities and other professionals.

312.8 demonstrate self-supervision through realistic self-evaluation of pastoral functioning.

C1: (sitting at the table) "Good morning, Ms. N. I am glad to see you today. How are you feeling today? (*I always enjoy visiting with Ms. N. I have warm and caring feelings for her.*)

N1: Not so good. (She stops smiling.)

C2: (soft spoken) Oh. (silent moment) I am sorry to hear that you are not feeling so good today.

N2: (with tears) I could not sleep.

C3: You did not get good rest last night?

N3: No. (still teary) (*My heart goes out to her.*)

C4: I have learned about you in the last years that you need your rest to feel good. What was keeping you awake?

N4: Spirits.

C5: Spirits? (*I am curious to learn more about her experience.*)

N5: (She nods her head.)

C6: Would you like to tell me more about last night and the spirits?

N6: They are bad. (She makes a scared face.)

C7: Last night the bad spirits scared you?

N7: Yes. All week long.

C8: Every night this week you felt scared by the spirits. (*I try to understand what was disturbing her rest.*)

N8: (She nods.) Since Elsie came. (Elsie is her new roommate.)

C9: Elsie moved in on Monday. Since then you could not sleep at night and felt bad spirits? It is Thursday today. You must be very exhausted by now and upset about your new roommate.

N9 (new tears) I am so upset and scared.

C10 (I pull my chair a bit closer and gently put my hand on her hand which she has put on the table—silent moment.) Ms. N., you have been through a lot this week. (*I feel so sorry that she could not rest well. I would like to hear more about her experience in this week since Elsie moved in.*)

N10 (She nods and cries quietly.)

C11 What is it that makes you feel so bad?

N11 Elsie uses bad words. Loud. (*I am familiar with Elsie. She frequently talks to herself in a loud voice and often uses swear words.*)

C12 When Elsie uses bad words and speaks loudly you feel bad spirits are in your room?

N12 Yes. Because of her bad words.

C13 And then you feel scared. It sounds like you miss the peace and harmony you had with Nancy, your old roommate. (Nancy died a week ago on Friday.) (*I am sure Ms. N. is grieving the loss of her good roommate who also became a friend. I feel for her since Nancy has been one of several roommates who died since Ms. N. moved to the nursing home eight years ago.*)

N13 (She nods.) We had peace. Much peace. I miss that. (pause) I miss Nancy.

C14 (silent moment) I remember that you and Nancy got along so well (I reminisce a bit about their relationship. Ms. N. smiled) And now everything is different and you do not feel happy and peaceful anymore. And you miss your good friend Nancy. (*I miss Nancy too. She was such a serene person. Nancy and Ms. N. were a good match.*)

N14 (tears)

C15 (*I feel sad. There are so many deaths in the nursing home and constant adjustments needed.*). (We sit quietly.) (*I am thinking of the spirits that Ms. N. experienced. Often after a death of a resident the staff calls me to report spirits and asks for a traditional blessing. I wonder whether Ms. N. would find comfort in a blessing. Her sense of peace is clearly disturbed.*)

N15 (squeezing my hand)

C16 Ms. N. what would help you to feel better? You miss Nancy, have not slept in days, you are scared about bad spirits and are upset about Elsie.

N16 (She nods.) Thank you for coming. (silent moment) It helps.

C17 I am very glad to be here with you. (silent moment) I am concerned about your well-being.

N17 I don't feel peaceful anymore. (silent) What now?

C18 I am thinking of two things: One is for you to speak with J., the director of nursing about finding another roommate who is quieter. The other is to have a blessing of your room so peace may be restored. Would you like that?

N18 Yes. A blessing (pause) and talking to J.

C19 I will ask J. to visit with you so you may share your feelings and distress with her. I will come back this afternoon at 4 p.m. to bless your room. Is that a good time for you?

N19 Yes. (She smiles). Please come back. (silent) I feel better.

C20 Ms. N., I will be back this afternoon. See you later. (standing up and leaving)

N20 (She gives me a little wave.)

(I approach the director of nursing after my visit with Ms. N. She was already aware of the situation and had discussed switching roommates with the care team. She said she would talk with Ms. N. and find another roommate.)

I returned in the afternoon. Ms. N. was in her bed, watching TV. She was alone in her room. She waved me in, switched off the TV. She smiled when she saw the ti leaves, ocean water and Koa bowl.

N21 Good.

C21 I am here to bless your room.

N22 (smile) Yes. Peace again.

C22 Yes. (I sit down next to her bed after asking permission. I show her the elements of the Hawaiian blessing. Ms. N. is familiar with them. They have been part of her life in Hawaii. She also remembered the annual facility blessings in the nursing home. I invite her to pray with me. We remember Nancy with gratitude and pray for peace in this room, restored harmony, restful nights, harmonious relationships and bad spirits to vanish. She puts some salt in the blessing bowl and says: "Peace." Then I sprinkle the salt water with the ti leaves in her room. After that I sit with her for a while, quietly. Ms. N. falls asleep, looking peaceful.

Verbatim Analysis

I Holistic assessment[21]

1.) *The medical dimension. What significant medical problems has the person had in the past? What problems do they have now? What treatment is the person receiving?*

Ms. N. is a 94-year-old Japanese American woman. Before coming to this skilled nursing facility Ms. N. had a history of transient ischemic attacks (TIA). She was admitted eight years ago to the skilled nursing facility because she had suffered a massive stroke (brain at-

---

[21] I follow the 7x7 Model for Spiritual Assessment developed by George Fitchett, Ruth-Presbyterian-St. Luke's Medical Center, Chicago, Ill. See also: George Fitchett. *Assessing Spiritual Needs: A Guide for Caregivers* (Minneapolis: Augsburg Fortress, 1993).

tack) leaving her with decreased reflexes, decreased sensation and muscle weakness of the face, balance problems, problems turning her head to one side, weakness in her tongue and a slight problem in speaking, some memory deficits, urinary incontinence, inability to walk, and her left side (arm and leg) is paralyzed. She can still feed herself and enjoys doing arts and crafts with the functioning right hand and participates in physical therapy. For the last four days she reported problems sleeping (N2).

2.) *The psychological dimension. Are there any significant psychological problems? Are they being treated? If so, how?*

Ms. N., despite her limitations due to her history with strokes, keeps up a positive outlook and attitude. She participates in many activities, has a strong sense of gratitude and is extremely cooperative and kind. She hardly complains and tries to bring a smile to other residents' faces. The fact that she expressed her negative feelings in this visit was rather unusual. I assess that Ms. N. is grieving the loss of her beloved roommate Nancy. She is in the ebb and flow of the dynamics of *grief*. After the *shock* of hearing about Nancy's death last Friday Ms. N gradually became aware of what has happened and began to express her emotions. When Elsie, the new roommate, moved in, Ms. N. began to feel and to hurt. She did not suppress her feelings but reported her discomfort to the RN and found some *emotional release* in meeting and sharing with the chaplain. Ms. N. expressed her feelings by talking about "spirits" (N4, N6). She *reported symptoms of some physical (N2) and emotional (N9, N13) distress* such as sleeplessness, feeling upset and scared, missing a sense of peace and missing the deceased Nancy. Psychiatrist John Bowlby[22] outlined the ebb and flow of grief processes such as shock and numbness, yearning and searching, disorganization and despair, and reorganization. I understand Ms. N is in a time of *disorganization and despair*. She lost her sense of feeling safe and secure with Nancy (N14).

3.) *The Family Systems Dimension. Are there at present, or have there been in the past, patterns within the person's relationships with other family members which have contributed to or perpetuated present problems?*

Ms. N was born the last of three children to a Japanese immigrant

---

[22] John Bowlby, "Process of Mourning," *International Journal of Psychoanalysis*, (42: 1961): 317–340.

couple. She is the only survivor. She married a Japanese American man and has one daughter and one granddaughter. Her husband died almost 20 years ago. The granddaughter is most active in care-taking of Ms. N. The family is extended with nephews and nieces who come to visit Ms. N. on a regular basis. The third generation does not speak Japanese anymore or only a little while Ms. N. is still bilingual. The family system is close-knit and caring, friendly, and positive. Being relational, appreciative and in harmony are impor-tant values for Ms. N.

4.) *The Psycho-Social Dimension. What is the history of the person's life, including, place of birth and childhood home, family of origin, education, work history and other important activities and relationships? What is the person's present living situation and what are the person's financial re-sources?*

Ms. N.'s mother came as a picture bride to Hawaii in 1908 when she was 18. She married a plantation worker and raised three children. Ms. N was the last born in 1913.[23]

---

[23] *Background information:* Between 1885 and 1907, thousands of Japanese men came to Hawaii to work on the sugarcane plantations in numbers so great that by 1897 the Japanese constituted the largest single ethnic group in the islands. In 1888, there were 6,420 Japanese in Hawaii; in 1890, 12,360; in 1896, 24,407; in 1900, 61,111. By 1900, the Japanese comprised nearly 40 percent of the population in Hawaii. They were not afraid of the hard plantation work—most were people born in the rural districts of Japan and were familiar with grass-thatched huts, communal cooking houses, communal baths, and physical isolation. The first major waves of Japanese "picture brides" began in 1908 and before all immigration was stopped from Japan in 1924, these tens of thousands of women would reshape the Japanese community in Hawaii. In addition to being wives and mothers who took care of the home, Japanese women immigrants also worked alongside their husbands in the fields. This early period of stabilization of the Japanese family coincided with a high birth rate. The birth of the second generation, the *nisei*, in effect established the identity of the first generation, the issei who became responsible parents and were beginning to view the Hawaiian Islands as their new home. The establishment of families was soon followed by the growth of Buddhist and Christian churches, a variety of language newspapers, and self-help organizations that served the needs of the immigrant community. After the 1920 plantation strike many Japanese immigrants realized that the plantations were a system that offered them limited futures. Thousands of laborers moved into the urban areas of Hawaii and began to enter the skilled trades, small businesses and other non-agricultural fields that gave them economic freedom and opportunity. Neighborhood pockets were created as the Japanese community found ethnic solidarity in their familiar associations. Clothing, food, customs, newspapers, stores and daily lifestyles of the town of Honolulu began to clearly reflect the Asian character and influence of the Japanese immigrants and their children.(Kayo Hatto in her film "The Picture Bride" (1994) tells the story of picture brides in Hawaii.) Ms. N. was born a nisei, graduated from high school in Honolulu, worked partially as a teacher for young children, married and raised one daughter. Her own and her husband's family came from plantation-worker background but by hard work they became a successful middle class family. Ms. N.'s husband worked in the banking business. Their cultural identity develop-

5.) *The Ethnic, Racial or Cultural Dimension. What is the person's racial, ethnic or cultural background? How does it contribute to the person's way of addressing any current concerns?*

Ms. N. was born and raised on Oahu, Hawaii as nisei, second generation Japanese in Hawaii. Ms. N. did not talk much about it but I assume that she, like many other nisei who lived in the period of World War II and internment went through a lot of hardship. Senator Daniel Inouye of Hawaii was 17 years old on December 7, 1941 (attack on Pearl Harbor), and later wrote: "The Japanese in Hawaii had wanted so desperately to be accepted, to be good Americans. Now, in a few cataclysmic minutes, it was all undone and there could only be deep trouble ahead. My people were only a generation removed from the land that had spawned the bombers and sent them to drop death on Hawaii."[24] Brian Sato, a local photographer, took photos of many nisei and spoke with them. He asked one woman what she would like to pass on to the younger generation, and she said "shimbo"—the strength to bear hardships and persevere. It's a stereotype, I know, but most of the nisei I met were quiet and reserved, with a lot of inner strength.[25] I can see this in Ms. N. as well, a quiet, reserved woman with lots of inner strength and perseverance. This is obvious in the way she deals with her physical struggles throughout the last years.

6.) *The Social Issues Dimension. Are the present problems of the person created by or compounded by larger social problems or dysfunctions of which the person is largely a victim? If the person is in part suffering from larger social problems, can they become aware of them and join with others in efforts to address those problems?*

a) As described above in 5.), Ms. N. comes from a generation of Japanese Americans who experienced discrimination and hardship in WWII. To fit in and belong, to have peace and harmony are important values for Ms. N.

b) Living in a skilled nursing care facility, needing to share a room,

---

ment happened in two worlds, within their parents' traditional Japanese world and the new world in Hawaii in the USA, with a desire to fit in, belong, not attract any attention and be good citizens. This explains why Ms. N comes across as very polite and quiet.

[24] Senator Daniel Inouye, *Go for Broke* (WWII–100th/442nd), condensed from his autobiography, *Journey to Washington* (Englewood Cliffs, N.J.: Prentice Hall, 1967). *Go for Broke* is the story of Senator Daniel K. Inouye's experiences during World War II.

[25] Brian Sato's portraits of Hawaii's *nisei* were on display at the Japanese Cultural Center of Hawaii's Community Gallery in July 2007.

needing to adjust to accepting help and being dependant are issues Ms. N. has to deal with, as well as facing multiple deaths and the loss of other residents. She is confronted with grief over and over. These are the facts of institutionalized care versus the family care model that Ms. N. has experienced in her Japanese upbringing.

II Spiritual assessment

1.) *Belief and Meaning. What does the person believe which gives meaning and purpose to their life? What major symbols reflect or express meaning for this person? What is the person's story? Are there any current problems which have a specific meaning or alter established meaning? Is the person presently or have they in the past been affiliated with a formal system of belief?*

Ms. N said she and her family have always belonged to a temple in Honolulu of the Honpa Hongwanji Mission. Ms. N. said that she did not go to the temple that much but followed the main teachings. I learned that her generation lived faith by doing and practicing the teachings in ordinary things. When I offered to contact her temple and asked whether she would like to see members of her temple and/or the minister, Ms. N. declined. Ms. N. said she also grew up with many Christians in the area, and that she was never dogmatic about faith, but quite open. She stated that of main importance for her is that people act kindly, compassionately, respectfully, and with gratitude for life. Ms. N. occasionally joined some of the Christian Sunday worship services. Her granddaughter is the one in the family who nurtures the Buddhist roots. She brings in Buddhist teachings to her grandmother and Buddhist friends to visit the nursing home.[26]

---

[26] *Background information:* The Honpa Hongwanji Mission of Hawaii is a district of the Nishi (West) Hongwanji, one of the major temples of Jodo Shinshu Buddhism, a school of Mahayana Pure Land Buddhism. Jodo Shinshu Buddhism was established in Hawaii as a result of the immigration of Japanese people to work the plantations on the islands. The first Hongwanji temple in Hawaii was dedicated in 1889. Since then, 36 temples and the Buddhist Study Center have been established statewide.

The Honpa Hongwanji Mission of Hawaii was initiated by Shinran Shonin (1173–1263), founder of Jodo Shin School on Pure Land Buddhism. Shinran Shonin was born during the Kamakura period in Japan. His teaching is based on the Pure Land tradition as a successor to Honen Shonin. Shinran Shonin concentrated his efforts on clarifying the necessity of being on the power of the Primal Vow as the inner dynamics of recitative nembutsu. The complete entrusting of self to the Primal Vow meant simultaneously abandoning all need to rely on self-power. This is the reason for Shinran's emphasis on Shinjin (Faith), "the true and real mind of Amida Buddha," which is the source of this entrusting. Through the working of Amida's wisdom

2.) *Vocation and Obligations. Do the person's beliefs and sense of meanings in life create a sense of duty, vocation, calling or moral obligation? Will any current problems cause conflict or compromise in their perception of their ability to fulfill these duties? Are any current problems viewed as a sacrifice or atonement or otherwise essential to this person's sense of duty?*

"Embraced by the Vow … in Harmony" (see above) and living a life of gratitude and in reverence of life and service of others have always been central for Ms. N. She raised her family that way. Her role as mother and wife appear to have been central in her life. She also was an active volunteer in several women's service groups in her temple and community. Her current roommate can be loud, yells at times and uses bad words (N11). This disrupts Ms. N.'s need for harmony and peace (N13).

3.) *Experience and Emotion. What direct contacts with the sacred or divine or with the demonic has the person had? What emotions or moods are predominately associated with these contacts and with the person's beliefs, meaning in life and associated sense of vocation?*

Overall Ms. N. has experienced her faith as giving her peace and meaning in life. In this verbatim Ms. N. speaks of "spirits" (N4) as the reason for disruption of the harmony in her room and life. Experiencing "spirits" is very much part of the multicultural "local" culture in Hawaii, a blend of diverse traditions and beliefs related to the understanding of life, death and the afterlife.[27] Because Ms. N. grew up and lived in an environment that speaks about "spirits," it was not surprising that Ms. N. would describe her experience of

---

and compassion, the followers are made to say the nembutsu, affirming the enduring power of Amida and acknowledging their limited human capacities. (Namu Amida Butsu—The original Sanskrit phrase was *Namo Amitabhaya Buddhaya*, which can mean either "I trust in the Buddha of Immeasurable Light and Eternal Life" or simply "Homage to the Buddha of Immeasurable Light and Eternal Life".) Thus, the central question for the Shin Buddhist becomes not "How can I attain satori (enlightenment)?" but "How can I be carried by the power of the Primal Vow?" Practices are: recitation of the nembutsu, bowing and gassho (putting hands together), chanting of Sutra, meditation and a life of gratitude, service and reverence. Motto: Embraced by the Vow ... In Harmony. (Introductory Guide to Jodu Shinsu Buddhism as distributed by Honpa Hongwani Hawaii Betsuin, Honolulu, Hawaii, 1998 and notes from lecture by Rev. Mari Sengoku.).

[27] *Background information:* In Hawaiian tradition "the animating force ("uhane"), which is present in the body, distinguishes the quick from the dead. And so "uhane" can be called "spirit." It is a vital spark that, departed from the flesh, lives on through eternity and is rewarded for virtue or punished for transgressions in life. Thus "uhane" is spirit in the immortal sense. It might return to visit the living. "Uhane" could be more specifically an "aumakua", a god-spirit of a long-dead ancestor, an "unihipili, a deified spirit of a recently deceased person, an "akua", god

disharmony and lack of peace as caused by "spirits," especially considering the recent death of her roommate and the arrival of her seemingly restless and loud new roommate. Ms. N. described her feelings as "upset and scared" (N9).

4.) *Courage and Growth. Must the meaning of new experiences, including any current problems, be fit into existing beliefs and symbols? Can the person let go of existing beliefs and symbols in order to allow new ones to emerge?*

Ms. N's recent experience of disharmony and lack of peace cause her to feel upset and scared (N9) and disrupt her ability to sleep well (N2). Ms. N. is hurting because she misses her roommate (N13). To allow the journey of grief to interrupt her desire for peace and harmony may be an important step in the following weeks.

5.) *Ritual and Practice. What are the rituals and practices associated with the person's beliefs and meaning in life? Will current problems, if any, cause a change in the rituals or practices they feel they require or in their ability to perform or participate in those which are important to them?*

I suggested to Ms. N. a blessing of her room (C18) knowing that Ms. N. has experienced numerous blessings in the nursing home and in her life in the Hawaiian community. In Hawaii and in the nursing home this is a common ritual of cleansing and for comfort.[28]

---

or any demi-god. "Makani" is a chill breeze—and any Hawaiian knows that this breeze means a spirit is present. Therefore, "makani" is the spirit." (Mary Kawena Pukui, E.W. Haertig, C.A. Lee, *Nana I ke Kumu—Look to the Source* [Honolulu: Hui Hanai, 1972, Volume I], 195.) Ms. N. is familiar with the Hawaiian way of speaking about "spirit" and the many local stories coming from the plantation world. She also is familiar with her own tradition of addressing "spirits" such as in the "Obon season." "In Hawaii, the summer months are known for their annual Obon Dance Festivals held every weekend at various Buddhist Temples around the islands. It all begins in June with the annual lantern-floating ceremony and continues for nine weekends of Obon Dancing. The tradition is to light the way for the spirits of ancestors who are greeted with offerings of flowers, food and incense in temple rituals and on family altars. The concept of dancing for the dead is based on a story about a disciple of the Buddha named Mokuren. The monk's vision of his dead mother in the realm of hungry ghosts, starving because of her greed while alive, led him to ask Shakyamuni Buddha how he could relieve her suffering. He was told to offer food to monks returning from a retreat. His mother's spirit was freed by his good deed, which led Mokuren to dance with joy. Although based on a Japanese religious belief, Bon Dances have become a favorite event celebrated in the islands by all different ethnic cultures and religious backgrounds." (See: http://islandlife808.com/my-family/its-obon-season-in-hawaii/)

[28] *Background information:* Blessing is a very public event in Hawaii. Blessings are seen as being a serious event, a religious rite, and should not be taken lightly. It involves remembering

6.) *Community. Is the person part of one or more, formal or informal, communities of shared belief, meaning in life, ritual or practice? What is the style of the person's participation in these communities?*

Ms. N.'s main community is her family who visits regularly and the "new family" in the nursing home. Ms. N. has become a leader in certain arts and crafts and received much recognition already for her talent and creativity. Some of her items were sold at the facility-wide craft fair. Her pleasantness and perseverance inspire other residents in the facility. In this sense Ms. N. has very much become a community-builder by her gentleness, positive attitude, and creativity in spite of her physical limitations. Ms. N. does not actively participate in her Buddhist temple, although her granddaughter has asked some of the temple members to come and visit Ms. N. As far as I know, Ms. N does not follow regular rituals consistent with her faith tradition, but practices the teachings of compassion and gratitude. She has regular visits from the facility chaplains.

7.) *Authority and Guidance. Where does the person find authority for their beliefs, their meaning in life, their vocation, their rituals and practices? When faced with doubt, confusion, tragedy or conflict, where do they look for guidance? To what extent does the person look outside themselves or inside themselves for guidance?*

Ms. N. respects and trusts the chaplains and likes spending time with us. In a time of crisis as seen in this verbatim, Ms. N. is open to the chaplain/minister to help with restoring harmony. To live a "life of gratitude" as outlined in the teachings of her faith group has been her principle and source of meaning acknowledging the deliverance and benevolent guidance of Amida Buddha. Living in harmony with all beings is the way of Jodo Shin Buddhism.

---

traditions and utilizing common elements of water, salt (sea salt) and ti leaves (a green leafy plant used for healing and to plant near houses for good fortune). It is based in a spirituality in which the sea and land and the place of people are honored. The salt is added to the fresh water in a wooden bowl (Koa wood). The ti leaves are held at the stems and are used to stir the salt and the water and to sprinkle the water over the area or persons to be blessed by ways of snapping one's wrist and letting the salt water 'fly'. The use of salt, water and the ti leaves is to "purify an area or persons from spiritual contamination and remove kapus (taboos) and harmful influences...." The term used for the ritual is *pi kai—pi* is to sprinkle, *kai* means sea or sea water. (Pukui, *Nana I Ke Kumo*, 179.) The use of ti leaves was "thought to protect against harm and invoke protection of the gods." (Ibid., 190.) Sprinkling salt water was a common practice not only in Hawaii but in many cultures, with salt having images of preserving, purifying, and flavoring, and water being seen as symbolic of purification and life-giving. Many Christian ministers have adapted this ritual. They use three ti leaves and sprinkle "In the name of the Father, the Son and the Holy Spirit."

III How did the chaplain feel about the patient/resident and/or situation?[29]

I felt warmth and caring for Ms. N. when entering the dining room. In these last eight years I have thoroughly enjoyed being in her kind presence. I was a bit concerned because of the charge nurse's referral since it was unusual for Ms. N "to be upset." She preferred to avoid any attention and focus on her. When I realized that Ms. N. was grieving and feeling without peace, I felt protective of her. I wanted to make her feel better (C16). While Ms. N. was grateful for my visit and even said "it helps" (N16), I wanted to do more and suggested two more approaches: talk with the DON (Director of Nursing) and provide a blessing C18). I recognize my desire to take good care of Ms. N. and restore harmony again. I am grateful that in the context of Hawaii there is a blessing ritual in place for times like this. At the same time I know that the journey of grief can be like an emotional roller coaster. I will continue to support/accompany Ms. N. on this journey. And I will remember that I cannot take away the pain from Ms. N. despite my attempts and best efforts.

IV Are there unspoken or hidden dynamics that affect this interview? If so, what are they and how did they operate?

I have always admired Ms. N. for her serene and gentle presence in the nursing home. Considering her severe physical limitations after the major stroke, I have been so touched by her gracefulness amid suffering. I have been moved by her ability to accept her suffering and make the best of her new life in the nursing home. "Could I ever be like her?" I asked myself. I doubt it because I am much too attached at this time to my life. But I surely would like to be like Ms. N. Experiencing Ms. N. feeling "upset and scared" was new and surprising for me in our relationship. At the same time I could understand the dynamic of grief in her situation. So, I followed two dynamics: my need to make it all better (C18) and at the same time my knowing the need to create space and words to address the death of Nancy (C13, C14). To be effective I need to accept my inability to take away the pain of loss.

---

[29] The verbatim analysis part III–VII follows a model used by Pacific Health Ministry, Hawaii, in CPE training.

*V How did the chaplain function and/or utilize the Spiritual Assessment
in giving care?*

I provided sensitive and respectful spiritual care utilizing the Spiritual Assessment (see above) and hearing Ms. N.'s need for harmony and peace. I offered a safe space for Ms. N. to share. I used reflective listening skills, acknowledged and explored her feelings of being upset, scared, and sleepless. I built on our pastoral relationship and history, offering a ministry of presence. I provided spiritual resources appropriate for the context and situation and blessed her room. I made sure that the Director of Nursing and the interdisciplinary care team were involved.

It was important for me, while providing spiritual care, to touch Ms. N.'s grieving heart. In N8 Ms. N. gave me the connection that with the arrival of her new roommate the loss of her old roommate became obvious. It became difficult for Ms. N. to escape her feelings. I tried to understand the meaning of "spirits" (N4) and of the arrival of the roommate (N8) and to walk with Ms. N. through the related feelings (scared, N6, N9; upset, N8; tears, N10). It is a slow process until in C13 I finally named the real issue, that is, missing the peace and harmony with Nancy (N13 "I miss Nancy."). This is followed by reminiscing about Nancy and their relationship (C14) and more tears (N14). I was intentional in assisting Ms. N. in addressing her emotional ties to Nancy despite the discomfort and sorrow it causes. I wanted to give her permission to grieve (C14). "What a griever needs most is acceptance and non-judgmental listening, which will facilitate the expression of emotions and the necessary review of the relationship with a lost loved one. The griever will then require assistance in integrating the past with the new present that exists."[30]

While Ms. N. described her experience of disorganization in this early stage of grief (N2, N6, N9, C14), I offered my presence, a sense of security and support to help her to reorient to a world that has gone out of focus and control with the death of Nancy. The appropriate physical contact in C10, N15 also provided support as well as several moments of just "being" together quietly but connected (N10, C15, C17). Ms. N. responded well to "just being," "not doing" (C16, C17). Yet, I wanted "to do" more. I knew that Ms. N. did not have any closing ritual at the time of her friend's death. Nancy died in the hospital. When the residents die in the

---

[30] Therese A. Rando, *Grief, Dying and Death* (Champaign, IL: Research Press, 1984),p. 79.

nursing home the chaplains offer bedside services for the staff and other residents. A traditional blessing of the room seemed called for as a ritual of closure and blessing of the new beginning. Ms. N. responded well to it (C22) and participated with the salt. As mentioned above, my own need of wanting "to do" more played into offering a ritual; but more important was my knowledge about the importance of rituals in times of grief and in Hawaii. Rituals can give structure and support in a time of loss and transition. I hoped that for Ms. N. the blessing would be helpful in managing her sense of disorganization and loss of control.

VI What are the plans for continued care and follow up?

I spoke with the Director of Nursing about Ms. N.'s roommate and will continue to work with the interdisciplinary care team. I will continue to visit Ms. N. and accompany her on her journey of grief. I will assist her in accessing and utilizing internal coping strategies to reorganize and incorporate the loss and in using her existing spiritual resources (e.g. Buddhist teachings) to reshape a sense of safety and security, by this means incorporating the changes that have occurred in her life.

VII What did the chaplain learn about the chaplain's faith, religious understandings, self-awareness, and caregiving?

I felt humbled that Ms. N. invited me to share her spiritual struggles, lack of peace and harmony, and her grief with me. As a Christian pastor from Germany serving as chaplain in an interfaith context in Hawaii, I am consistently challenged to learn as much as possible and be knowledgeable about the meaning making, history, stories, many faith traditions and practices here. This is shown in this verbatim about "spirits," nisei, Honpa Hongwanji Mission and traditional blessings. This is not clear-cut book learning, but the art of finding a "meeting place/space of exchange" in this process is important to me. The "between" becomes an essential dimension for spiritual care. As with Ms. N., offering a ministry of presence worked well, a ministry that is based on empathetic and compassionate care. I need to be authentic, genuine, warm, and real. I have experienced many Buddhist residents and patients as welcoming—just like Ms. N. Kindness and gentleness, open ears and mind, a listening heart, respect without judgment, and creating a space to share have been appreciated by the patients, families, and friends.

As a Christian spiritual caregiver I ask myself how to evaluate theologically the interfaith situation and interaction with the patients. Jesus is my model for healing relationships, love, dialogue, respect, and forgiveness. Through Christ I know that God reaches out in love to *all*. I am called to walk the path of holiness that Jesus showed me (he reached out to the Samaritans, "lepers", bleeding women, sinners, the poor …). God shows the face of mercy and love. I must be subject to all human beings, a servant, God's willing instrument. Jesus healed the ones in need, the marginalized. He loved them, ate with them, touched them, comforted them, blessed them, served them, encouraged them, taught them, and liberated them by his own suffering, death, and resurrection. Finally, Jesus breathed on them to infuse them with the power of the Holy Spirit. Jesus, full of compassion, journeyed with people.

Dialogue is about listening and learning rather than about arguing and convincing, and not about converting. It does not start with doctrines. It is not about labeling, but seeing through the eyes of compassion. It is about storytelling and listening. The Sufi poet Rumi said once: "Out beyond ideas of wrongdoing and right doing, there is a field. I'll meet you there."[31] Ms. N. and I met on this "field," a place to hear about gloom and sadness, a place to re-invite peace and harmony through the gift of the "I and Thou" relationship and meeting dynamic[32] and the power and mystery of ritual.

---

[31] Marshall B. Rosenberg, *Nonviolent Communication: A Language of Life* (Encinitas, CA: Puddle Dancer Press, 2003), p. 15.

[32] See Martin Buber's classic book, *I and Thou* (New York: Scribner, 1958).

Interfaith spiritual care: A view from Brazil

James R. Farris

The term *interfaith spiritual care* raises various complex and challenging questions, beginning with, what does "interfaith" actually mean?; what is "spiritual care"?; how do cultural contexts affect "interfaith spiritual care"? There are, obviously, no simple answers to these complex questions. In this chapter, I will begin by describing my understanding of the terms "interfaith" and "spirituality" and propose the concept of "communion" as a key to the discussion. From here I will set the stage with a summary of Brazil's socio-religious history and realities. This survey will shed light on the conversation about interfaith spiritual care and the views from Brazil. Existing dynamics of both intolerance and tolerance will be explored. Being a member of the Methodist Church, I will engage the topic from a Wesleyan perspective and then conclude the chapter by suggesting a vision of the way forward for interfaith spiritual care in Brazil.

Fostering communion

The concept of interfaith can be easily confused with interreligious dialogue, which generally deals with questions of how to communicate between different religious traditions. Interreligious dialogue deals with how to approach practical, ethical, and theological experiences between, for example, Christianity and Buddhism. Interfaith is a broader term. Assuming that faith involves the construction of universes of meaning, it includes both interreligious and interdenominational communication, and also dialogue with people of non-religious faith broadly speaking.

James R. Farris, Ph.D., is Professor of Pastoral Care and Counseling (Methodist School of Theology), and Professor of Psychology and Religion (Graduate School of Religion) at The Methodist University of São Paulo (UMESP), in São Paulo, Brazil.

The concept of interfaith includes how to share experiences between faith traditions.

Spirituality is another complex concept. However, in order to avoid the seemingly never-ending discussions regarding what spirituality is, I will use a fairly simple and common understanding of the term. Spirituality is the creation and fostering of communion between persons, groups, creation, and God. What this means and how to practice it is incredibly multi-faceted, and varies widely between religions and denominations. However, the essence, or ground, of spirituality seems to always return to one central question: "how do we create, foster, and live in communion, or community, with ourselves, our neighbor, our world, and our God?"

The idea of communion may be the key to this discussion. Communion is an ideal, much like the Kingdom of God. Communion suggests basic, even if very general, shared values, beliefs, understandings of who we are as human beings, what we believe to be true, and our images of God. However, such an ideal is often far from what we experience in day-to-day life. Human values, beliefs, understandings of who we are, what is true, and our images of God are incredibly diverse. This diversity often creates conflicts and can shatter communion. When communion is fragmented by the diversity of experiences and beliefs, interfaith spiritual care is very difficult.

The word "communion" suggests "community." To live in community means living with, and hopefully respecting the beliefs of the "other." Community generally refers to the kind and quality of relationships that we offer to each other or, in other words, how we can best live together. It assumes that what we have, what we can offer and who we are can be, at least to some degree, held in common. This does not mean that we live in an ideal world where everything is held in common. Community means that we recognize that we are not islands unto ourselves.

The opposite of community is immunity. To be immune means that we are protected from the dangerous "other," or from that which could threaten to infect us. Who we are and what is ours belongs to us and we do not need to share. Or, at best, we can share with those who serve our needs. Immunity implies a certain kind of community, but one which is finally self-serving. As long as the "other" serves our needs, there is no threat. They can be part of our circle of relationships. However, when they disagree with us, or pose some sort of threat, they can be quickly dismissed or defined as the enemy. The highest values in immunity are safety and security.

When communion or community directs our lives and faith, interfaith spiritual care can be a living reality because it invites living together, sharing, and mutual respect. To care for the "other" is not a threat. When immunity guides our lives, it is much more difficult to live together, share, and respect one another. One of the fundamental questions for interfaith spiritual care may be found exactly at this point. When and where do we feel at peace with caring for the "other" who may have values, beliefs, and faith that are very different from ours? Who is the "other"? How secure are we in our own beliefs? What are the limits of our understanding of "communion" and "community"?

The word "God" immediately raises problems because spirituality, in its broadest sense, does not necessarily include Western concepts of "God" and religious traditions often understand "God" in ways that are quite different. However, since interfaith is a broad and inclusive concept, it is well worth considering that, in the words of Paul Tillich, the concept of "God" reveals and expresses our "ultimate concern."[1] God does not necessarily reflect the beliefs of any one religious tradition, but is that which organizes, orients, and expresses our deepest beliefs and values. "God" is the "ground of our being," and orients our life, and the meaning of communion and community.

This is very similar to the idea of Rudolf Otto that "God" reflects a universal human experience that is a priori.[2] It is a part of our consciousness. The possibility of experiencing the "mysterium tremendum et fascinans"—the mystery, the power, and the attraction of the infinite— is built into our human existence. How we experience and express this deep reality varies enormously, but it is there. It is always a presence and potential. Interfaith spiritual care respects this presence and potential in all of its complexity and variety.

Finally, care is how our community seeks to create, foster, and live in communion and community, in practical terms. Or, in other words, how is it that we seek to live in such ways that are faithful to our beliefs about the nature, presence, and will of God, and at the same time live with those that believe in ways that may be very different? Within various religious traditions, care is intimately related to the "care of souls." Traditionally, it includes healing, sustaining, guiding, reconciling, and educating. It is an expression of deep mutual correction, encouragement, and solidarity which embraces the totality of life. In this case, the term "care of souls" refers to the totality and integrity of human beings in light of the nature of the Divine. Who is included and who is excluded

---

[1] Paul Tillich. *Dynamics of Faith* (New York: Harper Torchbooks, 1953), p. 20.

[2] Rudolf Otto. *The Idea of the Holy* (London: Oxford University Press, 1923), pp. 1–12.

in the "care of souls," communion, and community is a key question in interfaith spiritual care.

In sum, the ideal of interfaith spiritual care seeks to create and foster communion and community between persons of diverse religious and nonreligious spiritual traditions and denominations. It is how we express the love of God, the Ground of our being, both within our communities of faith, and beyond them. If there is one question that permeates interfaith spiritual care it is: "how do we build bridges, and at the same time maintain and respect our own identity and community of faith?" There are, of course, no simple answers.

Brazilian contexts

In order to understand interfaith spiritual care in Brazil, it is important to have some notion of Brazilian culture. To begin with, there is no one "Brazilian perspective" or "culture." Brazil is physically the size of the United States, and is composed of a great variety of cultures. Historically, the south of Brazil was influenced by German and Italian immigrations. The north of Brazil maintains African influences. The Amazon continues to reflect strong indigenous influences. The central regions of Brazil are a mixture of a wide variety of cultural influences that include European, South American, and Portuguese traditions. The major urban centers are a very diverse mixture of cultures and traditions, currently highly influenced by North American and European values. It is impossible to understand Brazilian cultures without taking into account the political, economic, and religious influence of Portugal, Europe, and the United States in the last five hundred years. Specifically, the religious landscape of Brazil has been, and continues to be, profoundly influenced by each of these.

This is the link to the current religious context of Brazil. Beginning in the 1500s, Brazil was almost exclusively Roman Catholic. Indigenous religious expressions were repressed and almost systematically eradicated. This situation did not change significantly until the mid 1800s, with the arrival of various Protestant missionaries, generally from the United States and Europe. These new religious expressions were generally tolerated by the Roman Catholic Church. Such tolerance was due, in great degree, to the perception that these religious groups, or "sects," generally concentrated their attention and ministry on members of their own group. Indeed, Methodist, Baptist, Lutheran, Presbyterian, Adventist, and Mennonite missionaries and pastors typically ministered to members of their own communities. The tendency was to care for one's own flock.

However, these religious groups grew and expanded. In the 1930s and

1940s Protestant denominations began to have an increasingly important presence in Brazilian culture. Their presence had religious, economic, social, and educational dimensions. This phenomenon represented a shift in social presence and power. While the Roman Catholic Church was still the dominant religious presence in Brazil, it was no longer the only Church in Brazil. This shift in religious power, presence, and expression was further complicated by the resurgence, in roughly the same period, of indigenous and African religious traditions that had been effectively underground, but still very powerful, for centuries. By the 1960s, the religious landscape of Brazil had changed radically.

In addition, the relatively small groups of Pentecostals, which had been present in Brazil since the 1920s, began to grow rapidly in the 1950s and 1960s. In the 1970s and 1980s a new expression of Pentecostalism, neo-Pentecostalism, also began to grow rapidly. It is difficult to describe neo-Pentecostalism. As a movement, it is neither Pentecostal nor Protestant. It has been influenced by a theology of prosperity, marketing theory, and a mixture of Roman Catholic, Pentecostal, Protestant, and Afro-Brazilian theologies. Its growth, over the past twenty years, has been phenomenal. In summary, the following figures represent formal church membership, according to the 1960, 1971, 1980, 1991, and 2000 Brazilian census.[3]

The following informal map reflects the reality that many "church members" also attend other religious worship services. The result is that there is tremendous competition between religious traditions for membership and for financial support. What was half a century ago a Roman Catholic country has become an incredibly diverse and competitive religious environment.

---

[3] A.F. Pierucci, "Bye bye Brasil: O Declínio das Religiões Tradicionais no Censo de 2000." *Estudos Avançados*, 18:52 (2005): 1–12. Total membership exceeds 100 percent because of multiple-church membership, which is not uncommon in Brazil.

Figure 1: Formal church membership

	1960	1971	1980	1991	2000
Roman Catholic	93.1%	91.8%	89%	83.3%	73.9%
Historical Protestant[4]	4%	5.2%	10%	11%	20.6%
Pentecostal	?	?	3.2%	6%	10.6%
Neo-Pentecostal[5]	?	?	?	?	?
Afro-Brazilian/ Other Religions[6]	?	4.5%	4.4%	7.8%	6.6%

To give some life to these numbers and this history I will provide an informal example of the religious diversity in Brazil. I live in a middle-class neighborhood in São Bernardo do Campo, one of the many cities that surround São Paulo, which is the second or third largest city in the world, with a population of approximately 12 million. In front of my home there is an Umbanda house church (an Afro-Brazilian religion). Up the street is an independent Pentecostal storefront church. Within a one mile radius of my home one finds: a Roman Catholic Church, which occupies a central place in the neighborhood square; one Candomblé center (an Afro-Brazilian religion); two neo-Pentecostal churches; six independent Pentecostal churches; two Japanese religious centers; one Mormon temple; one Methodist Church; one house church which I cannot identify; and the Methodist School of Theology in Brazil.

I have cable television, which is still a rarity in Brazil, but an influence that is both powerful and growing. Amidst the thirty-four channels that I receive, one is owned by the Roman Catholic Church, one by the Universal Church of the Kingdom of God (a neo-Pentecostal church), and one by the Rebirth in Christ Church (a neo-Pentecostal church). I do not have statistics regarding the number of independent religious programs broadcast on various channels, but it is an impressive presence.

---

[4] Baptist, Adventist, Lutheran, Presbyterian, Methodist, Congregational and Mennonite. These churches are also known as "Evangelical," in Brazil and elsewhere in Latin America and the Caribbean.

[5] Statistics regarding membership in neo-Pentecostal churches are very difficult to determine due to the lack of formal membership records.

[6] Kardecista, Umbanda, Candomblé, neo-Christian religions such as Jehovah's Witness, Mormons and Good Will League, and all other recognized religious groups.

The number of formal and independent and illegal religious radio stations is very difficult to calculate, but probably numbers in the hundreds.

In summary, religion in Brazil is very present, incredibly diverse, and highly competitive. This is not to say that religious diversity is something new, or exclusive to Brazil. Religious diversity and competition is a widespread phenomenon in the modern world. What marks the situation in Brazil are the complex interactions between social-economic context, the historical concentration of power in one religious tradition, and the current growth of some traditions in the midst of the near stagnation of others. These realities profoundly influence relations between religious traditions and denominations. These are at least some of the socio-religious contexts that influence the question and the practice of interfaith spiritual care.

Interfaith spiritual care in Brazil

Strictly speaking, there is very little interfaith care offered in church communities, universities, hospitals, and in the day to day lives of priests, pastors, and believers. This does not mean that interfaith care does not exist, but that it is fairly rare. This is due, in large part, to the current religious climate in Brazil that seems to reflect competition among religious groups, and the need to establish and maintain religious identity. For example, recently a friend of mine, a pastor in a city in the interior of Brazil, told me a story. The pastor is a woman, about forty years old, with considerable pastoral experience. An elderly member of her church asked her if she could visit a neighbor, who was not a member of that particular church. The neighbor was also elderly, and not a member of any church, but had, during her life, gone to the Methodist Church, the Baptist Church, the Roman Catholic Church, several Pentecostal churches and, from time to time, Afro-Brazilian churches. The pastor visited her fairly regularly, and offered her communion. That practice became common knowledge in her local church. When it came time for her pastoral evaluation, several members of her church council questioned her about the time she had spent with this person, and whether it was "advisable" to offer communion to a person who was not a church "member." The pastor responded that in the Methodist Church the Lord's table was open to all who seek the Grace of God. The members of the church council agreed in principle but questioned her for spending "so much time" with a non-member of the church. The pressure was subtle but powerful.

Without a doubt, moments of communion and grace do occur between different religions and denominations but, sadly, they are the exception and not the rule. The current religious climate in Brazil tends to promote an attitude where each cares for their own. Questions of religious competition and marketing appear to dominate the landscape. Furthermore, there are deeper questions that influence this situation. For example, it would appear that the Roman Catholic Church is attempting to maintain its historical dominance in Brazilian culture by reinforcing its traditional roles and theologies. Such practices and principles can, at times, exclude communion with other traditions. There are exceptions, but offering care to members of other religious traditions is uncommon.

Historical Protestant churches continue to be in the minority. They tend to create a form of "ghetto mentality" that protects these churches from other social and theological influences and at the same time isolates them from social and cultural realities. For example, my denomination, the Methodist Church in Brazil, recently voted against allowing formal membership and leadership in ecumenical organizations, a move that was directed against associations with the Roman Catholic Church. The Methodist Church continues to be nominally ecumenical but its members, pastors, and bishops cannot have formal membership or leadership in such organizations. This complicates any type of interfaith spiritual care on an institutional level and reflects an attitude of isolation within the daily life of church members.

Afro-Brazilian religions continue to be in a process of recovering and celebrating their social-historical-religious roots. For this reason, they tend to create their own "religious universe," and hesitate to enter into communion with dominant Western religious traditions.

Pentecostal churches have a delicate relation with charismatic Roman Catholic and Protestant traditions that does create a certain communion among diverse religious experiences but continues to be profoundly influenced by history and internal conflicts in each religious tradition. Pentecostal and charismatic religious traditions value highly the Spirit of God and the Bible but often have considerable difficulties ministering to those who do not believe as they do.

Neo-Pentecostal religious communities that emphasize a theology of prosperity, tend to accept any and all believers whatever their formal or informal religious affiliations, but the emphasis is on emotions and spirit-filled worship, and not on the ongoing care of souls. In terms of interfaith spiritual care, it is hard to evaluate neo-Pentecostal churches. On the one hand, they are very open to accepting persons from all religious traditions, and incorporate theologies and rituals from a wide variety of sources. On the other hand, they emphasize mass religion, have difficulty articulating a coherent theology, and often reduce spiritual care to emotion-filled worship services and the promise of miracles.

Another context where interfaith spiritual care might occur is in hospitals and related institutions. Once again, it is important to understand the Brazilian context. There are basically three types of hospitals in Brazil. There are government hospitals which are part of the Brazilian universal system of health care. Government hospitals do not include space for religious chaplaincy because of the constitutional separation of church and state. The same is generally true for hospitals related to federal universities. There are exceptions, but these are rare. A few hospitals related to federal universities are open to chaplaincy if that service is related to the department of medicine, usually psychiatry, of the university.

The second type of hospital is related to religious institutions. The vast majority of these hospitals are Roman Catholic. They almost always have some type of formal chaplaincy but it is very rare for other religious traditions to be included. There are a few hospitals related to historical Protestant traditions but they rarely have well-established chaplaincy programs. When they do, the chaplains tend to be volunteers related to the religious traditions that support the hospital.

The third type of hospital is independent. In many cases, these hospitals have roots in religious traditions but over the course of time, and for financial and administrative reasons, became independent. Other independent hospitals are formal corporations that include doctors and insurance companies. Independent hospitals rarely, if ever, have formal chaplaincy programs, generally for financial or philosophical reasons.

In the Methodist Church, in spite of our formal openness to other religious traditions, hospital visitations are almost always limited to members of the Church, or to members of other Protestant traditions. A Methodist pastor friend of mine recently visited a member of another Protestant church, a close friend of a church member, who was in the hospital. The patient spent much of the time asking about the beliefs of the pastor, his church, and why he was there. In the end, the patient accepted the presence and prayers of the pastor, but only with a certain reluctance. His pastor was his spiritual guide, and this visiting pastor was only a barely acceptable substitute. His prayers were very welcome, but only after considerable evaluation. They did not have the same value as those of "his pastor."

At an emotional level, this makes sense. When we are vulnerable, as all hospital patients are, we protect ourselves. When we are most vulnerable, we seek the familiar. We want our family, friends, and pastor. However, the deeper issue is that the question is more than emotional. The "patient," the person, was not totally comfortable with the presence of a pastor from another religious tradition, even if it was also Protestant. At a deep level, the "other pastor" was, at least to a certain point, perceived as an unknown. This reveals a great deal about the spiritual–religious environment of Brazil.

Given the context of the local church and hospitals, it becomes fairly obvious why Brazil does not have any form of Clinical Pastoral Education (CPE). There are training programs for chaplains, generally within the Roman Catholic Church, and for medical professionals, to understand the relationship between spirituality and health. However, there are no organized chaplain training programs that deal with the complexities and realities of interfaith spiritual care.

Beyond questions of religious and denominational histories and identities and the financial and administrative realities of hospital systems, there is another layer to the question of why interfaith spiritual care appears to be so difficult within Brazilian contexts. This deeper layer is related to questions of fundamentalism, tolerance, intolerance, and moral exclusion to which we now turn our attention.

Fundamentalism, intolerance and moral exclusion

There are several ways to understand religious fundamentalism. This kind of fundamentalism often identifies various beliefs, dogmas, and practices with the revealed nature of God. These become the guiding principles of the community, and are rarely questioned. The key is that these elements of belief are considered to be the divinely revealed foundation of the being and identity of the community. Still, fundamentalism cannot be exclusively identified with conservative religious groups. There are also theologically liberal fundamentalisms. There are philosophical, economic, and social fundamentalisms. In the case of non-religious groups, the "god," or authority, that reveals these truths may be very human. The fundamental dynamic is to identify the being and identity of the group with very specific beliefs and behaviors, which are often unquestioned.

Various fundamentalisms can live together relatively peacefully. The question of intolerance and moral exclusion enters when the hermeneutical, or interpretive, tradition becomes political. When a religious community, for a variety of reasons, seeks to impose its interpretation of God's truth on other traditions, usually in subtle fashions, then intolerance becomes a basic problem, and interfaith spiritual care becomes almost impossible. It would appear that this is often, though not always, the case in Brazil.

When a community translates its beliefs into the political or social realm, the result is often intolerance due to the need to "convert" others to certain ways of believing and being in the world, or a certain image of God and divine will. In this sense, the survival, identity, and being of a religious community depend on converting others to their belief system. To some extent, this explains why a patient visited by a pastor from another church can at times feel uneasy. "Why is he / she here?"; "what does he / she want?"; "where is my pastor?"

In general terms, the four main marks of religious identity of Evangelical churches in Brazil are:

- Jesus as the only way to salvation

- The need to combat idolatry

- A strong sense of "having the truth" and "being different"

- The need to evangelize, not only in the sense of spreading the seeds of the Gospel, but of "gaining souls for Christ."[7]

These marks of what it means to be Evangelical often reflect a subtle fundamentalism and a certain intolerance of other religious experiences. It may very well be that the third element, the need to be different, is what prompted my tradition, the Methodist Church in Brazil, to distance itself from ecumenical organizations, specifically from the Roman Catholic Church.

When dialogue regarding the nature of God and truth is hampered, then theoretical fundamentalism often becomes applied, practical, or political fundamentalism, and interfaith spiritual care is rarely possible. Such fundamentalism may be quite subtle or very public. In Brazil, fundamentalism is generally subtle. While there are fundamentalist religious communities, they do not have a great impact on religious life. When fundamentalism enters the religious scene it often expresses itself as intolerance, or exclusion, of other religious communities or experiences.

Due to a wide variety of factors, religious fundamentalism in Brazil expresses itself via the need to defend the identity, beliefs, and numerical growth of religious communities. This tends to generate intolerance and to make interfaith spiritual care very difficult because care is frequently transformed into proselytism.

Religious communities that understand their source as based in revealed truth sometimes categorize those who do not have the same be-

---

[7] Ricardo Bráulio Muniz, "Intolerância e Igreja Universal do Reino de Deus." Master's Dissertation, The Methodist University of São Paulo, 2001.

liefs as radically different, or other. This means that persons and groups who do not have the same religious and moral convictions are not necessarily included in their understanding and practices of love, justice, and compassion. Moral exclusion occurs when one sees the other as being outside the community in which the norms apply, and therefore in need of "conversion." At the extreme, those outside of the community can be viewed as heretics, or sinners. To a large degree, the interpretation of the other by the "faithful" determines how those outside the religious and moral system should be treated. Some communities may see the need to express compassionate care for the "lost soul." Others may see the need to convert the "lost soul." Once again, at the extreme there are others that may see the need to condemn. Amidst the complex landscape of religious life and being, interfaith spiritual care requires compassion, at the very least. Conversion and condemnation are attitudes that often contradict the very nature of *interfaith*, *spiritual*, and *care*.

One of my students in the Master of Religious Studies Program is a part-time, volunteer chaplain at a hospital in the city where he lives. The hospital has a well-known program of treating persons with HIV/AIDS. My student regularly visits these patients. He is an exception. On various occasions he invited other pastors to visit these patients. Only one pastor agreed to make one visit. Two pastors made it very clear that they believed that HIV/AIDS was God's punishment for sinful behavior. The HIV/AIDS patients were effectively excluded from the spiritual and moral community of these pastors.

The key element appears to be, therefore, how to treat those who are outside of "our" religious community. As previously noted, those outside of our community may be seen as somewhere on a continuum between neutral and evil. Where on this continuum my religious community places the other is a fundamental element in deciding how they should be treated: should they be cared for?; should they be converted?; should they be ignored?; should they be condemned? These are fundamental questions in understanding the role and identity of religious communities in interfaith spiritual care.

Solidarity, tolerance, and beyond

A few years ago, the term "solidarity" was very popular among more "liberal" churches and pastors in Brazil. Solidarity is difficult to define, but its essence is communion and community. It suggests building bridges and relations between people, groups, and institutions. The term reflects attitudes from various Latin American liberation theologies, and originally referred to solidarity with the poor and the oppressed. Over time, solidarity came to be understood as a basic pastoral attitude toward the whole human community, but with particular attention to the excluded. Solidarity involves communion, compassion, and care, all in the pursuit of justice in the light of God's love. As a principle, we can see it based on Mark 12: 28–31. "One of the scribes came near and heard them disputing with one another, and seeing that he answered them well, he asked him, 'Which commandment is the first of all?' Jesus answered, 'The first is, "Hear, O Israel: the Lord our God, the Lord is one; you shall love the Lord your God with all your heart, and with all your soul, and with all your mind, and with all your strength." The second is this, "You shall love your neighbor as yourself." There is no other commandment greater than these.'"

This is the meaning of solidarity in Brazil. The term is less frequently used now, and it has been roughly replaced with the idea of "communion." How do we create communion in the midst of such fragmentation and competition?

Communion and care require tolerance in addition to commitment to remain engaged in relationship. Without tolerance, communion and care can quickly become either superficial or transformed into self-serving intentions or actions. In Brazil, where religion is concerned with survival, numerical growth, or the declaration of a special, set apart identity, the care of all souls, or comprehensive compassionate communion, becomes extremely difficult. For that reason it is important to look at the concept of tolerance.

There are many types of tolerance. For example, there is tolerance that only exists to seduce. This type of tolerance serves the need of the "tolerant:" "I tolerate you in order to convince you that I am right." By tolerating your beliefs, my hidden agenda is to convince you that I am right. This is a veiled form of fundamentalism. There is tolerance that expresses power: "I am tolerant of you because you are not a threat. In the long run I believe that you will come to believe as I do, but there is no hurry. My position is secure, and I can wait." Another form of tolerance reflects passivity. Directly or indirectly it says: "We will see who is right in the long run." Such tolerance avoids the risk of living and expressing the truth and identity of the community. There is also the kind of tolerance that ultimately seeks to create alliances: "I tolerate you in order to create an alliance against a greater foe, or to gain power." Tolerance can also be based on curiosity: "What do you believe, and why?" Such tolerance can be the beginning of communion, or simply a way of reinforcing the beliefs of my community, depending on the intention.

With the exception of tolerance based on respect and sincere curiosity, each of those forms of tolerance is ultimately self-serving. Spiritual care based on such tolerance ultimately creates fragmentation, and not community. In this sense, it can never be genuinely interfaith. Tolerance that promotes deep interfaith spiritual care requires a secure sense of identity, respect for the other, and the desire to create communion. Fundamentally, it recognizes that God's Truth can only be discovered by sharing our partial truths. In this sense, the person and community respect and maintain their beliefs while, at the same time, they are open to learning from others. We recognize that each of us holds a partial truth, and all of us are seeking the Truth.

Such tolerance is fundamentally spiritual because it makes it possible to create and foster communion between persons, groups, creation, and God. It expresses care because the other is a Thou, and not an Object, or an It.[8] It is interfaith because it deeply respects the other, without denying self and identity. Needless to say, such quality of tolerance is rare, but it is possible.

The Methodist tradition and interfaith spiritual care

My tradition, the Methodist Church, has historically relied on the theology of John Wesley (1703–1791), the founder of the Methodist movement, to understand the meaning of care and communion. Wesley was deeply concerned with bringing the Gospel to all. This led to a deep respect for diversity and the need for a theology that both respected the fundamental authority of the Bible and the ways in which God speaks in the midst of human experience. The Methodist Church has a long history of accepting diversity and providing care to all. While the current religious climate in Brazil does not encourage interfaith spiritual care, the Methodist Church continues to have a deep sense of its importance.

Respect for diversity reflects the cultural realities of England in the 18th century and Wesley's personal religious experience. England was in the midst of an Industrial Revolution that changed the character of the country. In a relatively short period of time, England went from agriculture to industry, from rural to urban. This industrial explosion brought people from rural areas of England, as well as from Europe, Spain, and Portugal, to live and work in the cities. The result was tremendous growth in industrial centers, along with the accompanying problems of unemployment, poverty, violence, alcohol abuse, the fragmentation of families, and social disorganization.

The situation of modern day Brazil is in some ways very similar to

---

[8] See Martin Buber's classic, *I and Thou* (New York: Charles Scribner's Sons, 1958).

that of England in the 18th century. Over the past forty years there has been a mass migration to the cities in search of jobs. This has resulted in a wide variety of social problems, much the same as in Wesley's day. Many people who arrive in the cities come with very few financial or professional resources, and often find themselves living in *favelas* (slums) on the periphery of urban areas. Just as in Wesley's England, unemployment, poverty, violence, alcohol, and drug abuse, the fragmentation of families and social disorganization are pressing challenges for the church.

Wesley's religious tradition, the Anglican Church, was predominantly middle class, intellectual, and formal. It was often out of touch with the needs and experiences of the majority of people. Wesley saw this problem as more than religious and social. He perceived it as a question of spirituality, communion, and care.

At a crucial moment in his adult life Wesley experienced a personal religious conversion during a Bible study in Aldersgate Street, London. In his words, he felt his heart "strangely warmed." His conversion changed his life forever. While the Anglican Church of his day valued the Bible, reason, and tradition, there was little emphasis on personal religious experience. Because of his personal conversion, Wesley began to place great emphasis on personal religious experience. This turned his attention increasingly to daily life, the experience of God, and practical spirituality. He became less concerned with formal church practices, and more with the needs of people. For Wesley, true salvation meant experiencing God, recognizing practical needs in the midst of daily life, working to change society, and integrating the mind, spirit, and heart. While religious practice and presence continued to be of great importance, healing mind, body, and spirit became central in his theology and practice.

In almost all of Wesley's writings there is a profound concern for care and communion. For example, his Sermon of the 23rd of May, 1786 is entitled "About Visiting the Infirm".[9] The text of the sermon is based on Matthew 25:35, is very practical, and reflects the needs and fears of his time and ours. Summarizing the sermon, Wesley says that both pastors and members of the Church resist visiting the infirm. They are afraid of receiving, through the air or by contact, the illness of the person they are visiting. They resist visiting someone whom they "little know." The hospital "casts a shadow that is not well received." Wesley goes further to say that visitation is more than visiting the infirm at their bed side. It

---

[9] Helmut Renders, Rui de Souza Josgrilberg, Paulo Ayres de Mattos, José Carlos de Souza e Cláudio de Oliveira Ribeiro, eds., *Sermões de Wesley: Texto com duas traduções em português* (São Bernardo do Campo: EDITEO, 2006), CD-ROM, Sermão 98.

includes visiting those that are in a state of affliction, whether it be of the mind or the body, good or bad, that fear God or not.[10] Visiting the infirm is a fundamental Christian duty. The key is that Wesley does not exclude those that we do not know, or who do not fear God. Women are not excluded. Children are not excluded. The poor are not excluded. Persons of other religious traditions, or no religion, are not excluded. The "other" is included in communion. In the Wesleyan tradition, this is an essential basis for interfaith spiritual care.

Another basis for interfaith spiritual care is the Wesleyan Quadrilateral, which is the foundation of our theological reflection and social presence. We seek to discern the meaning and implications of care and communion in the Bible, tradition, reason, and experience. While the Bible is given priority; tradition, reason, and experience are also necessary for seeking and recognizing God's presence in our lives and evaluating the significance of care and communion. This balance of sources affirms that God is both transcendent and immanent.

To provide care reflects who we are—body, mind, soul, and spirit. This includes our personal and social past, our knowledge of self, world, and God, and our personal experience. All of these in turn influence our experience of God.

Wesley lived in a context where religion was often reduced to either moral precepts or to the authority of systematic theology and the tradition of the church. His response was to recognize the richness and complexity of life, always in light of faith. In the Methodist tradition we begin with the authority of the Bible, but recognize that to understand what God is saying we must include other elements. Tradition, reason, and experience are present in every moment of our lives, including how we understand the Bible and our faith. As shown in his sermon, "About Visiting the Infirm," Wesley was very practical. While he always began with the authority of the Bible, he did not separate faith from life. God was experienced in the midst of life. This stance has direct implications for care.

While the Bible is foundational for interfaith spiritual care, we can also draw from the wells of our tradition; from resources provided by psychology, sociology, and other human sciences (that is, "reason"); and from our personal experience of God. This is one of the true gifts that Wesley and the Methodist tradition offer today.

There is a story that circulates in the Methodist Church in Brazil, which may or may not be true: In a moment of exasperation in the midst

---

[10] Ibid.

of a very tense discussion regarding interfaith and interreligious dialogue, a now retired Bishop said, "Enough! Who is your neighbor? How would Christ treat your neighbor? That is what we should be talking about, and not the theological implications of Jesus Christ as the only Son of God."

Whether or not the story is literally true is of little importance. It points to a deep concern in the Methodist Church for people, for communion. "What does it mean to live in communion with God, neighbor, and creation?" In our time this is a fundamental question with regard to interfaith spiritual care. I am sure that the bishop did not intend to discard a fundamental theological principle. What the story says to me is that creating communion comes before defending ideas. Creating communion requires that we go beyond our comfortable boundaries and welcome and embrace the other, the stranger.

The Methodist University of São Paulo has a Methodist School of Theology and a Graduate School of Religion. Both the School of Theology and the Graduate School are ecumenical, and various students at the Graduate School come from non-Christian traditions. Many students who study at the School of Theology do their Master's course work at the Graduate School. Recently, I was giving a class on faith development theory at the Graduate School. In the class were five Methodists, one Presbyterian, two Baptists, one Roman Catholic, and one Umbandista. At the School of Theology, it is very common to begin class with prayer, which almost always ends with the phrase "in Jesus' name we pray," or something similar.

At the Graduate School we do not begin class with prayer. One student, a Methodist, asked, in a very respectful way, why we did not pray before class. The Methodist student, who was studying missions, did not know that one of his colleagues was not a Christian. I answered, also in broad terms, that the Graduate School was both ecumenical and interreligious. The student responded that we were studying at the Methodist University of São Paulo and since the vast majority of students are Christian we should respect "our" religious tradition.

At this point, the Umbandista student, who was studying sociology of religion, entered the discussion, saying, "So it is a question of power? We pray according to who has the most votes?" The Methodist responded, "The University is Christian. It is not a question of power but respect for our tradition." The Umbandista said, "Your tradition, not our tradition." Soon afterwards the Roman Catholic student said: "I do not ask you to pray to Mary, which is my tradition, and we are the majority in Brazil."

From there other students entered the discussion, at times supporting the Methodist, at times the Umbandista. Questions were raised about the relationship between the church and the academy, the meaning of being a Methodist University, academic freedom, the place of prayer in the University, the relationship between faith and religious practice, social and political power, the meaning of ecumenical, and so forth.

I felt lost much of the time, and only barely managed to organize the discussion. Still, it was an exciting and rich discussion which revealed a great deal about religious dynamics, power, compassion, communion, fear, and hope. In the end a certain communion was realized. All present agreed to have a moment of silence at the beginning of each class, each using the time as they wished. We did not resolve the conflicts or answer the questions, but we did find a way to live and learn together.

The way forward

My wife and I have a friend who left a middle class Protestant church, went to a Spiritist community for a few months, and is now attending a neo-Pentecostal church. She left the Protestant church in the search of a miracle for her cancer, and because she did not feel welcome because of her poverty. She is still not well, but her cancer is in remission. We see each other every week or so, and always pray together. At one point she told us a story that, for me, points the way forward, toward interfaith spiritual care in Brazil.

The pastor of her current church has never visited her, either at home or in the hospital, but preaches "Spirit-filled" sermons. When she is well she goes to worship services and feels welcome and renewed. She has friends there and feels a sense of communion with the members of the church, most of whom are, as she is, poor.

The pastor from the Protestant church that she attended continues to visit her at home, and when she is in the hospital. She feels a personal and spiritual bond with him that guides and sustains her, but says that the church community was very formal, and not "filled with the Spirit." She says that they prayed for her, but then made it clear that she was not truly welcome. She did not dress like they did. Grace entered when, at a certain moment, the pastor said that "God does not mind how you dress."

One pastor offers worship that is "Spirit-filled," and promises miracles. The church accepts her, even though she is poor and comes from another religious tradition. The other pastor offers her personal care and presence. He did not abandon her because she did not fit the traditional profile of his church. Her friends offer her the family that she does not have, as well as love and prayers.

Our friend is not Protestant, Spiritist, or neo-Pentecostal. She is not a member, in the traditional sense, of any church. She is poor, sick, vulnerable, and yet resilient. She is seeking care, healing, communion, and community.

At least in the context of Brazil, she is a metaphor for how interfaith spiritual care exists and may grow. It is informal. It is personal. Though it rarely exists on formal, institutional, or ecclesiastic levels, it is present between pastors, persons, friends, and families. In the midst of the various problems between religious traditions and communities, our friend has found a delicate balance that offers her care, communion, and community that often go beyond the bounds of traditional church membership, fidelity, and identity. This would seem to be the future of interfaith spiritual care in Brazil, at least in the near future.

The sacralization of identity
An interfaith spiritual care paradigm
for chaplaincy in a multifaith context[1]

Lindsay B. Carey, Ron Davoren, Jeffrey Cohen

In general terms, most scholars have broadly agreed that "... no convincing general theory of religion exists.[2] Indeed given the enormous cultural, theological and philosophical variability as to "what religion actually is," means that the undertaking of any serious social and scientific study of religion continues to be difficult. Indeed for some it is simply too complex. Likewise, despite the increasing contemporary interest in "spirituality," 'there is no widespread agreement on what spirituality [actually] means'[3] and thus, similar to 'religion' there is no common general theory

Lindsay B. Carey, M.App.Sc., Ph.D., is a Lecturer and Research Fellow in Pastoral and Palliative Care at the School of Public Health, Palliative Care Unit, La Trobe University, Melbourne, Australia. He is also the National Research Fellow for the Australian Health & Welfare Chaplains Association and Specialist Reserve Chaplain with the Royal Australian Air Force, R.A.A.F. Base Williams, Laverton, Victoria.

Ron Davoren, M.Min., CP., is a Passionist Priest at St. Paul's Monastery in Adelaide, South Australia and former President of the Australian Health & Welfare Chaplains Association.

Jeffrey Cohen, D.Min., D.D., FRSA., is a Rabbi, Lecturer and Visiting Senior Research Fellow at the School of Public Health and Community Medicine, University of New South Wales, Sydney, Australia.

[1] Acknowledgement is given for the research support provided by the Australian Health & Welfare Chaplains Association (AHWCA), the Palliative Care Unit of the School of Public Health, La Trobe University (Victoria, Australia), the School of Public Health and Community Medicine, University of New South Wales (Sydney, Australia), the Melbourne College of Divinity, (Victoria, Australia), the Adelaide Theological College (South Australia), the Uniting Church Centre for Ministry (Victoria Synod, Australia), the Roman Catholic Passionist Community ('Holy Cross' Victoria, 'St. Paul's' and 'All Saints' South Australia), plus Rev. Dr. Roy Bradley (Victoria, Australia), Rev. Dr. Brian Gleeson, C.P., (Melbourne, Australia) and Rev. Dr. Noel Brown (The Orere Source).

[2] S.E. Guthrie, "Religion: What is it?," *Journal for the Scientific Study of Religion*, 35:4 (1996): 412–419.

[3] H.G. Koenig, "Religion, Spirituality and Medicine in Australia: Research and Clinical Practice", *Medical Journal of Australia* 186:10 (Supplement, 2007): S45–46.

"concerning the things of the spirit." Reflecting a lack of consensus given countervailing discourses and that no academic discipline or profession dominates the field sufficiently to provide an acceptable definitive paradigm.[4] Yet the lack of a commonly accepted theory or paradigm by which to gauge the contribution of various religious and spiritual beliefs and their relevance in society (if any), has become particularly and currently pertinent within economically rationalist medical environments where religious professionals (e.g., chaplains, pastoral care workers), are being called upon to justify and defend the value and relevance of their religious/spiritual services, in terms of a health care outcome, particularly given a multicultural and multifaith society.[5]

It is the position of this paper that one theoretical paradigm, the *"Sacralization of Identity,"* [6] developed by sociologist and theologian Emeritus Professor Reverend Hans Mol, has largely been overlooked by analysts and critics of religion and spirituality. Yet Mol's theoretical social scientific paradigm may provide some in-depth understanding concerning the common contribution that all religious and spiritual beliefs make to the identity of their members and the community. Given the development of multicultural and multifaith policies that are increasingly required within many Western countries, Mol's theory may also prove particularly helpful when exploring and researching the interfaith ministry of hospital chaplains and other religious workers (of whatever religious/spiritual beliefs). Given such a potential, this paper will also provide an overview of research findings concerning the involvement of chaplains in providing pastoral care to people of non-Christian faiths by making use of the mechanisms of Mol's "sacralization of identity" paradigm.

The "sacralization of identity" as a resource

During the twentieth century various theologians and religious leaders have strongly advocated for an interfaith paradigm that would encourage a pragmatic and reciprocal pastoral care relationship between people of different religious and spiritual beliefs.[7] For example, and perhaps the

---

[4] B. Rumbold, *Spirituality and Palliative Care: Social and Pastoral Perspectives* (Melbourne: Oxford University Press, 2002), p. x.

[5] L.B. Carey, & C. Newell, "Economic Rationalism and the Cost Efficiency of Hospital Chaplaincy: An Australian Study," in L. VandeCreek, ed., "Professional Chaplaincy: What is Happening to it During Health Care Reform?" *The Journal of Health Care Chaplaincy*, 10:1 (2000): 37–52.

[6] H. Mol, *Identity and the Sacred: A Sketch for a New Social-Scientific Theory of Religion* (Oxford: Blackwell, 1976).

[7] D. Donnelly, *On Relationship as a Key to Inter-Religious Dialogue* in D. Kendall and G. O'Collins, *Many and Diverse Ways* (New York: Orbis Books, 2003), p. 136.

most progressive, was that of the Catholic Benedictine, Bede Griffiths (b.1906–d.1993) who held that the various religions were like the fingers on the hand. That is "... *the baby finger is Buddhism, the next is Hinduism, the middle one is Islam, the forefinger is Judaism and the thumb is Christianity. Buddhism is miles from Christianity, and they are all divided separately, but as you go deep into any religion, you converge on the centre, and everything springs from that centre and converges at that centre.*"[8] The Second Vatican Council (1963–1965) published *Nostrae Aetate* and *Lumen Gentium*, both unprecedented declarations affirming the relationship of the Christian church to non-Christian religions[9] and which acknowledged that there are "*seeds of the Word in other religions and grants that adherents of these (non-Christian) religions may come to salvation by way of their religion.*"[10]

Johannis (Hans) Mol

Often overlooked when considering multifaith issues is the work of Hans Mol (b. 1922) who was renowned within many universities and theological colleges for his extensive sociological inquiry into the religious and spiritual beliefs and practices of people living within many Western countries,[11] but particularly in Australia,[12] New Zealand,[13] and Canada.[14] Mol's research interests, however, were not just confined to those countries that have become dominated by Christianity. In his search for a scientific paradigm via which to study religion, Mol also explored other popular faith systems in countries such as India and China.[15] During the

---

[8] J. Swindells, *A Human Search: Bede Griffiths Reflects on His Life* (Ligouri, Missouri: Triumph 1997), p. 94.

[9] W.M. Abbott, *The Documents of Vatican II* (London: Geoffrey Chapman, 1967), p. 34–35.

[10] D. Nicholl, *Other Religions (Nostrae Aetate)* in Adrian Hastings, ed., *Modern Catholicism: Vatican II and After* (London: SPCK, 1991), p.126–34, 132.

[11] H. Mol, *Western Religion: A Country by Country Sociological Inquiry* (The Hague, The Netherlands: Mouton & Co, 1972). This text explores the countries of Austria, Belgium, Bulgaria, Canada, Czechoslovakia, Denmark, Finland, Germany, Great Britain, Hungary, Ireland, Netherlands, New Zealand, Norway, Poland, Portugal, South Africa, Spain, Sweden, Switzerland, United States of America, Russia, and Yugoslavia.

[12] H. Mol, *Religion in Australia: A Sociological Investigation* (Melbourne: Nelson, 1971) and H. Mol, *The Faith of Australians* (Sydney: George Allen & Unwin, 1985).

[13] H. Mol, *Identity and Religion: International, Cross Cultural Approaches* (Sage, London: International Sociological Association, 1978).

[14] H. Mol, *Faith and Fragility: Religion and Identity in Canada* (Canada, Trinity Press, 1985).

[15] H. Mol, *Wholeness and Breakdown* (Madras, University of Madras, 1978) and H. Mol and E.G. D'Aquili, *The Regulation of Physical and Mental Systems: Systems Theory of the Philosophy of Science* (New York: Edwin Mellen Press, 1990).

1960s, 1970s, and 1980s, Mol's sociological quest into worldwide religious and spiritual belief and practice was, and arguably still is, comprehensive.[16] Predominantly it involved descriptive data and interpretative information, which, while historically invaluable, is already outdated due to the almost predictable and rapidly changing effects of secularization and post-modernism upon religious belief throughout the world. Yet the ramifications of Mol's accumulated country-by-country statistical and social inquiry were significant in terms of Mol's formulation of a general theory of religious belief that would withstand time and cultural comparison. Indeed Mol's theoretical social-scientific paradigm of religion—"the sacralization of identity"—may well be considered 'classical' in years to come due to its potential ongoing contribution to interfaith dialogue and pastoral care ministry within multifaith contexts.

Mol's "sacralization of identity"

There are many ways one could approach Mol's thesis on the "sacralization of identity." Whichever way is chosen it is practically impossible to fully describe Mol's complex dialectic paradigm—the "sacralization of identity"—within this short paper. Indeed, one could describe Mol's social scientific theory as a psycho-social-spiritual and religious 'Rubik's cube.' Nevertheless, it is hoped that this attempt will at least introduce the reader to Mol's theoretical process, particularly for example as it may relate to chaplaincy.

If 'secularization' (from the word secular) is defined as "the process by which sectors of society, it's people and their culture are removed from the domination of religious institutions and symbols,"[17] then 'sacralization' (from the word sacred), could be explained as, "the process of setting apart, reserving, dedicating, consecrating and/or instituting something or someone, as especially acceptable to, and coming under the auspices of a religious organization/spiritual movement, deity or deistic principles." In very simple terms, then, Mol's concept of the "sacralization of identity" could be considered, given the dialectic of "secular" and "sacred" just mentioned, as the "process by which a person's identity predominantly develops under, or is transformed by "sacred" principles in contrast to "secular" influences." According to Fallding (1974) "...

---

[16] Mol's writings should, perhaps, be also given credit for having provided a springboard for sociologists and many other professionals, (e.g., psychologists, anthropologists, political scientists, theologians, plus many "lay-analysts"), to either gain a solid grounding in, or provide a launch for, their own understanding and studies into religious/spiritual belief and practice.

[17] See for example: P. Berger, *The Sacred Canopy* (New York: Doubleday, 1969) or B. Wilson, *Religion in Sociological Perspective* (New York: Oxford University Press, 1982).

secularization is the analytical process that has sacralization for the complementary synthesizing process. They form a dialectic. Secularization, through the operation of reason, breaks down; sacralization, through the operation of faith, builds up."[18]

Mol likewise recognized that through the process of "identity sacralization" that another dialectic opposite will more than likely also occur—'desacralization.' That is, "... the sacralization of one [identity] may weaken another [identity]". Indeed Mol suggests that in reality a spiritual-psycho-social dialectic process of 'jostling systems' is constantly ongoing during the "sacralization of identity" process:[19]

> ... sameness (identity) is wrestling with change (difference), order is fighting it out with chaos, salvation (wholeness, integrity) conquers, yet is constantly threatened by sin (breakdown, fragmentation), the feminine mode (inclusion) is in collusion, yet also in concert with the masculine mode (intrusion), yin alternates with yang, purusa (the static) is polluted by prakriti (the dynamic), dharma is subverted by adharma, consolidation is undone by expansion, integration is foiled by differentiation ... crucifixion versus resurrection, freedom versus constraint, chaos verses order ... the sacred versus the profane....

To the current authors, it is this 'dialectic' jostling which is the crux of the "sacralization of identity" theory and the key to understanding the importance of religious/spiritual beliefs and the role of the chaplain in encouraging the 'man/woman in the street' (or the patient in the intensive care hospital bed, as the case may be) to find stability in times of crisis *or* to encourage change/conflict when there is need for progression. As Mol infers, religious/spiritual beliefs reinforce conflict that leads to change but can also reconcile conflict that leads to stability. Or, in terms of social or community organization, religious/spiritual beliefs encourage both the dialectics of 'contention and cooperation' or 'differentiation and integration.' Yet amidst this contention and cooperation of dialectic systems which allow 'flexibility to permit survival,' Mol suggests that religious/spiritual beliefs sacralize identity that, in turn, provides stabil-

---

[18] H. Fallding, *The Sociology of Religion* (Toronto: McGraw-Hill/Ryerson, 1974), p. 210.

[19] H. Mol, "Religion and Identity: A dialectic interpretation of religious phenomena." In: V.C. Hayes, *Identity and World Religions*. Selected proceedings of the fifteenth Congress of the International Association for *The History of Religions* (Netly, Adelaide: Wakefield Press, 1986).

ity, continuity or sameness and a system of defense and reinforcement to ensure the preservation of that sameness.[20]

Key mechanisms of "identity sacralization"

As a sociologist and theologian Mol was fully aware of the enormous theological, social, and cultural diversity within and across the various religions and spiritual movements, but more importantly, he recognized many practical similarities in the way various religions/spiritual movements sacralize the identity of its societal or community members. Challenging the classic psychological and sociological theories of Freud and Marx, Mol postulated that the various religious and spiritual enterprises around the world have a very real, powerful, and pragmatic influence upon people's lives due to four key 'mechanisms,'[21] common to all religious and spiritual expressions cross-culturally,[22] namely:

(i) **Objectification** or transcendental ordering (e.g., superior being, spiritual realm)

(ii) **Ritual** (e.g., rites, enacting dramatization)

(iii) **Myth** (e.g., sacred legends) and

(iv) **Commitment** or emotional anchoring

According to Mol each of the various "sacralization of identity" mechanisms developed by various religious and spiritual beliefs (for further detail refer to Figure 1) help to sacralize a person's identity (leading to one's integration into a particular belief) by helping to *reconcile conflict* that leads to *stability* or *reinforce conflict that leads to change.* Mol called this functionary process—between change and stability and vice versa—"dialectic jostling." Following Mol's paradigm, Carey argued that it is the "sacralization of identity" 'dialectic jostling' function that is helpful in understanding the importance of religious/spiritual beliefs in terms of aiding an individual's well-being and useful in comprehending the potential interfaith pastoral care role of a chaplain within a multifaith context.[23] Chaplains may, for example, be required to help a person (irre-

---

[20] H. Mol, *Identity and the Sacred*, p. 5.

[21] Ibid., p. 5; and H. Mol, *Meaning and Place: An Introduction to the Social Scientific Study of Religion* (New York: Pilgrim Press, 1983).

[22] H. Mol, "New Perspectives from Cross-Cultural Studies," in P.E. Hammond , *The Sacred in a Secular Age: Toward Revision in the Scientific Study of Religion* (Berkeley: University of California Press, 1985), p. 90–103.

[23] L.B. Carey, "The Sacralization of Identity: A Cross-Cultural and Inter-Religious Paradigm for Hospital Chaplaincy." *The Journal of Health Care Chaplaincy* (February, 1998), p. 15–23.

Figure 1: Mol's "Sacralization of Identity" Mechanisms

Objectification (Transcendental Ordering)

is "... the tendency to sum up the variegated elements of mundane existence in a transcendental point of reference where they can appear more orderly, more consistent and more timeless." This ordering process of religious/spiritual belief, according to Mol, can enable those experiences of individuals and communities that may seem 'disorderly and disparate' to be interpreted meaningfully given the existence of a rarefied realm, "...where major outlines of order can be maintained in the face of temporal dislocations." This objectification reference to another realm helps to give life meaning, even under tremendous adversity and thus sustains the "sacralization of identity" and indeed encourages the creative opportunity to "... profoundly transform conceptions of existence or provide the leverage for transformation." It has 'two faces.' The first face is the conservative one that manages discord, disorder and disruption and legitimates by relating relevance to a transcendental order. The second face diminishes the legitimization and declares that the penultimate and mundane is only relatively important and therefore the transcendental order becomes a catalyst for change.

Myth ... comprises the, "narratives, tales or speculations sacralizing meaning and identity by outlining and anchoring the definition of what life and its relationships are all about." Myths dramatize the dialectic between chaos and order, sin and salvation. According to Mol, myths hold arbitrariness and chaos at bay; they usually contribute to the resolution of basic conflicts; and, they help to interpret and make meaningful objectification, ritual and commitment, thus sacralizing the meaning of life and one's identity within that life.

Sacralization of Identity

Ritual ... is "the repetitive enactment of human systems of meaning." Mol argues that it is through the: "... repetitive, emotional evoking action that social cohesion and personality integration are reinforced—at the same time that aggressive or socially destructive actions are articulated, dramatized and curbed ... ritual also restores identity, particularly when disruption has occurred, for example, through death, personal or social loss or when rearrangements in family relations become necessary." Rituals recall old lines of demarcation before drawing new lines around new or changed identities.

Commitment (Emotional Anchoring)

... that is, the "emotional attachment to a specific focus of identity," is another mechanism of "sacralization of identity." In the face of modern skepticism, rationality and competition, religious/spiritual commitment is the deliberate, "... anchoring of emotions in a salient system of meaning, social group or personal beliefs, whether abstract or concrete." Religious/spiritual commitment according to Mol shows loyalty, clarifies priorities, demands sacrifice, inspires awe, and as such, defines one's religious/spiritual identity as having integrity (being 'consistent' and 'predictable') and thus sacralizes one's identity to that to which one is committed. Its dialectic is that it requires "de-commitment" or "detaches" or "distances" from the evil, chaotic and anxiety-ridden past towards present future hopes.

Source: H. Mol, *Identity and the Sacred: A Sketch for a New Socio-Scientific Theory of Religion* (Oxford: Blackwell, 1978). H. Mol, (1983) *Meaning and Place: An Introduction to the Social Scientific Study of Religion* (New York: Pilgrim Press, 1983; L.B. Carey, "Sacralization of Identity: A Cross Cultural and Inter-religious Paradigm for Hospital Chaplaincy, *Journal of Health Care Chaplaincy* (Cambridge: February, 1998): 15–23.

spective of their faith) to encounter issues challenging their religious or spiritual beliefs and (by using one or more of the sacralizing mechanisms) assist with their stability in the midst of crises; or, alternatively, a chaplain may need to help encourage change when there is a need for progression. Thus, by making reference to one or more of the "sacralization of identity" mechanisms, the chaplain becomes both empathetic supporter yet gentle confronter. Carey argued that because of the relevance of Mol's paradigm within a multifaith context, it can serve as an excellent 'frame of reference' in the study of health care chaplaincy, which increasingly necessitates cross-cultural and interfaith ministry involving patients, their relatives and clinical staff enduring various levels of religious/spiritual contention within contemporary clinical and multifaith contexts.[24]

The role of chaplains within the clinical context

It has been suggested by researchers such as Idler (1983), following the work of Emile Durkheim (1912) and others, that there are at least four religious psycho-social ways in which religious and spiritual involvement might alter a person's health. These are in terms of: (i) a patient's/client's health behavior, (ii) social cohesiveness, (iii) cognitive coherence, and (iv) (positive) theological understandings.[25] Carey's review and synthesis of scientific research suggests that past and future research considering the correlation between religion, spirituality, and health can be categorized (in terms of a health outcome) into one or more of Idler's four categories.[26] Overall much of this literature and research suggests that, "... even given an increasing technological society and the scientifically tenuous links between religion and health that the relationship between the two dimensions of religion and health, are substantial enough to warrant further investigation and significant enough for health care practitioners to encourage a holistic practice that includes the spiritual/religious dimensions of a patient's/client's healing needs."[27]

It has been argued that by making use of chaplains, health care institutions can assist in creating better health outcomes for patients and

[24] Ibid.

[25] E.L. Idler, "Religious Involvement and the Health of the Elderly: Some Hypotheses and an Initial Test" in Social Forces, 66 (1987): 226–238.

[26] L.B. Carey, "Religiosity and Health: A Review and Synthesis," New Doctor: Journal of the Doctor's Reform Society, Sydney, 60 (1993): 26–32.

[27] L.B. Carey, "Religiosity and Health: A Review and Synthesis," New Doctor: Journal of the Doctor's Reform Society, Sydney, 60 (1993): 26–32.

staff by helping to ensure that hospitals are holistic in their practice and not just practicing tokenism.[28] To some, however, 'chaplaincy' simply provides a symbolic framework for the official recognition that there may be a need for the provision of spiritual care in the hospital setting. It is important to note, of course, that the role of chaplains varies enormously depending upon their specialist skills, the environment in which they minister and the medical and psycho-social religious needs of patients. Some of the most common roles of hospital chaplains which have been researched thus far have included counselor, liturgist, and sacramentalist, ethicist, teamworker, thanatonist (carer at times of death), prayer intercessor, witness, and teacher.[29]

Much of the literature to date commenting about the contribution of hospital chaplains in promoting the possible salient psycho-social religious benefits for patients, their families, and staff within the hospital environment, reflects a positive attitude to health care chaplains.[30] Various quantitative and qualitative research exploring the role of chaplains,[31] locally and internationally, also suggests that the role of the "clergy" working as hospital chaplains, though affected by such social processes as secularization,[32] modernization,[33] professionalization[34] and marginalization,[35] nevertheless seems predominantly to be very much accepted and professionally appreciated by medical practitioners, nursing staff, and allied health professionals who have experienced chaplaincy

---

[28] L.B. Carey, R.A. Aroni and A. Edwards, "Health Policy and Well-Being: Hospital Chaplaincy," in H. Gardner, ed., *Health Policy in Australia*, 1st ed. (Melbourne: Oxford University Press, 1997), pp. 190–110.

[29] Ibid.

[30] L.B. Carey, "Clergy Under the Knife: A Review of Literature on Hospital Chaplains," in *Ministry: Journal of Continuing Education* (Sydney, Summer, 1991), p. 7–9.

[31] R. Shook and L. Fojut, "Measuring What Chaplains Do" in *Health Progress* 85 (2004): 2 and B. Rodrigues, D. Rodrigues, and D.L Casey, *Spiritual Needs and Chaplaincy Encounters: A National Empirical Study on Chaplaincy Encounters in Health Care Settings* (Medford: Providence Health System, 2000).

[32] Secularization: see P. Berger, *The Sacred Canopy* , or B. Wilson, *Religion in Sociological Perspective* (New York: Oxford University Press, 1982).

[33] Modernization: see S. Acquiaviva, *The Decline of the Sacred in Industrial Society* (Sydney: Basil Blackwell, 1979).

[34] Professionalization: see B. Turner, *Medical Power and Social Knowledge* (California: Sage Publications, 1992).

[35] Marginalization: see G. Bouma, "Chaplains as Marginalized Professionals," Conference Paper, Australian Health & Welfare Chaplains Association, February, St. Mary's, Melbourne University, 1990.

services.[36]

However, as stated by Gardner, "... although [the] evaluation of the utility of hospital chaplaincy appears to be largely positive for staff and patients, it is an intangible, difficult to quantify service that could disappear within a health system which is making decisions on the cost-effectiveness of hospital services and where chaplains face competition from a number of other professions."[37] In addition, according to some chaplains and their clinical colleagues (e.g., medical practitioners, nurses, and allied health staff), an important issue facing chaplaincy in the future is the inclusion and provision of religious representatives from non-Christian faiths as chaplains, and an appropriate model for understanding and teamwork.[38] Consequently, it can be argued that a cross-culturally appropriate interfaith model for chaplaincy that is functioning within a multifaith context is needed.

Chaplains and the "sacralization of identity"

Mol hypothesized that through the various religious mechanisms of sacralization (i.e., objectification, ritual, myth, and commitment), that people gain a sense of identity and meaning which can consequently influence their social behavior towards others (positively or negatively)[39] and can affect the way they organize and provide for themselves.[40] It has been argued that all the clinical staff within hospitals, chaplains, and other pastoral care workers (no matter what their faith) are at a decisive advantage (through reference to the various sacralizing mechanisms), in promoting the potential positive psycho-social religious and spiritual benefits that may enhance a patient's well-being and assist clinical staff

[36] R. Carey, *Hospital Chaplains: Who Needs Them?* (St. Louis, USA: The Catholic Hospital Association, 1971) and L.B. Carey, "The Role of Hospital Chaplains: A Research Overview" in *The Journal of Health Care Chaplaincy*, Cambridge (May 1997) p. 3–11, and L.B. Carey and C. Kenworthy, "Pastoral Care: Nurses Suffering from Grief and Loss" in *Ministry: Journal of Continuing Education* 5:4 (Winter 1995), p. 20–22, and L.B. Carey & H. Elliot, "The Hospital Chaplain's Role in an Organ Transplant Unit" in *Ministry, Society & Theology* 10:1 (1996), p. 66–77.

[37] H. Gardner, *Health Policy in Australia* (Melbourne: Oxford University Press, 1997), p. 8.

[38] L.B. Carey, "The Utility of Chaplains within Health Care Institutions." Master of Applied Sciences Thesis, Faculty of Health Sciences, La Trobe University, Melbourne, 1995.

[39] It is important to note that some of the examples indicated by Mol (e.g.: religious mass suicide, "Peoples Temple" commune, Guyana, 1978), rightly suggest that the sacralization of identity may not necessarily lead to a religious/spiritual phenomena of salutary results, but indeed may be deleterious. Hence the importance of "chaplains" in promoting the potential positive psycho-social benefits of religious/spiritual belief.

[40] H. Mol, *Meaning and Place: An Introduction to the Social Scientific Study of Religion* (New York: The Pilgrim Press, 1983).

in their beneficent patient care.[41]

People entering the modern hospital environment, whether they be "in-patients" or "out-patients," Christian, Buddhist, Maori, Aboriginal or of other spiritual praxis are usually subordinated to the demanding processes of technical medical intervention; consequently, some patients may experience radical and even rapid changes to their normal routine of living and decision-making. Hospital institutionalization most often also necessitates a change in lifestyle and sometimes, due to circumstances beyond human control, a change in identity. The loss of physical health, the loss of limb, the loss of employment, the loss of a loved one, the loss of meaning and direction in life, the loss of culture, the loss of faith and the loss of self worth, are just some of the factors that can cause identity crises. By making use of Mol's paradigm, with specific mechanisms, it is possible to systematically hypothesize how religious/spiritual beliefs (regardless of type) can be important in assisting the well-being of a patient's and clinical staff's sense of identity, and indeed integrity, particularly at times of crises.

The religious/spiritual representative within a medical environment, especially the appointed chaplain, has a specialist opportunity to assist patients, their families, and staff to reinterpret their lives (particularly given 'hard to believe' and overwhelming circumstances that seem void of any transcendental meaning) as well as encouraging a sense of (i) meaning by the objectification reference or inference to an ongoing order that, unlike penultimate occurrences, remains the same 'yesterday, today, and forever.' The 'chaplain' can encourage an ongoing (ii) commitment by reference to (iii) religious/spiritual texts and myths that idealize characters and commandments, that, for patients and staff in the face of challenge and change, help provide resources that define and anchor the meaning of life and call upon endurance and inspiration to remain committed and strive for new goals. Through various (iv) rituals such as baptism, Eucharist, prayers, marriage, anointing of the sick and funeral rites, the formalization of life's events are expressed, celebrated and mourned, providing for reinforcement and change and also the shaping, controlling, and sacralizing of a future identity.

A study of interfaith chaplaincy in Australia

The importance of establishing a general theory of religious/spiritual beliefs, such as the "sacralization of identity," particularly within multifaith

---

[41] L.B. Carey, "The Sacralization of Identity: A Cross-Cultural and Inter-Religious Paradigm for Hospital Chaplaincy," pp.15–23.

contexts, has never been more apparent given the current interfaith and interreligious dynamics within many Western countries. Within Australia, for example, over the last thirty years the face of health care within all Australian capital cities has changed substantially, particularly in terms of meeting the various needs of people from other cultures who have migrated from distant shores as a result of poverty, persecution, and war. Ministering to an increasing number of people who are from different cultural backgrounds and from non-Christian religions has the potential to present various challenges to Christian chaplains working within clinical contexts. Past research suggests that health care chaplains within Australia have provided pastoral care to people facing a variety of issues within the clinical context.[42] These issues have included such areas as pain control,[43] withdrawal of life support,[44] resuscitation,[45] abortion,[46] euthanasia,[47] invitro-fertilization,[48] organ donation, and transplantation.[49] It is, nevertheless, an assumption to simply believe that Christian chaplains can, have, or do minister to those adhering to non-Christian beliefs.

It is important to note that the newly established 'Pastoral Intervention Codings' (i.e., 'pastoral assessment,' 'pastoral ministry/support,' 'pastoral counseling/education,' and 'pastoral ritual and worship') by the National Centre for the Classification of Health (NCCH) in conjunction with the World Health Organization (WHO), do not discriminate

---

[42] L.B. Carey, R. Aroni and A. Edwards, "Health and Well Being. Hospital Chaplaincy" in H. Gardner, *Health Policy in Australia* (Melbourne: Oxford University Press, 1997), p. 190–210 and L.B. Carey, B. Rumbold, C.J. Newell, and R. Aroni, "Bioethics and Care Chaplaincy in Australia," *Scottish Journal of Health Care Chaplaincy*, 9 (2006): 23–30.

[43] L.B. Carey, C.J. Newell and B. Rumbold, "Pain Control and Chaplaincy," *Journal of Pain and Symptom Management*, 2006, 32 (6) p. 589–601.[44] L.B. Carey and C.J. Newell, "Withdrawal of Life Support and Chaplaincy in Australia," *Journal of Critical Care and Resuscitation*, 9:1 (2007): 34–39.

[45] L.B. Carey and C.J. Newell, "Chaplaincy and Resuscitation," in *Journal of Resuscitation* Vol. 75, No. 1 (2007): 12–22.

[46] L.B. Carey and C.J. Newell, "Abortion and Health Care Chaplaincy in Australia," *Journal of Religion and Health*, 46:2 (2007): 315–332.

[47] L.B. Carey and C. J. Newell, "The Euthanasia Debate and Hospital Chaplaincy within Australia," *Journal of Health Care Chaplaincy*, Cambridge, (June 1998): 8–16 and C.J. Newell and L.B. Carey, "Euthanasia and Hospital Chaplains in Australia," in C. Newell & D. Prior, "Dying Matters: Faith and Death," *Interface Journal*, 4:2 (2001): 86–100.

[48] L.B. Carey and C. Newell, "Invitro-Fertilization and the Role of the Chaplain: An Exploratory Study," *Scottish Journal of Health Care Chaplaincy*, 11:2 (2008) [In press].

[49] H. Elliot and L.B. Carey, (1999) "Organ Transplantation and Chaplaincy," *Ministry, Society & Theology*, Melbourne, 10:1 (1999): 66–77.

in terms of who is entitled to pastoral care.[50] Further both the British 'Health Care Chaplaincy Standards' and the Australian 'Health Care Chaplaincy Guidelines' clearly state that, as a matter of professional ethics, chaplains are to provide pastoral care to people irrespective of creed or race.[51] From January 2008, the 'Public Hospital Patient Charter' within Victoria (Australia) came into effect, translating in 18 different languages that services are to be provided to patients in a culturally sensitive way: *"You have the right to be treated in a way that respects your culture and beliefs."*[52]

While chaplains do not have the automatic right to minister to people of other faiths, they do have an obligation to respond equally to the needs of people of any faith and to ensure that people of all religious/ spiritual beliefs have the right of access to religious/spiritual care.

Yet it is possible that some Christian chaplains, perhaps due to theological, doctrinal or pragmatic reasons, may not see interfaith ministry as their priority and may avoid or neglect such ministry. Indeed Kirkwood noted, when exploring pastoral care within one hospital (which had a clientele of 54 percent Muslim patients), that: *"… to my amazement and disbelief not one of the clergy had visited a Muslim patient. One [clergy] made the comment that he did not consider it part of his ministry to visit Muslims."*[53] Yet research undertaken among clinical staff suggests that the majority of medical, nursing, and allied health clinicians believed that it was irrelevant as to whether the religious faith of a chaplain was the same as the patients/families, as long as chaplains were readily available to provide pastoral support to patients and their families at times of crisis.[54] This then raises several fundamental questions worth exploring, for example:

- Do Christian chaplains provide pastoral care to people of non-Christian faiths?

---

[50] *NCCH Pastoral Intervention Codings, International Classification of Diseases*, Vol. 10 – Australian Modification (ICD-10-AM), World Health Organization & the National Centre for the Classification of Health, Sydney University, Sydney, 2002.

[51] Australian Health & Welfare Chaplains Association, *AHWCA Health Care Chaplaincy Guidelines*, (Melbourne, 2004).

[52] Victoria Government Australia, "Services provided in a culturally sensitive way," Public Hospital Patient Charter, Victoria Government Department of Human Services, Melbourne, January 2008.

[53] N. Kirkwood, *Pastoral Care to Muslims: Building Bridges* (New York: Haworth Pastoral Press, 2002), p. 7.

[54] L.B. Carey, R. Aroni, and A. Edwards, "Health and Well Being: Hospital Chaplaincy," in H. Gardner, *Health Policy in Australia* (Melbourne: Oxford University Press, 1997), p. 190–210.

- If chaplains have provided pastoral care to people of non-Christian faiths, to which non-Christian faiths are chaplains ministering?

- If chaplains have provided pastoral care to people of non-Christian faiths, what approaches, strategies, and techniques have chaplains used to provide care?

- If chaplains are providing pastoral care to people of non-Christian faiths, have chaplains found their own knowledge about those faiths adequate?

- If chaplains have found themselves unable to provide adequate pastoral care to people of non-Christian faiths, how have they sought to help those people?

- Does Mol's "Sacralization of Identity" theory/paradigm have any pragmatic relevance to above issues and the field of multifaith pastoral care?

Interfaith pastoral care research

Davoren and Carey's research[55] sought to address such questions. However a lack of empirical material within the available literature (regarding interfaith ministry) prevented the researchers from using unobtrusive research techniques.[56] Thus a social scientific methodology using a two stage non-experimental cross sectional retrospective study collating descriptively both quantitative data (using a uniquely designed 'interfaith pastoral care survey')[57] and qualitative data (using the in-depth interview technique based on the survey)[58] were utilized in order to maximize their collection of material for analysis. Though time consuming, using two methods was deemed to be particularly advantageous, given that the exploratory study involved the activities of a specialist occupation. It has also become increasingly accepted among behavioral and public health analysts[59] that the combined use of quantitative and quali-

[55] R. Davoren and L.B. Carey, "Interfaith Pastoral Care and the Role of the Chaplain," *Scottish Journal of Health Care Chaplaincy*, 11:1 (2008): 21–32.

[56] A. Kellehear, *The Unobtrusive Researcher*, (Melbourne: Longmann, 1996), pp. 5–6.

[57] C. Peterson, "Quantitative Approaches to Evaluation in Health Care," in H. Gardner, *Health Policy in Australia* (Melbourne: Oxford University Press, 1997), pp. 98–115.

[58] V. Minichiello, R. Aroni, E. Timewell and L. Alexander, *In-Depth Interviewing: Researching People*, (Melbourne: Longman Cheshire, 1995).

[59] S. Thomas, I. Steven, C. Browning, E. Dickens, E. Eckermann and L.B. Carey, "Patient Knowledge, Opinions, Satisfaction and Choices in Primary Health Care Provision: A Progress Report" in D.P. Doessel, *The General Practice Evaluation Program: The 1992 Work-in-Progress Conference* (Canberra: Australian Government Publishing Service, 1993).

tative methodologies is considered the most effective in obtaining the best empirical results from descriptive studies.[60]

As noted by VandeCreek, et al[61] and Swinton and Mowat,[62] this social scientific dual approach has also been affirmed as being appropriate for assessing religious and pastoral care issues, and, indeed, has repeatedly been used successfully within Australia to study health care chaplaincy.[63] It is important to note at the outset, that the primary focus of Davoren's and Carey's research was upon the provision of interfaith traditional 'religious pastoral care,' which while inclusive of spiritual issues, did not seek to specifically measure chaplaincy involvement with nontraditional or contemporary spiritualities.

Research method

All accessible Christian health care chaplains who had provided interfaith pastoral care during a ten year period (1995–2005) within the culturally diverse North Western Health Care Network of Melbourne, Victoria, Australia (N=43) were issued an 'Interfaith Pastoral Care Survey' which explored their involvement, or lack of involvement (as the case may be), with people of non-Christian faiths within the clinical context. Of the forty-three chaplains receiving a survey, eight (n=8: 18.6%) did not respond and five did not wish to participate, arguing that their ministry to people of other faiths was negligible (n=5: 11.6%). A positive response was received from thirty chaplains (n=30: 69.76%) providing a favourable rate for basic descriptive statistical analysis (Figure 2).[64]

---

[60] S. Polgar and S. Thomas, *Research in the Health Sciences*, 3rd ed. (Melbourne: Churchill Livingston, 1995) pp. 116–117.

[61] L. VandeCreek, H. Bender and M.R. Jordon, "Research in Pastoral Care and Counseling: Quantitative and Qualitative Approaches," *Journal of Pastoral Care Publications* (New York, 1994).

[62] J. Swinton and H. Mowatt, *Practical Theology and Qualitative Research* (London: SCM Press, 2006).

[63] L.B. Carey, R. Aroni and A. Edwards, "Health and Well Being: Hospital Chaplaincy," in H. Gardner, *Health Policy in Australia* (Melbourne: Oxford University Press, 1997), p. 190–210 and L.B. Carey and C.J. Newell, *Chaplaincy in the Clinical Context* (Melbourne: AUSCUR Publications, 2004).

[64] S. Polgar, S. Thomas, *Research in the Health Sciences* (Melbourne: Churchill, Livingstone, 1995) p. 47.

Figure 2: Chaplaincy Survey Respondents and Interview Informants

	Chaplain Population	Negative Response	No Response	Total Positive Response
Survey 'Respondents'	43	5 (11.6%)	8 (20.9%)	30 (69.76%)
In-depth Interview 'Informants'	30	0 (0.0%)	0 (0.0%)	30 (100%)

NB: Chaplaincy respondents/informants had ministered at: The Royal Melbourne Hospital (n=13), The Royal Children's Hospital (n=4), The Royal Women's Hospital (n=4), The Mercy Hospital for Women (n=2), The Freemason's Hospital (n=2), North Western Rehabilitation Hospital (n=1), The Peter McCallum Hospital (n=1), The Western Private Hospital (n=1), the Western Hospital (n=1) and the Werribee-Mercy Hospital (n=1).

Basic demographic data is provided in Figure 3. In summary, of all the respondents who had ministered in the Western Health Care Network of Melbourne, the majority of respondents were female (76.6%), part time (n=18: 60%) and had served between 6–10 years as chaplains. There were near equal numbers of Protestant (n=16: 53.3%) and Catholic chaplains (n=14: 46.7%) and exactly equal numbers of ordained chaplains (including those of religious orders) (n=15: 50%) compared to lay chaplains (n=15: 50%). All survey respondents consented to being interviewed (n=30: 100%; Figure 2). The 'in-depth' model of interviewing[65] was used to gain greater explanation from respondents with regard to their survey responses.

While this research was reliant upon a chaplain's very subjective interpretation of their own experience and knowledge about another religious faith, nevertheless it was deemed that the obtained results would help to provide a gauge of a chaplain's level of self-confidence concerning the tenets of certain non-Christian beliefs and their perspective about their pastoral care provision to people of non-Christian faiths. Following the signing of consent forms chaplaincy informants were tape-recorded for up to 60 minutes. All interview data gathered was fully transcribed, thematically collated and analyzed using the 'Non-Numerical Unstructured Data Indexing, Searching and Theorizing' qualitative data computer program.[66] This ensured that all transcribed interviews were collated and processed systematically, enhancing accurate identification of thematic categories.

---

[65] V. Minichiello, R. Aroni, E. Timewell, and L. Alexander, *In-Depth Interviewing: Researching People* (Melbourne: Longman Cheshire, 1995).

[66] T. Richards and L. Richards, *Manual for Mainframe Non-Numerical Unstructured Data, Indexing, Searching and Theorizing* (Eltham, Victoria: Replee Pty Ltd, 1990).

Figure 3: Chaplaincy respondent and informant demographic data (n=30):

Gender	Female	23	(76.66%)	Male	7	(23.34%)
Denomination	Protestant *	16	(53.3%)	Catholic**	14	(46.7%)
Status	Ordained/Religious Order	15	(50.0%)	Lay	15	(50.0%)
Time	Part Time	18	(60.0%)	Full Time	14	(40.0%)

* Protestant: Anglican = 11, Uniting Church = 3, Lutheran = 1, Presbyterian = 1: Total = 16.
** Catholic = Roman Catholic: Total = 14.

Results

Overall, one of the key results from Davoren and Carey's research was that a substantial majority of chaplaincy respondents (93.3%) indicated that they had provided pastoral care to people from non-Christian religions. One chaplain was 'unsure' (3.3%) and another chaplain replied in the negative (3.3%). Of those respondents who had engaged people of non-Christian beliefs, the majority indicated that they had provided pastoral care to people from the Jewish faith (76.66%) and the Buddhist tradition (76.66%). The next largest religious category identified by respondents was the provision of pastoral care to people of Islamic belief (70.0%), followed by that of 'others' (53.33%), comprising Aboriginal, Maori,[67] Shinto, Baha'i, Sai Bala, Jehovah Witnesses, Mormon, and Confucianism. Finally, there were those of the Hindu faith (50.0%) and the Sikh faith (10.0%) (Figure 4).

Figure 4: Percentage of chaplaincy respondents (n=30) providing Pastoral Care to people of non-Christian faiths.

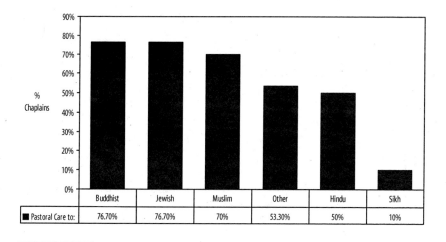

	Buddhist	Jewish	Muslim	Other	Hindu	Sikh
■ Pastoral Care to:	76.70%	76.70%	70%	53.30%	50%	10%

---

[67] Maori: New Zealand has two unique faiths, namely the "Ringatu" and "Ratana" churches.

As the survey required categorical responses from chaplains regarding gender, denomination, status, and time fraction (Figure 3), chi square tests were subsequently undertaken to compare (*vs*) chaplaincy sub-populations (i.e., male *vs* female chaplains; part time *vs* full time chaplains; ordained *vs* lay chaplains; Catholic *vs* Protestants) with regard to their pastoral care to people of non-Christian faiths. Only the results that were found to be statistically significant are presented here. As might be expected, a chi square test revealed that the degree of association between the employment status of chaplains (i.e., 'full time' *vs* 'part time') and the provision of pastoral care was statistically significant indicating that full time chaplains (100%) had significantly more involvement than part time chaplains (50%) in providing pastoral care to people of non-Christian faiths, but particularly with those of Islamic faith (p=0.0034). A chi square analysis also revealed that the degree of association between the denominational affiliation of chaplains (i.e., Catholic/Protestant) and their involvement with people of the Hindu faith was statistically significant (p=0.0281) indicating that Catholic chaplains (71.4%) were significantly more involved with people of Hindu faith than the surveyed Protestant chaplains (31.2%). There was, however, no statistically significant difference between Catholics and Protestants in their perceived knowledge about the Hindu faith (p=0.0921).

Interfaith knowledge

As illustrated in Figure 5, in overall terms the majority of chaplaincy respondents believed they had an 'average' knowledge of most non-Christian faiths (e.g. Islamic: 63.33%; Buddhist: 60%; Jewish: 56.6%; Hindu 53.3%)—except concerning Sikhism about which the majority indicated their knowledge regarding this particular belief system was 'poor' or 'nil' (63.3%). The only non-Christian faith, however, that the majority of chaplains believed they had a 'very good' or 'good' knowledge about, was that of Judaism (56.67%). 'Other' religious faiths received only a minority of chaplains indicating their knowledge level was 'very good' or 'good' (10%) or 'average' (23.33%). It is important to note however that 53.3% of chaplains did not indicate involvement with people from any 'other' religious faiths and thus could not provide a response about their knowledge level of such faiths. Of those who did indicate involvement with people of 'other' faiths however, only 13.3% indicated that their knowledge was 'poor' or 'nil' (Figure 5).

Figure 5: Percentage of chaplaincy respondents (n=30) indicating their level of knowledge about the fundamental truths of Non-Christian faiths.

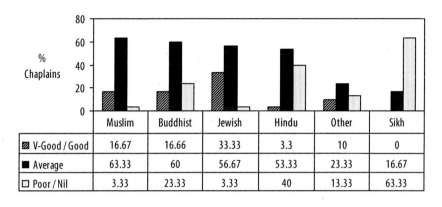

	Muslim	Buddhist	Jewish	Hindu	Other	Sikh
▨ V-Good / Good	16.67	16.66	33.33	3.3	10	0
■ Average	63.33	60	56.67	53.33	23.33	16.67
☐ Poor / Nil	3.33	23.33	3.33	40	13.33	63.33

NB: 'Other' = Aboriginal, Maori, Shinto, Baha'i, Sai Bala, Jehovah Witnesses, Mormon, and Confucianism

Statistical analyses were undertaken comparing chaplaincy sub-populations with their perceived knowledge of non-Christian faiths. Chi square tests revealed that the degree of association between the denominational affiliation of chaplains (i.e. Catholic/Protestant) and their perceived knowledge of the Buddhist faith was statistically significant (p=0.0122), indicating that Protestant chaplains having a 'good' (31.25%) or 'average' level of knowledge (68.7%) were more confident about Buddhism than Catholic chaplains ('good' 0%; 'average' 50%), a considerable percentage of whom acknowledged a 'poor' level of knowledge about Buddhism (42.8%).

Interfaith care

Figure 6 indicates what action chaplains pursued when they were unable to provide pastoral care of people from 'other' faiths. The majority of chaplains (60%) referred to their own pastoral care department for advice. Other chaplains (56.7%) simply referred people to their own particular religious leader. Approximately 46.7% of chaplains however made the effort to gain advice directly from the patient's/family's non-Christian religious leader. Forty percent (40%) of chaplains undertook 'other' means of ensuring some form of pastoral care. Ten percent (10%) of chaplains referred patients to another pastoral care department outside of their hospital. Approximately 6% of chaplains made no provision to minister to people from 'other faiths.'

Figure 6: Percentage of chaplaincy respondents (n=30) indicating their strategies for assisting people of non-Christian faiths.

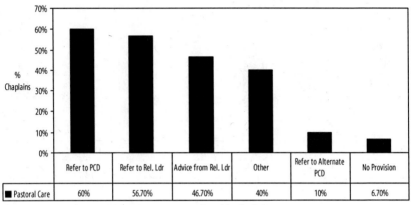

	Refer to PCD	Refer to Rel. Ldr	Advice from Rel. Ldr	Other	Refer to Alternate PCD	No Provision
■ Pastoral Care	60%	56.70%	46.70%	40%	10%	6.70%

Pastoral Care Provided

NB 1: Refer to PCD = Referred to/sought advice from other chaplains within their own Pastoral Care Department (PCD).
NB 2: Refer to Rel. Ldr. = Referred patients/family to a religious leader of the patient's/family's own religious faith.
NB 3: Advice from Rel. = Sought advice/made contact directly with the patient's/family's religious leader.
NB 4: 'Other' = Variety of strategies used (e.g., consulted clinical staff; used interpreter, used religious literature).
NB 5: Refer to alternate = Alternate PCD (at another hospital) for advice about a patient's/family's religious issues.

Statistical analyses were also undertaken comparing chaplaincy sub-populations with the strategies used to assist people of non-Christian faiths. Chi square tests revealed that the degree of association between the religious status of chaplaincy personnel (i.e. ordained/lay) and their contact with non-Christian religious advisors was statistically significant (p=0.0281) indicating that ordained chaplains (66.6%) tended to be more involved in contacting non-Christian leaders to help people of non-Christian faiths than lay chaplains (26.6%). Further, chi square tests investigating the degree of association between the religious affiliation of chaplains (i.e., Protestant/Catholic) and whether they referred issues of pastoral care to religious leaders of non-Christian faiths was found to be statistically significant (p=0.0303), indicating that Catholic chaplains (66.6%) were significantly more involved than Protestant chaplains (26.6%) in providing contact details to patients and their families about religious leaders of other faiths whereas a greater percentage of Protestant chaplains (56.2%) tended to take the initiative and contact non-Christian religious leaders directly to help ensure the continuity of pastoral care.

Interfaith skills, techniques and functions

The qualitative data gathered from the in-depth interviews revealed that chaplains had a variety of ways of assisting people of non-Christian faiths. Given the volume of material gathered from the in-depth interviews, a summary table of the qualitative data is presented at Figure 7. The qualitative data was thematically coded into three main categories: (i) Pastoral 'religious functions' were noted, such as the reading or provision of 'religious literature' (e.g., Qu'ran), discussions about the patient's beliefs or 'theology' (particularly effecting bioethical decision-making), the conduct of, or assistance with appropriate rituals, and ultimately, the reinforcing of the patient's religious identity and commitment to their faith. These specific religious functions were found to be easily sub-coded using Mol's "sacralization of identity" mechanisms; (ii) General pastoral skills which included 'being there' with patients and their families experiencing crises, 'listening' or 'hearing their story,' 'developing rapport' and 'providing reassurance' that their religious beliefs would be respected; (iii) The application of 'pastoral approaches, strategies, and techniques' were also identified, such as chaplains giving an appropriate introduction, the provision of religious resources, appropriate physical comfort, exploration of any relevant personal religious experience and the provision of referral information about available religious leaders of the patient's faith (Figure 7).

Interfaith challenge

Given the involvement of the majority of Christian chaplains in assisting people of non-Christian faiths, it would not be surprising that chaplains may have found their own faith challenged by regularly ministering to people of different philosophies and beliefs. Indeed, sixty percent of chaplains indicated that their faith had been challenged by learning about 'different ways to God;' whereas, 6.67% were not sure, while 33.3% stated that their faith had not been challenged—some refusing to be 'syncretistic' in their thinking. Several reasons were given by those who felt that their faith had been challenged, namely: (i) they developed an understanding about, and thus tolerance to, other faiths, (ii) they acknowledged, given other people's unique religious journeys and experiences, that there were 'matters beyond our comprehension,' and (iii) that there were 'areas of common ground' such as: (a) the existence of sacred texts and/or teachings, (b) the common practice of the ritual or act of prayer, (c) the common practice of reverence or respect towards a superior being/spirit, transcendental order or sacred objects, and (d) the practice of a 'commitment according to their beliefs,' symbolized and expressed in a

Figure 7: Summary table of qualitative data derived from in-depth interviews listing chaplaincy pastoral religious functions, general pastoral skills plus specific approaches, techniques and strategies provided to people of non-Christian religions.

I Pastoral religious functions	(Utilizing Mol's "sacralization of identity" mechanisms)
Objectification/Transcendental Ordering/Theology	Expression/sharing of specific faith, knowledge, theology, philosophies, beliefs, structure, values and ethics particular to non-Christian faiths.
Myths/Sacred Literature	Reading of sacred texts (e.g., Qu'ran; Psalms) and recounting of non-Christian significant religious stories, legends and religious/spiritual leaders.
Ritual	Provision, organization and/or assistance with non-Christian religious blessings, prayers, worship services, funerals and other rituals.
Commitment	Through the use of non-Christian sacred literature, expression of faith specific theology, support from other relevant religious leaders and the enactment of rituals, the patient's faith commitment is encouraged, maintained and developed during times of crises.

II General pastoral skills	
Being There/Presence	Through physical presence, chaplains encountered patient feelings of aloneness or alienation in a 'foreign context,' provided advocacy, support and comfort.
Listening/Hearing	Time was spent with patients listening to their life story/religious perspective and discerning/assessing their deep feelings and concerns.
Developing Rapport/ Relationship Building	Rapport and chaplain-patient relationship developed through the acknowledgement and respect for patient's life and religious experiences; Emotional and practical support provided to assist with addressing issues.
Providing Reassurance	Chaplains reinforced principles of unconditional love, affirmation and encouragement of religiously sensitive/culturally respectful practice that helped to enhance patient well-being.

III Pastoral approaches, techniques and strategies	
Pastoral Introduction	Sensitive self introductions and offers of support: clear identity badge, wearing of Christian cross/badge on lapel, wearing of colorful clothes, flowers for women, toys for children.
Physical Resources	Provision of Sacred texts (e.g., Qu'ran, Torah); faith specific pamphlets; faith specific pictures and icons; pastoral care manual/reference.
Physical Expression	Appropriate physical touch (e.g., holding hand), gesturing or physical posing of respect (e.g., Buddhist greeting).
Personal Experience	Exploration of a patient's personal experience or background to explore faith connection/development and any religious issues/concerns.
Professional Referral	Use of non-Christian religious leaders; social workers; interpreters; genetic counselors; bereavement support, etc.

variety of ways. Interestingly, each of the 'areas of common ground' identified by interview informants paralleled that of Mol's "sacralization of identity" mechanisms.

Conclusions

A common general theory of religious/spiritual belief is desirable to serve as a tool or frame of reference that will encourage a greater understanding of the common processes of different religious/spiritual faiths. Further, any such paradigm could also assist in terms of how religion/spirituality (of whatever construction) intersects with health and well-being. It is one argument of this paper that Mol's "Sacralization of Identity" paradigm serves as a convincing general theory canvassing the common mechanisms across all religious/spiritual beliefs.

An overview of Mol's paradigm has been provided in this paper with specific reference to the intersections of religion, health, and the role of the hospital chaplain in providing pastoral care within a multifaith context. Given the specialist nature of some dimensions of chaplaincy (particularly in relation to sensitive bio-ethical issues alluded to earlier), there can be no question that further research and examination of Mol's paradigm would be required to explore its ongoing utility. Nevertheless, the relevance of the "sacralization of identity" theory, while seemingly quite amendable for a general scientific theory of religion, was found to be relevant and very useful for chaplaincy in terms of it being a systematic, theoretical, educational, and methodological frame of reference for interfaith ministry within a multifaith context (refer Figure 8).

Figure 8: A fivefold affirmation of the value of the paradigm proposed for the practice of interfaith spiritual caregiving. The paradigm provides:

- A general theory of religious/spiritual belief highlighting common dynamics of different beliefs.
- A common 'frame of reference' to assist chaplains/pastoral care workers in the systematic provision of religious/spiritual ministry to people of 'other faiths.'
- A common 'frame of reference' to enhance interfaith dialogue/pastoral care language between religious/spiritual practitioners.
- An educational framework for the systematic training of chaplains and other pastoral care workers in interfaith situations and multi-faith ministry settings.
- Common methodological categories for empirical research and quality assurance into interfaith ministry.

In overall terms Davoren and Carey's research indicated that the majority of Christian chaplains had provided pastoral care to people of non-Christian faiths, particularly those of the Buddhist, Jewish, and Islamic traditions, and that chaplains believed they had an average knowledge of these traditions with the least knowledge about Hindu and the Sikh traditions. Chaplaincy informants indicated a variety of pastoral skills, methods, and specific religious functions that were undertaken to ensure the provision of pastoral care to people of non-Christian faiths. It was found that it was possible to thematically categorize all the various religious/spiritual functions undertaken by chaplains according to Mol's "sacralization of identity" mechanisms, irrespective of the particular religious faith of the individual.

When chaplains were unable to provide pastoral care to those of non-Christian faiths, the majority contacted their own pastoral care department for advice and/or referred the patient and their families to their respective religious leaders residing within the local community. Other chaplains, rather than simply referring or directing patients to where they could find help for themselves, went the 'extra mile' and contacted non-Christian religious leaders directly so as to personally ensure the provision and continuity of adequate pastoral care for those of non-Christian faiths.

Interfaith chaplaincy pastoral care: positive and negative

While it can be argued from Davoren and Carey's research that the amount of interaction between chaplains and people of other faiths simply reflects the particular religious adherence of inpatients and outpatients attending their respective hospitals; nevertheless, the results provide evidence that even though the chaplains surveyed were of the Christian religion, the majority were non-discriminatory in applying their pastoral care ministry. A minority of chaplains however seemed some-what indifferent (adopting a 'sink or swim' attitude) or deliberately avoided people of non-Christian faiths and thus their ministry beyond their 'own' was negligible. While it can be argued that some chaplains do not minister to people of other faiths simply due to a lack of opportunity, the research results of Davoren and Carey's study suggest that the non-compliance of some chaplains to care for people of non-Christian faiths was more than likely due to a lack of knowledge and interfaith training and thus, motivated more by the 'unknown' and possibly fear, rather than understanding, consequently failed to provide for those people of non-Christian faiths.

Indeed, from a critical perspective it could be summarized from the results that chaplaincy respondents were only 'average' in their knowledge concerning non-Christian religions, but particularly poor with regard to the Hindu and Sikh faiths; that some chaplaincy respondents did not refer people to religious leaders of non-Christian faiths, particularly lay chaplains; that while Catholic chaplains were more involved in helping people of the Hindu faith, Protestant chaplains tended to be more proactive (even more helpful) in terms of making direct professional contact with non-Christian religious leaders, irrespective of their faith; further, despite the research being conducted within a high density multifaith region, approximately 16% of the total chaplaincy population (n=7/43: 16.2%) were either 'not sure' or had not provided pastoral care to adherents of non-Christian religions or were fully aware that their ministry to people of other faiths was negligible. This then begs another question. How effective are some chaplains in multicultural/ multifaith contexts if their ministry to non-Christians is negligible?

Chaplain effectiveness

For chaplains to be more effective at interfaith pastoral care it can be argued that continuing education needs to be provided for all chaplains (irrespective of gender, denominationalism or employment status) concerning the fundamental tenets of non-Christian faiths (but particularly with regard to the Sikh, Hindu, and Buddhist beliefs). Such training will help to ensure that chaplains will be able to communicate more effectively and thus demonstrate a *'language care'* ensuring that care-receivers *"… feel heard, understood, and encouraged …"*[68] For chaplains and other pastoral care workers to achieve such improvements, comparative religious studies could be encouraged and resourced at theological colleges and within secular universities (by federal and state governments in conjunction with religious institutions). Chaplains will thus be assisted with the care of non-Christian patients plus their families, and thus also encourage the development of a health-promoting policy supporting multifaith care and social inclusion within the community.

Further, given that the majority of chaplains (93.3%) in a high multifaith area such as the Western Health Care Network of Melbourne had, at some point, provided pastoral care to people from other faiths, it seems obvious that these chaplains may require additional support to assist them in their ministry. Additional support could be given particularly with regard to those from Jewish, Buddhist, and Islamic faiths, simply because of the substantial and increasing number of these people

---

[68] L.D. Bueckert and D. Schipani, "Interfaith Spiritual Caregiving: The Case for Language Care" in L.D. Bueckert and D. Schipani, eds., *Spiritual Caregiving in the Hospital: Windows to Chaplaincy Ministry* (Kitchener, Ont.: Pandora Press, 2006), p. 246.

seeking support, and thus, the increasing likelihood of chaplains engaging with people of other non-Christian faiths. Additional support could be provided, for example, by the various government health services in conjunction with established chaplaincy associations by conducting special in-service training of Christian chaplains, aimed to meet increasing interfaith needs. In addition, the appointment of non-Christian chaplains to health care facilities could also be supported by government, Christian, and non-Christian communities alike. There could also be a role, in highly populated multifaith cities, for a 'Multifaith Community Chaplain' to be appointed by governments as a coordinator and liaison for multifaith activities and support—which would be particularly valuable during times of community crises.

Finally, assistance could be provided to chaplains with regard to physical resources such as improved multifaith chapels for patients and their families plus multifaith information kits to assist clinical staff. As noted (Figure 7: III 'Physical Resources'), the production of an interfaith pastoral care manual for the support and help of chaplains and clinical staff has commenced within some pastoral care departments. This resource concept could be expanded for the benefit of those working in welfare, defense, mental health, aged care, and correctional institutions. It is important to acknowledge, however, that there is a need to extend beyond an exploratory study of chaplaincy to include a larger sample of chaplains engaged in interfaith ministry. Quality assurance research could also be undertaken surveying/interviewing those of non-Christian faiths who have received support from Christian chaplains. Such additional studies would more than likely produce other informative strategies and techniques to aid interfaith ministry.

<u>Figure 9</u>: Summary of strategies for improving chaplaincy effectiveness in developing multi-faith ministry.

- Continuing education programs for current chaplains, supported by health care institutions and religious/spiritual organizations, about the fundamental tenets of other religious/spiritual beliefs.

- Comparative religious/spiritual studies to be implemented and resourced within secular and theological colleges by governments and religious/spiritual organisations as part of a health-promoting policy supporting multifaith care and social inclusion.

- Additional resources and materials provided by health care institutions, governments and religious institutions to facilitate multifaith ministry.

- Appointment of a 'Multifaith Community Chaplain Coordinator' to facilitate multifaith ministry on behalf of religious organizations, local communities and governments.

- Appointment of non-Christian chaplains within health care and other institutions/ organizations.
- Additional research and quality assurance to assess and aid interfaith ministry.

Sacralization education

Following Mol's "sacralization of identity" mechanisms, and the paralleling 'pastoral religious functions' identified by chaplains, it would seem that Christian and non-Christian religious/spiritual beliefs may have more in common than what first seems apparent. Using Mol's "sacralization of identity" mechanisms not only provides a general theory of religious/ spiritual beliefs, but, more pragmatically, will assist in a more systematic method of chaplaincy education about various religious/spiritual practices that in turn (through chaplains using the "sacralization of identity" paradigm) will advance pastoral care for the benefit of all. Certainly any argument questioning whether Christian chaplains can provide pastoral support to people of non-Christian faiths is addressed by Davoren and Carey's research. The answer is 'Yes!' Chaplains can and have done so, through the use of specific pastoral religious functions that encourage the "sacralization of identity" process (via objectification, ritual, myth, and commitment). Using such mechanisms ultimately seeks to aid the spiritual care of people (irrespective of their religious or spiritual adherence) and, in turn, their sense of health and well-being. Given the rapid growth of non-Christian faiths within traditionally Christian regions, it can be argued that there is an immediate need for an improvement in training and resourcing of current Christian chaplains so as to enable pastoral care ministry to progress with the increasing interfaith and spiritual demand that will most certainly continue throughout the 21st century.

How is it that you, a Jew, ask a drink of me ...?

A study of interfaith care in a Norwegian context

Iselin Jørgensen

But he had to go through Samaria ... and Jesus, tired out by his journey, was sitting by the well. It was about noon. A Samaritan woman came to draw water, and Jesus said to her, "Give me a drink."... The Samaritan woman said to him, "How is it that you, a Jew, ask a drink of me, a woman from Samaria?[1]

Jesus and the Samaritan woman encounter each other by the well. She prays to her god at "this mountain," he goes to the temple in Jerusalem. In the end, she serves him water. They talk about intimate topics, life. This story about meeting the other has particular relevance in Norwegian society today as the population becomes ever more ethnically diverse.

Pastoral care with Muslims was the focus of my thesis for my theology degree. For the last thirty years Norway has experienced a growing number of Muslim migrants to the country. As a result, many pastors have expressed that they often have Muslims knocking at their door seeking care and counseling. In 2007 I conducted a research project involving pastors[2] in the Lutheran Church of Norway[3] who experience this situation. I visited six pastors in the region of Oslo, and became acquainted

---

Iselin Jørgensen, Cand. Theol., is Project Coordinator for Integration and Migration Issues in the Christian Council of Norway, based in Oslo.

[1] John 4: 6–9a.

[2] "Pastors" is the word used throughout this chapter as the umbrella term that refers to all theologically trained spiritual caregivers, including those who work as chaplains.

[3] Norway still has a state church. This is the majority church to which more than 80 percent of the population belongs.

with their experiences. There were three women and three men, all with at least two years of experience, ranging in age from 35 to 60. I interviewed one student chaplain, one hospital chaplain, two prison chaplains, one pastor in a diaconal organization and another pastor in a regular congregation. It was a qualitative research project with in-depth interviews lasting about two hours each. Simply put, this is the hypothesis I wanted to test out: *pastors have a role to play in Norwegian society as spiritual caregivers and they can become good conversation partners with Muslims.* I assumed that, learning from the story of the Samaritan woman, it is in the sacred space of truly meeting the other that a more peaceful and humane society can be created.

In this article I would like to share from my findings. I begin by highlighting key insights from intercultural pastoral care. A brief outline follows of some of the assumptions and attitudes with which the pastors regard pastoral care and counseling. The experiences of Muslim care seekers, as relayed by the pastors, is discussed next, including biographical and geographical insights and reflections on the content and context of the spiritual caregiving situations. Switching focus from the care seekers in the encounter to the caregivers, the pastors' own views about their role with Muslims are then explored, with attention to the ways in which they handle similarities and differences. Finally, several conclusions are drawn that respond to the hypotheses that I wished to test.

Insights from intercultural pastoral care and counseling

Some of the theory I considered in my research is found in the published work of Emmanuel Y. Lartey.[4] He is a pastoral theologian who reflects systematically on his own significant practical experience. In a few words, Emmanuel Lartey, like Howard Clinebell before him, sees the functions of spiritual care as including the dimensions of *healing, sustaining, guiding, reconciling,* and *nurturing.* He adds *liberating* and *empowering.*[5] To realize the goals pertaining to each dimension, the caregiver must be aware of how people interact, how words communicate and how symbols shape and explain peoples' lives. Spiritual caregivers have to be aware of their own distinct positions and points of view. In this way one is able to take people seriously as being both similar to and different from oneself. Lartey is experienced as an *intercultural caregiver and counselor*[6] and proposes

---

[4] Lartey, Emmanuel Y., *In Living Color: An Intercultural Approach to Pastoral Care and Counseling,* 2nd ed. (London: Jessica Kingsley Publishers, 2003) and *Pastoral Theology in an Intercultural World* (Peterborough: Epworth, 2006).

[5] Lartey, *In Living Color,* pp. 67–68.

[6] Ibid., pp. 171–177.

and intercultural approach to the practice of pastoral care. He asserts that all people must be viewed in terms of universal, cultural, and individual categories and that there are no complete answers regarding the role of spiritual caregivers. In other words, all human beings are like everybody else, like some others, and at the same time like nobody else.[7] This realization has to be taken into consideration in spiritual care situations.

Lartey guides the reader around the world to get a broader understanding of current challenges and approaches to spiritual care.[8] He underscores that individualism is a very European and North American value, and suggests there is something to learn from the Asian, African, and Latin American collective way of thinking. According to traditional cultures in those regions, when people see others face to face, and affirm and respect each other, the whole society is improved and may become more peaceful. Lartey also points to Emmanuel Levinas' philosophy as illumining the dynamics of the encounter with another person.[9] According to Lartey, Levinas is a phenomenologist and follower of Husserl, but the two differ on one main issue. While Husserl emphasizes empathy and identification with the other person, Levinas, as a Jew who experienced World War II, does not believe this is really possible. It is more important to value *being otherwise*. God's creation is so rich and complex that we have to discover new elements of God by discovering new elements in creation like our fellow human beings. An encounter with another face is an encounter with Mystery. *Otherness* is therefore an important resource in human encounters; one searches for this by being respectfully curious about the other person and asking pertinent questions. The pastors I interviewed reflected on their own understandings and convictions about good pastoral care.

Attitudes toward pastoral care and counseling

All of the pastors who participated in my project have a clear understanding of what it means to be a counselor and pastoral caregiver. Even though they do not explicitly identify with a certain theoretical tradition, it is clear that these caregivers work with what might be called a "client-oriented" approach. They express an open attitude by listening

---

[7] Lartey, *Pastoral Theology in an Intercultural World*, p. 132. Lartey has drawn from the contribution of David W. Augsburger in *Pastoral Counseling Across Cultures* (Philadelphia: Westminster Press, 1986). Augsburger's theology of culture includes the categories of "universal," "cultural," and "unique" (pp. 48–78).

[8] Lartey, *In Living Color*, pp. 50–70.

[9] Lartey, *Pastoral Tehology in an Intercultural World*, pp. 132–135.

to the seeker's own experiences in an inductive way. All of them said that the focus of pastoral care should be based on the care seekers' wishes and felt needs. They also emphasized the importance of taking time and being accessible.

All of the pastors pointed out that respect for privacy and confidentiality is important. Empowerment and respect were words that were frequently used. They focus less on *kerygmatic* (viewed as "evangelistic") pastoral care,[10] in the sense that they don't want to impose Bible content or their own theology on the care seeker. At the same time, however, they do call themselves missionaries, as expressed by one of the pastors: *"being available to deal with hard topics, providing space and time. In this sense I think that I am evangelizing. Because this is how I want the church to be, as well as the faith."*

This ministry of presence and focus on the agenda of the care seeker guides the pastors in their conversations with Muslims, as with other Norwegians. All of the participants said that they are not concerned with categorizing their care seekers, hoping to offer care receivers the opportunity to define themselves. They all commented on the realization that a "Muslim" is one who calls him or herself a Muslim.

Biographical and geographical considerations

None of the pastors reported having had conversations with Muslims of ethnic[11] Norwegian origins. From the descriptions it is apparent that Muslim care seekers come from all of the same countries that any Norwegian migrants come from. Regions mentioned often are Africa, the Middle East, and former Yugoslavia. Some also came to Norway as guest workers in the 70s, often from Pakistan or Turkey.

In my research I did not make a special effort to collect numbers. All of the participants had difficulties calculating concrete numbers concerning their ministry. The pastors also work in different fields with different conditions. Both the hospital chaplain and the prison chaplain expressed *"Oh, they are many!"* They claim that almost 50 percent of all care seekers are Muslims. The others say it might be between five and 30 percent. The prison chaplain thinks it is a mirror of the rest of society. Since people with the same cultural background often settle down in neighbourhoods close to each other, a pastor in a congregation often encounters people from a particular selection of cultures.

---

[10] Berit Okkenhaug, *Når jeg ser ditt ansik*, 2nd. Ed. (Otta: Verbum, 2006) p. 24.

[11] This is not a good term, but maybe the best to explain persons born in and brought up with Norwegian traditional culture, with Norwegian-born parents.

Almost all Muslim care seekers do not go to a pastor for the purpose of converting. When compared to other care seekers, the pastors see more of a tendency to protect traditional identity. In fact, according to one of the pastors, one migrant said in a so-called "faith group": *"I guess I am Muslim, but I did not know before the war started."* This is also the reason why many of the pastors I interviewed expressed problems with stereotyping. One's religion can sometimes be misconstrued by society. The prison chaplain points out that Muslims especially are very concerned about protecting their religious identity and that one can see this developing. From praying in the private room, they now want to be more visible in the common room by, for instance, holding special meals during Ramadan. One pastor commented: *"They find it important that their Muslim identity plays a natural role in today's society. Before, one accepted more that the country was Christian and one had to adjust oneself to the majority. Now it is much more a confrontation. Religion can be used for making alliances and identity-making."*

In one of my interviews the pastor got confused while referring to one care seeker and mixed him up with a Coptic Christian from Ethiopia. The person was mentioned thus because he was very much associated with the Ethiopian Muslims. Religion easily gets mixed with culture. Yet Muslim care seekers all carry different life stories. They come from different cultures, where religion is practiced in different ways. For the pastors there can often be many similarities between talking to a Muslim Somali and a Christian from the same area. And talking to a Bosnian Muslim can also be very different from talking to a Pakistani Muslim. This may show that significant differences can be found within religions. My group of pastors emphasized that all individuals are different. As a prison chaplain says: *"my experience is that people are differently independent, no matter where they come from. At the same time one can see some cultural commonalities. For instance, some prisoners from Africa feel close to others from the same place. They have different religious traditions but much in common in terms of culture. But, you know, they are also unique individuals."*

It does not look like there is a pattern relating to whether Muslim care seekers turn up once or come steadily. They have personal stories like all other care seekers. What often differentiates the migrants from other Norwegians is the reasons for immigrating. In many ways the Muslims in Norway are unique because almost all of them arrived as refugees or economic immigrants. This means that a great number of them have experienced suffering and crises. In my chosen hospital, in both the prisons and in the environment of the pastor who serves in an organization, there are many Muslims who are traumatized and struggle with mental illness.

The pastors were asked if there are certain kinds of Muslims who seek them. I wanted to find out whether or not the care seekers were unsure about their religious identity and wanted a "taste" of Christianity, as it were. This does not seem to be a pattern. The hospital chaplain answered that Muslim care seekers can be just as confused as any others, but it is very rare that they want to change their point of view. One prison chaplain laughed and said that talking about "wandering" and "faith shopping" is maybe mostly "*Christian and Western*." *Muslims are in a different way connected ethnically to their religion and it is not something you easily step out of.*" The other prison chaplain continued: "*They are not necessarily concerned about being Muslims while talking to me, but they just need to talk to someone when they suffer. They do not have to express for me that they are Muslims.*" At the same time, as mentioned, Muslims are more often aware of their religious identity than others are. One pastor says that Muslims often show more piety than many Christians do.

Why the Muslims seek pastors the participants do not know for certain. The hospital chaplain says that many people go where they feel safe. Even though they are very religious and aware of their own identity, some of them seem to feel safer in a church than a mosque. Whether or not this is linked to relational issues and not wanting to meet certain people is unclear. The hospital chaplain also spoke about some special occasions when the care seekers asked for baptism. He thinks that "*some people believe that baptism means becoming Norwegian, rich, valued, and accepted in society,*" and therefore finds it problematic to respond to such a request. At the same time, he says that there is a discussion among chaplains about what to do in this situation.

One of the pastors believes that Muslims come "*first of all because they do not have many others to talk to.*" This pastor works at a place where people in general are facing difficult life situations, are often vulnerable, and therefore frequently want to talk about existential and religious topics. This pastor supports the hospital chaplain in underlining the need to feel safe, saying: "*Many people are not able to get to the mosque for several reasons.*" Many Muslims explain that they feel marginalized in the mosque because of moral conflicts over issues such as drug use. Some feel marginalized because they live with a mental illness. Muslim women seek women pastors because of gender issues. Two pastors underscored that they are one of the few who are present for these types of conversations, especially because they know Norwegian society and understand the context more than imams from foreign countries do. The process of attaining independence, the student pastor mentions, may be about standing on one's own feet in relation to family and the mosque. The last point to be mentioned here about the pastors' role is the significance of being different than a doctor wanting to find a diagnosis or having the functions of an imam. This is also the case in the hospital where the chaplain is a unique part of the interdisciplinary care team.

Content of the spiritual care encounters

All the pastors reported that the care seekers want to talk about a variety of things. Many migrants have family and friends still in war and crisis situations. Common topics are what it means to be a woman in Norwegian Muslim society and what it means to live in an institution; also illness, crime, dreams, and hope. The line between talking about practical issues in life and more religious ones is often blurred.

One of the prison chaplains does not want to define what is most important in the care seeker's life. It must always be on the care seeker's terms. *"It is fine if we talk about God. But it is also fine when it is about problems in marriage. I think that my job is to talk about the topics the care seekers want to talk about. That is my job. Full stop."* This chaplain does not have time for long theological discussions. *"There are so many personal crises here that need to have first priority,"* the chaplain asserted. The other five pastors, on the contrary, reported that they often do have theological conversations and that is important for them. The hospital chaplain is one of these and says that theological issues are often raised. Grief over being seriously ill is very common. The thought of being punished by God for not being faithful enough is often repeated. The fact that many have psychological struggles also means that the pastor has a role in helping to find clarity in the midst of chaos.

The student chaplain experienced that existential issues are important for those who seek pastoral care. Moral issues put into the Norwegian context are often discussed. The topics are often connected to family and religion. These are often hard for a young person to carry alone. One of the participants said: *"Many are concerned about finding out what is religion and what is just tradition."* Practicing Ramadan, contraception, and circumcision might be examples. The pastor with the organization also identified moral issues as very common and often connected to faith. Topics such as "shame" and "guilt" are raised by many of the participants as being important, not only in the prison context, but everywhere. Many religious care seekers have a need for confessing their guilt. Since many of the Muslim care seekers are religious, this topic is often raised. One prison chaplain commented: *"They feel like getting further in relation to*

God.... *They often hold a strong sense of punishment, these Muslim care seekers. They often think that everything happening is God's will and there is nothing more or less one can do to change that. At the same time they feel they did something wrong and have to make up for it."*

In this sense most of the participants experienced being sought out as counselors regarding religious and spiritual issues. Some care seekers ask if they can pray together. The hospital chaplain found it very touching that especially one patient wanted to continue visits. They would always end by praying for each other. It is important for the patient to give something back to the pastor, and prayer is the best gift. *"The patient wishes me the best, and I wish him the best,"* this pastor remarked.

Context of the encounters

The pastors expressed that there are always special opportunities but also limitations, according to where they work. It is also clear that the care seekers are influenced by their surroundings. Certainly more people seek the pastors in institutions than those in "freer" contexts. In institutions everyone knows about the chaplain, and they are much more part of the whole team. In this sense it is easier for these pastors to think about the "whole" person, together with other colleagues and therapists. It is also often easier to follow up with each care receiver, as long as it is not a short term stay.

Care seekers in institutions are in a different life situation than the rest of the population. They are separated, and some even isolated, from the rest of society, which means that: *"this situation [incarceration] does something to all human beings that is quite universal, no matter what background you have,"* one of the prison chaplains commented. The hospital chaplain expressed the same sentiment.

Most of the participants were asked whether the geographical background of the care seekers influenced their search for spiritual care. It does not sound like any of them have thought about that. Two say they see a big difference between the European and non–European Muslims. This may have to do with their life stories, but also different ways of thinking. All the pastors have many individual conversations with people from all over the world. At the same time, some of them said that there are many Muslims who need rituals and they often go to the services that pastors lead.

Pastors reflect about themselves as caregivers to Muslims

All the chaplains in institutions felt a bit uncertain in the beginning on how to respond to the Muslim care seekers' needs. They searched for knowledge and contacts that could help them support care seekers in a more informed way, both religiously and culturally. In other words, they did not see themselves as ideal and competent enough to be caregivers to all people. To a certain extent this is still the case for most of them. They all wish that there were more opportunities for people to choose someone who more readily understands their way of thinking. They wish, for instance, that cooperation with the mosques was better.

All of the pastors have the impression that the role of imams is different in their community than the role of Christian pastors in Norway. One of the prison chaplains said that they have been trying for many years to give prisoners the opportunity for Friday prayer and conversations with the imam. Some of the Muslims go to prayer, but just a few seek imams as spiritual care givers. The impression is that the imam is respected as a wise person who knows the scriptures and organizes the rituals. He is a counselor on ethical issues and operates as a teacher. According to the hospital chaplain: "*Having an imam on a visit is very much a big family thing. In the hospital the family can come together with an imam. If it were a Norwegian, the family would usually leave the room when the pastor arrives, because it is an individual and intimate thing for them.*"

The hospital chaplain also expressed that there is a difference between general and psychiatric clinics. In a psychiatric hospital, there is much more loneliness because imams and family very seldom go for a visit. "*That there are many taboos about mental illness is not only something that I discovered, but something that you can find well-documented research on,*" the hospital chaplain underlined.

Pastors do find themselves in a position to care also for Muslim care seekers. As they become more knowledgeable and experienced, they feel more confident in their role. The pastor in the congregation puts it this way: "*We always have to search for the best ways to be present. But we are valued and trusted. We can show ways to the sacred. And then others can do it in their own way.*"

This is similar to what the student chaplain explains: "*In the beginning I tried to refuse. But that was mainly because of my own fear. I thought it was too scary. I was too afraid to step across their borders. I thought that this is not something I can do. In a way I do not know how to do it. But where should I tell them to go then? They had already decided that I was the right one to talk to. Then I could not be the one not accepting their choice. They just knew so very well what they did by knocking on my door. Much more than what the ethnic Norwegian students do, when they are just dropping in, not really thinking about it. When it is such a big choice for them, it would be too bad to send them away, at least with religious arguments.*"

When the pastors were asked the question whether or not they fulfill the care seekers' expectations, they all said they never ask about this. At the same time they believe that they do, because the same Muslim care seekers come back, often again and again.

When asking about the importance of professionalism, experience, and theological education, all the participants replied by saying that these are indeed essential. The congregational pastor says it is *"important to be visible and well known."* One prison chaplain said: *"The pastor having experience can make it safer for them to think that the person is good to talk to."* The hospital chaplain believes that it is important that there is a person with whom it is easier to talk to about spirituality. The other prison chaplain expressed something similar, believing that the pastor has a special authority.*"They respect me. I am a leader of spiritual services and have authority to do this. I believe that is important."* Another mentioned that some Muslims put the pastors into a role that the pastors themselves do not often recognize. *"Muslims may ask for a religious leader who is more authoritarian, in front of all these confused Norwegians."* Privacy is something all the pastors emphasized as very important. One of them also wondered if there are different traditions for this in different cultures. This pastor had heard care seekers' disappointment about trusted people in the mosque.

The general attitude toward pastoral care does not seem to change in encounters with Muslims. All of the participants said that they can never be something other than what they are. They are committed to letting care seekers define their own agenda. Time, availability, and respect are terms repeated as very important. They also all emphasize that their Christian faith and belief in loving our neighbour is what encourages their work. Some of them expressed that *"liberating from different kinds of oppression"* is an aim for their conversations. On the one hand, one of the pastors said, *"I have to be careful that I do not let out all my own thoughts about God."* This makes it sound hard sometimes to keep the care seeker in focus. On the other hand all, except one, confessed that they sometimes use their own ideas to challenge the care seeker when they find it helpful for giving care. If they see that the care seeker has very destructive and unhealthy images of God, several pastors say they would try to strengthen and empower them by helping care receivers to reflect on new possible ways to imagine God. At the same time the pastors are afraid of putting their own faith in focus, and want to let the care seeker find their own answers to live with. The hospital chaplain expresses it this way: *"This is about complex empathy. The patient has to experience a pastor who is credible when saying that he or she wants to listen.... I have to make sure that I am a living person, not a machine in order to show that I am listening to you and I am with you in what you are saying. But you should not have to hear my own story and carry me."*

Responding to differences and similarities

The pastors' experiences vary somewhat regarding the similarities and differences that become clear in encounters with Muslim care seekers. Whatever their experience, it certainly alters what they think. None of the pastors have experienced many spiritual care encounters with Muslims of a gender other than their own. If they have, it is because practical, not personal issues, are concerns they wish to address.

There is a difference in how the male and female pastors experience the encounter with Muslim care seekers. The women pastors underline that they themselves have a very different life situation than their care seekers. One of them puts it this way: *"I sometimes feel that I am talking to my great grandmother."* This may indicate that many Muslim women are not yet well integrated into society, at least not living a life similar to the ethnic Norwegian female pastor. Two of the female pastors say explicitly that the care seekers' gender role is very different from their own. Much of their life is influenced by the way their husbands treat them. The pastors experience that migrant women, both Christian and Muslim, sometimes seem alienated from things happening to them. Some are denied much personal freedom.

The male pastors seem to have different experiences. Two of them in particular underline, first of all, the importance of encountering the other with an attitude of finding something common, finding a "meeting point," so to say. *"We are very much the same by both being religious persons. It often strikes me that we do believe in the same things,"* says one of them, and continues: *"I believe that we have to find the similarities first.... There are so many prejudices and news reports around us that are destroying our good constructive dialogue. We have to find meeting points and get to know each other first.... We have many common images of God, and it is important to find them."* At the same time this person says: *"But I have not yet heard someone saying something bad about women and so on, though."* When I challenge him to reflect on what he does when controversial issues are raised, such as homosexuality, he replied: *"This topic has not been raised yet."* Another male pastor says: *"The differences are in our life stories and what brings us here. I work at this institution, and the care seeker lives here."* This participant also stresses practical and social distinctions, when asked about differences. To be university-educated and living a life outside the building, are the most important things. This is the same with both Muslim and other care seekers.

Even though the women also see practical differences, one of them emphatically commented that the images of God are *"definitively different!"* At the same time she noted a point of agreement: *"but we both believe in one God and there is respect for each other."* Regarding my follow-up question about whether or not the different images of God challenge the relationship, she replied: *"Yes, I think so, and it is my need that I have to keep on hiding many times. The fact is that I stand for a much stronger idea of liberation. I have a religiously grounded self-confidence. There is a legitimating thing inside me. That is also why I cannot push it further."*

One of the pastors emphasized the shared experience of being religious. It usually does not make any difference what tradition one belongs to. *"It is important to find the bridge,"* this pastor commented. When asked what to do when it seems that the care seeker's faith is hurtful for him or her, this pastor replied: *"I believe that all have negative perspectives and images of God sometimes. When human beings are fundamentalist in their way of expressing themselves, it is entirely impossible. I cannot be really present in a conversation with a person who does not open up."* Not all the pastors agree on this. Another, as earlier mentioned, said: *"I do sometimes hide myself, because I stand for a much stronger liberating theology. I cannot push it, but just respect that that they are where they are."* As we see, some of them side-step a conversation which does not open up, while others "hide" themselves by avoiding some contacts or circumventing certain issues. Nevertheless, most of the pastors challenge unhealthy images of God in a way that still keeps the care seeker in the center.

One of the female participants commented: *"The similarities are not so important. Respect for differences is just as important. It is important to be open to the ways that others look upon reality. This also opens up my own horizon."* Another said: *"Differences may vary according to the personal encounter. At the same time I believe that the image of God, especially for people who are raised in a spiritual language as a way of reading reality, will both find it familiar and not."*

Another female pastor believes it is important that the spiritual care giver is a believer, but at the same time is very concerned about the effectiveness of being different in ethnicity and religion. On the question about experiencing the pastor's role, this person said: *"I get positive feedback on my role. And then I think it is very much about getting a mirror in front of them that is quite brave. I believe that I am brave, that I am spontaneous in a way, that I give back what is being related to me. This can in many ways trigger some processes that may hurt, but also can be quite useful. They may see things from an angle other than their own."*

It may look like at least two of the male pastors have a philosophy close to Husserl's notion of empathy and search for common meeting points. All the female participants' answers, on the other hand, evoke Lartey's interpretation of Levinas. The differences are so clear that they believe there is nothing else to do but look at the other as a unique *other*. This may mean that full empathy is harder, but according to Lartey and the women's answers, neither is it the aim. If one is concerned about it, seeing another person as completely different from oneself may mean that it is easier to respect her or him. In this way one can also bring in new perspectives; this is the advantage of placing respect for differences first. At the same time, when both are religious and the caregiver's faith serves as a basis, it may provide opportunity for the care seeker to recognize the importance of their religious outlook and horizon.

One of the male pastors stressed that we sometimes hear news through the media that may lead to the formation of stronger prejudices. This is an important element. Even as we talk about searching for the otherness in faces that may provide new perspectives, this is not always the case on the level of the whole society. The world feels closer and smaller today now that we have quick means of communication. This may mean that we also make quick analyses of other people. If we do not take the opportunity to encounter others face to face and get to know human beings with other backgrounds, negative opinions about others will split more than gather people.

Even though the participants disagreed about how much one should read about the other's religion, all agreed that curiosity is important. The wish to learn something by listening to the other's point of view and even different images of God is mentioned. As Lartey recommends, it is best not to just shallowly and quickly read through an introduction to Islam. This may merely lead to the strengthening of prejudices because one might think that the content of the book is more revealing than the personal expressions of care seekers. [12]

Recapitulation

All the pastors interviewed regard pastoral care to Muslims as something that has been part of their everyday lives for several years now. They think that, as long as they put the care seekers' needs in focus, they can be good counselors to them. Also, in encountering Muslims, all of them tend to be aware, as Lartey puts it, that all human beings are like all others, like some others and like nobody else. They all try not to gener-

---

[12] Lartey, *In Living Color*, p. 165.

alize the care seekers. From what they have said, I understand that many Muslim care seekers tend to be very concerned about their own identity, and they are seldom what we, in Christian terms, might call "seeking." Especially in recent years pastors have experienced indications that Muslim identity is stronger or at least more apparent.

Conversation topics may cover almost everything and are often concerned with practical issues. At the same time many need to talk about religious and existential issues when going through vulnerable times in life. All the pastors are concerned, in these instances, to avoid imposing their own experiences on them. When I asked whether or not they challenge negative and unhealthy images of God, most of them replied that they try to challenge in a way that the care seekers will find out themselves what is best for their lives.

From the information I have compiled it seems that Muslim care seekers know very well whom they seek for help. The pastors also believe that it is important that they are religious leaders. In this way they express the idea that religious persons tend to seek therapists with a religious perspective and philosophy. The pastors also believe that Muslims seek them because they trust their commitment to confidentiality. The Norwegian pastors are available and they know the Norwegian society. Some Muslims experience being marginalized and indicate that they look at the pastor as a safe environment. For instance, the pastors believe that female care seekers often want to talk to other women. The importance of being different from a psychologist, but at the same time separate from the mosque and family relations, seems to be positive. All the pastors interviewed believe that they traditionally have a different role than the imam. This is something several imams also have documented for me.[13]

Even though the pastors expressed that they wish to have close communication with imams and other religious leaders, they all believe that they have a role as pastoral caregivers also for Muslims, in the future. This is because they know that many Muslims refuse the offer of talking to an imam.

The male pastors all expressed that talking about differences is mainly about *all* people being independent human beings, across religion and culture. The female pastors agreed that there are differences between individuals, and it may be the case that they communicate better with some Muslims than with other Christians. At the same time, they said

---

[13] Six imams attending my lecture on October 16, 2008, at the University of Oslo, reported that they did not have any education on how to be a spiritual caregiver for individuals. They also indicated that imams do not necessarily have a role in helping people grieve, for example, because that is taken care of by the family.

that, culturally, they differ very much from Muslim women. This leads to certain challenges, but all the women pastors believe that this difference is often a resource in the encounter. The women in particular believe, like Levinas, that looking for the *otherness* of the other is important. The fact that they have different images of God and look at religion from another angle is a good thing, according to them. Most of all, they find that they think differently than their care seekers do about family structure and empowerment. A female, ethnic Norwegian pastor is, therefore, something totally different for the women care seekers than, say, a Pakistani imam is.

The question now is whether or not this modest research project might provide some guidelines for how to answer the alarming stories we find in the newspapers about clashes of religion. When I hear the stories of these pastors, I believe that religious care and counseling is giving a lot of people new hope in their lives. I also have a stronger interest in making safe places for people to meet each other. Respectful encounters where people feel acknowledged is indeed essential for creating a more peaceful society. When we never encounter the other face to face and listen to what the other person says, it is easier to distance ourselves and resort to superficial prejudices, often supported by the media. As one pastor expressed: *"The voice of the church has, and will continue to keep, an important role in society as long as we are taking human faith and experience seriously. Church can also influence politics. It did a lot during the fights about the Muhammad cartoons."*[14]

Why not look at spiritual care as the perfect place for a starting point, where listening to the other is exactly the nature of the encounter? There is no dialogue without clear and distinct positions, and that is why it is important to know where we are situated and what kind of "glasses" we are wearing. The pastors in this research all agree that you should never try to change the other, but rather try to get to know him or her. Even though all people have prejudices in encounters with another person, we can all train ourselves to be aware of and deal with them. It is through trust, respect, and being open that one often finds new treasures. *"It is important to open up to consider the ways that others look upon reality. That also opens up my own horizon,"* one of the pastors said.

According to my participants there is still a long way to go in terms of responding to the needs of Muslims in Oslo. These pastors wish there

---

[14] This episode took place in Winter 2006. Norwegian and Danish newspapers printed pictures of Prophet Muhammad that many found offensive. Both countries' embassies in Lebanon and Syria were under fire. In Norway there is a Muslim umbrella organization and a good dialogue with the churches that made the situation better than in Denmark.

were much broader possibilities for guiding care seekers to people who have knowledge about the religion and culture that is closer to the care seekers' own. In this way they think all faith communities should prioritize care and counseling and invest time and money accordingly. At the same time, it is important that institutions speak about the need and help to make it easier to get there. If one looks at *otherness* as an indispensable recourse for perceiving with a more open view, as a Christian one should not exclude the idea of also seeking an imam. Curiosity for new rituals, prayer, and more piety and passion, for example, may lead people to seek an imam. We could learn from other countries that offer spiritual care from a number of different religious traditions and in different languages. We must continue giving proper basic education in spiritual care for all religious leaders.

Regardless of where the encounter takes place—on the street, in the prison yard, in the office of the pastor, in church or in an institution—something special happens when two human beings encounter each other. If there is no well there before, it may be created in this moment. In the eyes of the other, in the plurality of God's creation, is a well built with life-giving water, water that restores meaning and safety and offers glimpses of hope. Let us take with us the story from the Bible and, putting it into our own context, ask: *"How is it that you, a Christian, ask me a Muslim man for a drink?"* *"How is it that you, a Muslim, ask me a Christian woman for a drink?"* The one holding the jar is longing for wisdom and life-giving water from the well. It is an encounter with two different lives and two different religious traditions. One can recognize that there are prejudices and uncertainty hidden in the words. At the same time, the two of them stay by the well, engaged in the conversation. Both are vulnerable when giving something of themselves and of their time. The two of them give and receive respect and care. The encounter is between two human beings as well as between two cultures and faith traditions.

Interreligious and intercultural pastoral care and counseling
Notes from a German perspective

Helmut Weiss

In this article I would like to give an overview of intercultural and inter-religious pastoral care and counseling in Germany. To do this, I have chosen the following procedure:

First, I will begin with a historical review, in order to reveal the rich traditions of pastoral care and counseling. Pastoral care and counseling has always been contextual and, by focusing on people's particular needs, has been determined by the respective cultures and religious currents.

Around 1970, the pastoral care and counseling movement began to take the psychological aspect of humans into account and repositioned itself to a pastoral-psychological point of view. It recognized that pastoral care and counseling is occupied with humans as psychological subjects. It soon became clear, however, that not only the inner dynamics of biography and life situations are decisive, but also the real context, i.e. economic, societal, cultural, and religious factors. This became apparent through the perception of cultures and differences—and through encounters with foreigners. I will quickly describe how Germany became a multicultural and multireligious society in the last few decades, and how new challenges for pastoral care and counseling have arisen from this change.

Second, starting around 1990, the Society for Intercultural Pastoral Care and Counseling (SIPCC) has been intensively engaged with the question of contextual perception in pastoral care and counseling, as well as with changes in German society. Issues surrounding

Helmut Weiss is the founder and President of the Society for Intercultural Pastoral Care and Counseling, Dusseldorf, Germany. He is an ordained minister of the Lutheran Church, and a retired CPE supervisor.

235

interculturality, as well as intercultural and interreligious competence in pastoral care and counseling, are the focus of the SIPCC. I will name a few basic principles that were formulated by the SIPCC on this subject and that need to be developed further. Here, the development of an understanding and meaning of culture and religion is important—both are areas which are now receiving more and more attention in pastoral care and counseling in discussions and literature.

Finally, two transcripts of counseling situations are discussed, in order to demonstrate the difficulties and possibilities of pastoral care and counseling with people of other religions in a German context. They come from work in hospitals—an area where interreligious pastoral care and counseling is possible and necessary. These encounters were discussed in various groups with the goal of learning about interreligious pastoral care and counseling.

I would like to point out the following terminological nuance in the German language: the word "religion" does not refer to the various Christian denominations, but rather to the major religious groups, such as Hinduism, Judaism, Buddhism, Christianity, Islam and various animist religions. In our situation, "interreligious" pastoral care and counseling is primarily concerned with the interaction between members of these different religious groups. The German term for pastoral care and counseling between members of various Christian denominations is "ecumenical pastoral care and counseling."

The rich history of pastoral care and counseling

Over centuries, intensive and differentiated pastoral care and counseling has been practiced in Germany—as in other European countries—in response to the *Zeitgeist* and peoples' needs and questions.[1] How can people best live meaningfully and beneficially? How can they arrive at their purpose in life? How can they enter into a moral relationship with themselves, God, and their role in the world? How can they cope with sickness and death?

Women and men posed these questions and gave answers in dialogue with others and in faith in God. These answers were influenced by Christian faith and mediated by the church. The church has been the place and institution of pastoral care and counseling for its members well into modern times.

Hildegard of Bingen (born in 1098) was a famous and respected nun

---

[1] Cf. Klaus Winkler, *Seelsorge*, Berlin 2. Aufl. 2000; Jürgen Ziemer, *Seelsorgelehre* (Göttingen, 2. Aufl. 2004).

who was not only connected to the important leaders of her time, but also, because of her life and faith experiences, she drew many people who were seeking advice. She reflected on the essence of humanity, the efforts and obliquity of humans, and wanted to offer orientation and comfort.[2] Another woman, *Mechthild of Magdeburg,* joined the pauper's movement. Around that time, many people slipped into poverty and dependence, particularly in cities. Widows who became single mothers, orphans, and the sick and needy were rejected; the dying were left without pastoral care. Together with a community of pious women, the Beghards, Mechthild dedicated herself to these people.

Monks were important spiritual advisors during the Black Death, a time of much dying. They cared for the sick, accompanied the dead to the cemeteries and attended to the survivors.

Thomas á Kempis, born around 1380 in a small town about 20 kilometers from Düsseldorf, where I live, joined a lay movement at an early age and wrote *"The Imitation of Christ."* This book, which encourages life formation and *praxis pietatis,* had an extraordinary effect and influenced many generations. In this book, pastoral care and counseling becomes a "way of wisdom."[3]

The *Reformation* gave pastoral care and counseling new accents. One could say that the Reformation began and was carried out for reasons of pastoral care. The people's conscience should be freed from the weights and burdens that the church in Rome had placed upon them. Pastoral care became a fundamental dimension of *Martin Luther's* life and work (1483–1545).[4] He was personally active in pastoral care and counseled and comforted people in many situations. It is no coincidence that he was away working on resolving a marital conflict during the last couple of days before his death.

While general pastoral care (*cura animarum generalis*) was administered by priests and their sacramental advice, a specialized form of pastoral care, was developed, oriented on individuals and their situation. In addition to one-on-one counseling, Pietism developed pastoral care and counseling in a group setting with the call for a life pleasing to God. In

---

[2] Margot Schmidt, Hildegard von Bingen, in: Christian Möller (ed.), *Geschichte der Seelsorge in Einzelporträts,* Band 1 Von Hiob bis Thomas von Kempen (Göttingen, 1994), p. 265–286.

[3] Gerhard Ruhbach, Thomas von Kempen, in: Christian Möller (ed.) *Geschichte der Seelsorge in Einzelporträts,* Band 1 Von Hiob bis Thomas von Kempen (Göttingen, 1994), p. 341–352. For a reframing and reorientation of pastoral counseling in terms of *wisdom* as a form of knowing holistically and of doing practical theology, see Daniel S. Schipani, *The Way of Wisdom in Pastoral Counseling* (Elkhart: Institute of Mennonite Studies, 2003).

[4] Christian Möller, Martin Luther, in: Christian Möller (ed.), *Geschichte der Seelsorge in Einzelporträts,* Band 2 Von Luther bis Matthias Claudius (Göttingen, 1995), p. 25–44.

groups, people related their concerns and needs, as well as their transgressions and sins. Groups gave support but also exercised social control. The great leaders of Pietism, like *Philipp Jakob Spener* (1635–1705) in Frankfurt am Main, Dresden, and Berlin, *Gerhard Teerstegen* (1697–1769) in Moers, a city neighboring Düsseldorf, or *Nikolaus Ludwig von Zinzendorf* (1700–1760) became pillars of orientation for many peoples' souls with their conversations, sermons, and hymns.[5]

Friedrich Daniel Ernst Schleiermacher (1768–1834) was not only the founder of practical theology as an academic theological discipline, but he was also the founder of a modern theory of pastoral care. He influenced pastoral care in the 19th and 20th centuries more than any other.[6] For Schleiermacher, individual pastoral care meant helping to deliver salvation, living a self-determined life and still being integrated in the community. Subsequent pastoral care teachings and practice have been oriented on that norm. The most important textbooks on pastoral care emerged in the 19th century. The industrial revolution and the resulting societal shifts (urbanization, the collapse of extended family structure, uprooted youth, the emergence of the proletariat) were examined and the question of how pastoral care could be helpful was posed. The specific hardships and needs were observed—pastoral care and counseling's differentiation began and has advanced greatly since then.

New accents came into play after World War II. Young German theologians became acquainted with *Clinical Pastoral Education* around 1965 in the U.S. They discovered how important it was to draw on insights from the areas of psychology and psychotherapy for pastoral care. They then developed a *therapeutic* approach to pastoral care and pastoral psychology with the help of clergy who knew the benefits of psychoanalysis. Questions were posed concerning the psychological dynamics that take place in a person's soul, the relationship to one's parents, to others and to the world, the interaction with affects and emotions and inner conflicts, and questions concerning personal identity. And questions were answered, and were answered with the help of various therapeutic processes. These questions were very beneficial for pastoral care and also gave the church many new impulses. Pastoral care and counseling—like pastoral psychology—is concerned with accompanying and interpreting life from the perspective of Christian faith, through which people are perceived with their inner complications and possibilities. Psychological insights were

---

[5] Ibid. p. 261–316.

[6] Volker Weymann, Friedrich Daniel Ernst Schleiermacher, in: Christian Möller (ed.), *Geschichte der Seelsorge in Einzelporträts*, Band 3 Von Friedrich Schleiermacher bis Karl Rahner (Göttingen, 1996), p. 21–40.

incorporated into pastoral care and made fruitful. It is important to note that pastoral care as a pastoral act can and should be taught and practiced. There are methods to make it competent and verifiable. Like theology, pastoral care and counseling learns from many other disciplines that have knowledge about humans. In that way, pastoral care and counseling becomes a multi-disciplined cooperation in human encounters.

Admittedly, the shortfalls of a psychological pastoral approach soon became apparent. It was made clear from various sides that pastoral care needed to view people as social beings. Narrative research has shown that each individual fate is tied to a collective history. Authors have shown that pastoral care and counseling is frequently concerned with day-to-day realities that need no therapeutic treatment. Encounters with strangers show to what extent cultural contexts dictate interpretations of life and form life narratives. Human existence cannot just be understood from the perspective of inner movements; it has manifold contexts, which need to be appropriated, realized, and valued by pastoral care. This was ultimately the reason why the motif of intercultural and interreligious perspective was introduced.

Toward an intercultural and interreligious approach to pastoral care and counseling

Until the last couple of decades, pastoral care and counseling focused on people of one confession, with a few exceptions. The teaching of the Roman Catholic Church formed the center of the unified worldview of the Middle Ages; the church alone mediated salvation. Following the Reformation and the formation of the reformed churches, it was not common for pastoral care to be given to those belonging to other denominations. Even in hospitals and social institutions where people of various confessions lived next to one another, everyone had their own clergy. Catholic priests visited Catholic patients in the hospital and the Lutheran and Reformed went to the beds of their sick. It has only been in the last two decades that there have been modest efforts towards cooperation and ecumenical pastoral care and counseling among the churches. So, it is not surprising that there is no tradition of intercultural or even interreligious pastoral care and counseling in Germany, because both are only in their beginning stages.

At the same time, because Germany has experienced significant demographic changes, it has become necessary to develop forms of pastoral care and counseling that recognize people in their cultural and religious diversity and adjust to them. After the Second World War, millions of people were forced to leave areas that were no longer part of Germany.

The population, and church membership, became fundamentally more mixed. Many more Protestants lived in areas that had previously been dominated by Catholics and vice versa. Through the arrival of workers and their families from other European countries, Turkey, Africa, and Asia starting in 1960, about 10 percent of the German population is now immigrants with quite different religions. The largest group is Muslims from Turkey, consisting of approximately three million people.

In Germany, many people have left the church; church membership lies somewhere between 70 percent and 30 percent in larger cities, and sometimes even lower. Forty years ago it was around 90 percent. From 1945 to 1989, religious socialization was heavily constricted in Eastern Germany under the communist regime of the GDR. Even after Germany's reunification, churches from these areas still have very few members. For this reason, it is not just a question of how people from other cultures and religious backgrounds can be helped by pastoral care and counseling; it is also a question of what pastoral care and counseling can look like for people who do not see themselves as religious.

One other aspect should be mentioned: non-Christian religions, like Islam and Buddhism, are gaining more and more adherents among those who grew up in Christian or non-religious homes. What kind of of challenge is that for interreligious pastoral care and counseling?

At any rate, there are a variety of answers offered by very different religious beliefs and worldviews to help all kinds of people with different lifestyles find meaning. Peoples' concerns, which were clearly influenced and motivated by Christian motifs in earlier times, have taken on an infinite number of forms, from highly professional help through psychiatry and psychotherapy to counseling and advice in magazines. Pastoral counseling and spiritual guidance compete with psychological, philosophical, esoteric, and atheistic life-orientations. German society still needs to adjust to this sort of diversity, which has been taken for granted in other countries for some time. The churches have to deal with it and pastoral care and counseling has to adjust to it.

As mentioned above, there have been international contacts within the pastoral care and counseling movement in Germany starting around 1970. In 1979, a large delegation from divided Germany, from the West (FRG) and East (GDR), participated in the first international congress of the *International Council on Pastoral Care and Counseling (ICPCC)* in Edinburgh, Scotland. I also took part and can remember various encounters well. The first president of the ICPCC was Werner Becher, a pastor from Frankfurt am Main. The German clergy members were represented at all congresses. In 1986 I led the first international seminar in Germany for pastoral care and counseling in Düsseldorf—since then a seminar has taken place almost every year. Constant encounters with people from many countries with different cultures and religions transformed the international to *intercultural* and *interreligious* and posed new questions for pastoral care and counseling, such as, how we can discern the various cultural and religious contexts. The challenge was to realize that people from one country could belong to completely different cultures and religions, completely different classes and races, to completely different castes and ethnicities. Interculturality is a challenge for interpersonal relationships in this diversity, for the co-existence of societies, for political and economic designs, for cultural participation and religious appreciation. All of these questions have also come up in Germany following reunification. It became apparent that people in the East and West had been practicing different cultures and acted accordingly; different political, economic and social systems had been established. All that leads to high levels of uncertainty and tensions that still are not overcome to this day. We have experienced this painfully in many international seminars.

In intercultural encounters one can quickly discover that despite all the similarities that can be experienced, there are still significant differences. Again and again these differences are emotionally straining and strenuous. Intercultural competence is demonstrated less by rational understanding of other cultures and accommodating other conventions and customs than by enduring the emotional tension, by recognizing conflicts and being willing to withstand them and make them tolerable.[7] It is a special experience when one is successful in resolving conflicts. These considerations are also decisive in interreligious dialogue. Intercultural competence also means being able to engage in encounters with strangers and being willing to listen to them. Interculturality is precisely the opposite of blocking off a stranger; it is the encounter and discovery of the foreign.

The *Society for Intercultural Pastoral Care and Counseling (SIPCC)*[8] has been intensely involved with questions concerning the meaning of culture for pastoral care and counseling since 1995. As a vital context, culture cannot be disregarded in one's perception of peoples' situations and the way they interpret their lives. Issues of interculturality and the definition of intercultural pastoral care and counseling are being delib-

---

[7] Elisabeth Rohr, Intercultural Competence, in: *Intercultural and Inter-Faith Communication—Materials from the International Seminar 2005*, SIPCC Magazin Nr. 13 (2006): 26–29.

[8] More on the SIPCC under www.sipcc.org.

erated and discussed in the SIPCC. Approaches to a hermeneutic of intercultural communication have been developed. Which types of intercultural expertise are necessary for pastoral care and counseling and for interreligious dialogue are being discussed. Interreligious issues are moving more and more into the spotlight.

The Handbook of Intercultural Pastoral Care and Counseling[9] from 2002 expresses this in the following way:

Interculturality

- describes encounters and exchanges between cultures—while preserving one's own cultural identity;

- perceives and appreciates cultural diversity in people, ethnic groups, and subgroups—which is especially important in times of globalization and cultural assimilation;

- recognizes that people are similar in many ways—and for that reason works on overcoming racist, sexist, and other inhuman attitudes;

- challenges us to recognize foreignness and engage in dialogue;

- exposes how many people, cultures, and ethnicities influence each other—and forces us to critically examine our own lifestyle;

- encourages us to encounter people of other cultures in our own neighborhoods with less fear, fewer prejudices and more helpfulness;

- views every individual person as distinctive with inherent worth.

Intercultural Pastoral Care and Counseling

- connects interculturality with religious truths, Christian faith, and psychological insights;

- helps people who work in pastoral care, counseling, therapeutic and other helping professions connect their professionalism with their cultural identity;

- develops approaches and methods of offering support and being there for people from various cultures in a competent and professional way.

In my opinion, we still need more involvement in understanding cul-

---

[9] Helmut Weiß, Die Entdeckung Interkultureller Seelsorge, in: Karl Federschmidt / Eberhardt Hauschildt / Christoph Schneider Harpprecht / Klaus Temme / Helmut Weiß (edrs.), *Handbuch Interkulturelle Seelsorge*, (Neukirchen-Vluyn, 2002), p. 36.

ture and religion. I want to elucidate this briefly.

Culture

For a long time culture was defined as the sum of human activities and values and as human interaction on values towards a collective goal. If a community created material or ideal values, then one defined this as culture. In that way, culture was something predetermined; and, although it could be transformed by continuing processes, it was a nearly ontological entity, like a possession of a certain community. Hence, it was easy for negative views of cultures other than one's own to develop.

Since then, a different, and in my opinion more viable notion of culture has been asserted, namely that of culture as a "thick description"[10] of meaning towards understanding human social behavior. According to this conception, culture creates symbols of values, which express meaning of human behavior. Human behavior can only be understood in the context of the respective social and cultural interpretation patterns, which is important for all pastoral work.

In this light, culture is no longer an entity, but rather a symbolic expression, an interpretation that places behavior in a situation (context) and makes it comprehensible through "description." Culture is defined by this understanding of "interpretation of contexts" and not by given values. It is a dynamic conception of culture—culture as social discourse, which leads to the descriptions of social behavior under examination.

Religion

There are many responses to the question, "what is religion?" From the perspective of phenomenological sociology religion is understood *functionally*: religion performs a function for individuals, groups, and societies, which can be observed and described. Religion aids in the formation of individual identity as well as communal orientation of values. Religion is sometimes even a necessary part of societies. However, a weakness of this definition is the vague determination of religion's content. What makes religion different from other functions?

Religious studies have attempted to describe the various forms of religion and discover their common contents. This *phenomenological definition* of religion presupposes the "holy" or "cult" or "magic" or other forms of religion. However, today the manifestations are becoming more and more blurred. One could pose the question, for instance: is football (soccer) a "religion" or similar to a religion in Germany? Many religious

[10] This term was introduced by Clifford Geertz in *The Interpretation of Cultures* (1973).

forms are represented in the worship of this "game." Sports are a type of substitute for religion for many people today. I think that we cannot characterize religion without clarification in regards to content. I would like to follow Gerd Theißen in *The Religion of the Earliest Churches: Creating a Symbolic World*. This renowned New Testament exegete writes, "Religion is a system of cultural signs which promise a better life by responding to a final reality."[11] With this, Theißen makes clear: even religion is made up of a discourse in a certain cultural environment—comparable with culture. Like culture, religion aims for life formation and gains. It also leads us to decisive and differentiating criteria: Religion finds a language of signs and symbols in the "counterpart to a final reality." Religion is tied to culture but does not originate from culture; it orients itself around a "final reality," a reality that exceeds or experiences or ascertains reality. Different religions can describe this "final reality" in different ways—but this point of reference to transcendence constitutes religion. This is already expressed in the original Latin word "religio" as "connection to the divine."

If religion is concerned with "ultimate reality," it is essential for clergy to clarify what this means. Because they stand in a tradition of faith, pastoral care always has to connect this tradition with the present time and with the present context. Theological work always involves the discourse connecting the present needs and the message of the "ultimate reality". Christian pastoral care and counseling has its foundation in the gospels and Christ—in other words in the humanity of God and God's commitment to humans. For that reason, it can concentrate on the challenges of humanity in interpersonal encounters and perform its task in that way. Other religions have their own premises and fundamental assumptions on human becoming and life orientation. If various religious forms were to enter into dialogue about their foundations, they could learn from each other and develop joint activities.

At any rate, those involved with pastoral care and counseling need to be more engaged in the discussion about culture and religion in the future in order to clarify and arrive at theories of intercultural and interreligious pastoral care and counseling. This is foreseen in another book from the SIPCC, which is in the planning stages.

---

[11] Gerd Theißen, *The Religion of the Earliest Churches: Creating a Symbolic World*, cited from: *Die Religion der ersten Christen: Eine Theorie des Urchristentums* (Gütersloh, 2. Aufl. 2001), p. 19. Cf. too: Christian Danz, *Die Deutung der Religion in der Kultur: Aufgaben und Probleme der Theologie im Zeitalter des religiösen Pluralismus* (Neukirchen-Vluyn, 2008).

Examples of interreligious pastoral care and counseling

In the following, I would like to demonstrate the difficulties and possibilities of interreligious pastoral care and counseling using transcripts of two conversations. They come from work in hospitals, a place where patients from different religious backgrounds come together. In the hospital Christian chaplains and clergy come into contact with Christians from various confessions, atheists, Muslims, Buddhists, and many others. The need for interreligious pastoral care and counseling is increasing also in other areas, such as schools and prisons. In order to help the reader understand the background of these conversations, I would like to make a few comments about chaplaincy in Germany. This service generally does not reside directly within the structure of the hospitals; it is a service of the church—Roman Catholic or Protestant churches—and is also funded by the churches. Small denominations (free churches, Baptists, Methodists, etc.) offer this service in their own affiliated hospitals, but not everywhere. By law, the Roman Catholic and Protestant churches have the opportunity to offer and carry out pastoral care and counseling in hospitals. In larger hospitals (starting around 400 beds), there are usually full-time chaplains. This situation has advantages: Pastoral care and counseling is clearly defined as a service of the church and therefore has a clearly formed pastoral profile. The disadvantage is that chaplains are anchored to the institutions but can still find themselves on the margins. It is often unclear what the institutions should do with these services. However, pastoral care and counseling is often welcomed by patients and workers.

Currently there are no non-Christian chaplains working full-time in hospitals in Germany. Of course, Muslim, Buddhist or other non-Christian patients can be visited by their clergy or other spiritual caregivers. However, a continuous spiritual care only exists to a limited extent.

In the following two examples, full-time Christian chaplains encounter Muslims. They recorded these cases and presented them in groups in order to learn from them. There will be a reflection following the depiction of both cases.

"I saw souls..."

In the intensive care of a large hospital in a large city in Germany

S: fulltime Chaplain, around 45 years old, deacon of the Roman Catholic Church

P: patient, 41 years old, Pakistani, speaks good but somewhat broken German

P: *had asked for a chaplain*

S1: Hello, I'm the chaplain. My name is X.

P 1: It's nice that you came. I was in a coma for ten days and my wife says that I experienced a lot, terrible things.

S 2: Tell me about it. I'll get a chair.

P 2: I made three trips. The first was with my ancestors. I saw souls, you know, souls, and I was in a church... (*Seems like someone who tries to tell everything at once.*) I don't know what it means.

S 3: You experienced a lot of internally exciting things in the coma. Tell me about it calmly, then we can sort things out some so that we can understand it better (*I take more time for the patient than planned and mentally reschedule my lunch; I am satisfied with that*).

P 3: The journey was with a ship. My ancestors were along and they steered the ship; I was sick. There were borders, soldiers inspected us.

S 4: You were afraid.

P 4: Yes, no one said anything; it was dismal.

Then we arrived at my country. You know, I come from Pakistan and they brought me back to the land that I come from. (*Up to this point I had thought he was Indian based on his appearance.*)

And suddenly I was in a church. There were souls there, you know, souls.

S 5: What did they look like?

P 5: Yes, souls, they were there.

S 6: Like humans, just that they didn't have a body and could walk through walls and everything?

P 6: Yes, it's good that you listen; there were so many and I don't understand it.

S 7: You are becoming a little more calm and clear.

P 7: The church was not in Pakistan, it was in Germany, in the city I lived in; I had been there a couple times at Christmas.

S 8: What kind of souls were they? Did they know you?

P 8: They were praying and I was sick, but they were praying that I would die and they wanted money from me. And I always say that they should forgive me, that I forgive them too. I also told my parents-in-law from my first wife that they should forgive me.

S 9: What should they forgive you for?

P 9: I got a divorce even though my wife didn't want one. She was a German.

S 10: Are your parents-in-law mad at you because of that?

P 10: I don't know them. They were already dead. Now they were there.

S 11: What did they say?

P 11: They didn't say anything. I said that they should forgive me.

S 12: You didn't say what they should forgive you for?

P 12: That I have my limitations and my pride; they should forgive me and I will forgive them.

S 13: It won't work like that.

P 13: They wanted me to die and I was supposed to pay money; they prayed that I would die.

S 14: That must have been terrible for you...

P 14: I was shaking ...

S 15: You were afraid ...

P 15: They were very angry with me. (*Pause*)

I believe in Jesus Christ, he is a prophet, it's in the Koran, I am a Muslim, Jesus was a prophet like Mohammed, he was sent by God.

S 16: But it wasn't your temple that you were in ...

P 16: No, I was there, we always went to church on Christmas, I believe in Jesus Christ, I lit candles in the church, in other churches that we went into too. There is only one God.

S 17: Yes—What is the situation with you and God? Was he in the church too?

P 17: No. Up in heaven.

S 18: And God was looking down at you?

P 18: He wants me to live. I have a new life. Prophets have traveled such journeys too. Maybe I now have special gifts from God, what should I do...

S 19: Yes, I too believe that God wants you to live.

P 19: But what was with these souls? I'm afraid.

S 20: You need to leave this church but I know that you can't just leave; you have to find a way.

P 20: They don't let me leave. I know that I won't die but they are silent.

S 21:   I think that there is a big cultural difference here. Contrition plays a big role with us in Christianity. Do you regret the things that should be forgiven here?

P 21:   My pride, that is very important, I can't give it up.

S 22:   This could be difficult. Two cultures are clashing in your soul.

P 22:   The woman was not good. I now have a wife from Pakistan. I never have to say: "I'm hungry. Please get up and make me something to eat." My new wife thinks: "My husband is coming home from work, I'm sure he's hungry," and makes me something to eat and it is done when I get home. (*My hair starts to stand up on end.*)

S 23:   I can imagine that your first wife was very different.

P 23:   As a man I have to be responsible for what happens in the family, accountable to God. I can't always discuss and do what a woman wants.

S 24:   You know, with your first marriage you really engaged with our Western culture. Now you have big conflicts close by and haven't completely processed what happened. You will need to find peace ...

P 24:   I have a good wife now ...

S 25:   That's good. I need to go now. This conversation was very interesting for me. Would you like for me to come again?

P 25:   Yes, please come.

A couple of days later I meet P in a three-bed room. His wife is there. He wants to send her away so that I can sit next to him. I already have a chair in hand and make it clear that I want his wife to stay. That is not a problem.

After a couple of words I say ...

S 26:   You are personally stuck between two very different cultures.

P 26:   No, they are not cultures, I didn't feel wrong in this church, and it's the religions.

S 27:   We could call it the religions if you like ...

Once again P relates selected parts of his visions, this time many details. He hints that he understands them as a vision with which God has given him special gifts.

P 27:   I sometimes see a glowing point in front of me which moves around the room.

S 28: What does the point remind you of, what does it look like?

P 28: Like a glow worm.

S 29: And what does it do? Does it tell you something?

P 29: No, it sometime moves like this, sometimes like that. (*I have to think about eye movements.*)

S 30: And when you close your eyes, is it still there?

P 30: Then it's gone.

S 31: Maybe it has something to do with your eyes, with seeing?

P 31: No, I don't think so.

S 32: Do you think this is a sign from God?

P 32: (*Nods*). I have to tell you something. My wife rode here to the hospital from the neighboring city with the train when I was in the coma. A woman approached her, a Jew, no, a Buddhist, with a necklace and a star around her neck, she said to my wife: You have a very sick husband who is in a coma, there is someone who wants him to die, but he won't die, he will live. She said this right away and then got off the train at the next station. My wife says it was an angel. Do you think that it was an angel?

S 33: It is possible.

P 33: We were so "spiritual" earlier. Those are spiritual forces that wanted to hurt me. What does it mean, tell me as a pastor.

S 34: I'll say the following: You were very, very sick and standing on the edge of life and death. You saw that and received power where you could, even at your roots, with your ancestors.

P 34: But they were really concrete and like earlier, there weren't any cars and they were dressed so old ...

S 35: Yes, those are your roots; they reach back hundreds of years.

P 35: (*Nods*).

S 36: And the second thing that is important for this situation: You're alive. And you are alive because God wants you to live; he fought on your side. That is the foundation on which you can base your life from now on.

P 36: (*Nods*).

S 37: And there is still a poor relationship with your first wife.

P 37: Yes, (*immediately starts to talk about the divorce, etc.*)

S 38: You need to try to let go of this relationship, so that you are free from it.

P 38:   That's not good for my wife (*looks at her*), that makes her sad.

S 39:   Yes, try, maybe with a telephone conversation.

I have to go. We'll see each other again; I'll come by once more this week

Initial questions

It is immediately clear that this is a difficult conversation. What the patient says is really confusing. Are his pictures and dreams fever-induced fantasies? Do they have to do with his psychological situation caused by the serious illness? He is clearly in the situation in which he came close to death, and is processing his past—a painful past. Or does it seem like that which the patient relates is only confusing for the chaplain and has a clear logic which isn't understood?

To pose the question more concretely: What is the patient referring to when he talks about "traveling?" What does he mean by: "I have seen souls, you know, souls"? Is he processing current events in his life with his sentences ("The journey was by ship. My ancestors were along and they steered the ship; I was sick. There were borders and soldiers examined us."), about an escape, or are they a symbolic expression of his life, or are both mixed?

The patient then brings the "Church" and his belief in "Jesus Christ" and "God" into the conversation. As a Muslim what does he mean to say by that? Is he trying to speak about his religiosity? Or is it about his experience with the church and with his Christian wife and his Christian parents-in-law? Does he want to emphasize the similarities between himself and the chaplain in order to establish a connection? Is he trying to underscore his faith, that he is not a bad person and innocent? Does he want to say that he did not deserve the illness?

In P 8, a marital conflict and a conflict with the parents-in-law and relatives becomes clear. Relationship conflicts, cultural distinctions, and religious differences all blend together. How could they be unscrambled? The subject of "forgiveness," which is central for a Christian theologian, is touched upon. What meaning does it have for *this* Muslim? Is it possible that a Muslim theologian would talk about it completely differently than this believer? Another point that makes communication difficult between the patient and chaplain is the understanding of gender roles. The chaplain's "hair stands on end"—a clear physical expression of disapproval.

The questions remain unresolved in the second conversation as well.

In addition, the patient speaks of "the glowing point" as a "sign from God." And he relates a story from the train where a woman becomes an "angel": a person between "spiritual" and "satanic" powers.

Connected to the excursus concerning culture and religion, the conversation is concerned with the question of how these concepts are understood by the patient and chaplain. They play a role in the dialogue. I could imagine that a practicing orthodox Muslim or a Muslim theologian could characterize the patient's comments as "popular belief" or even as "non-Islamic" because there is little reference to devotion to God. Islamic popular piety, in turn, is quite familiar with the world of spirits and powers that appears here. The world of spirits and powers can be a tremendous help for people in need if they are understood as good— and this world can be very frightening for them if understood as evil. But this is not just a Muslim phenomenon; something very similar can be observed in many Christian communities. How could the chaplain talk about culture and religion in this situation in a way that is helpful for the care receiver? How should a chaplain deal with these questions? The patient pressures him to answer his questions. But has he understood the questions? Apparently not.

General reflections

Biographies and cultural and religious views are always mixed

In this encounter, various levels are clearly present at the same time: the biography as an emigrant, descent from a foreign land, familial ties to the original family and to the German relatives, relationship conflicts in the marriage, serious illness, cultural and religious differences, and emotional sensitivities like fear (also of death), disappointment (over a broken marriage), aggression (towards the first wife and the parents-in-law) and satisfaction ("now I have a good wife") are interwoven. That means we never have a cultural or religious perspective without a personal or biographical perspective. The personal biography interprets culture and religion; and culture and religion determine and interpret the personal history and situation. The patient cannot separate these aspects. The chaplain tries to make the different levels clear, which only helps the patient understand his experiences to a certain extent.

The importance of emotions for relationships

The attitude of not knowing[12] is very important in intercultural and in-

---

[12] Julian Müller, Intercultural Exchange—A discovery of being different, in: Traditions: Shadows of the Past—Sources of the Future, SIPCC Magazin Nr. 2, 1997, p. 4–8.

terreligious encounters. The experience described is so foreign to the chaplain that he can hardly understand—it is probably not any different for us readers. But how should I act if I don't understand? Should I ask questions? Should I have him explain that which is strange for me? At any rate, I can't act as though I understand. It is also not helpful to interpret what is said based on my own presuppositions and my own experiences. However, I can judge how what is said affects me. It appeals to me that the patient uses many images to express his experiences and emotions. He sees "souls," that is spirits, who are close to him and pressure him but also protect him. What he means is unintelligible; at any rate, these "souls" provoke emotions in the patient. Perhaps they are even an expression of his feelings. Would it have been helpful to ask him about that? He tells of a journey on "a ship with the relatives." While in great danger, the relatives surround him. Do they give him a sense of security or do they make him afraid? I would have liked to ask him. The next image, "the souls in the church," is emotionally charged as well. Although it is very hard to understand on the rational level, there might be a way to come closer emotionally, if one pays attention to the feelings in the comments and images. Emotions lie deep in our "consciousness" as biological and physical messages about our experiences. Feelings can establish relationships to others where "understanding" fails. This is quite evident in relationships with children. I am convinced that this is also a possibility in encounters with people from other cultures, religions or different biographies.

Support relationship despite differences

The differences experienced by the patient and the chaplain are not easy to bear. But accepting differences is an important element of the relationship. Time and again the patient tries to enter into a relationship with the chaplain. At the same time, the differences cannot be overcome. The way of expressing oneself and understanding, as well as the experiences of both, are too disparate. It is a hard request to ask of people to stay in a relationship and tolerate each other in such a situation. If it is possible and successful, then both partners gain. The patient did not succeed in this aspect with his first marriage. Both of them came from different walks of life and remained in them to an extent that they had to separate. For the man from Pakistan, marriage meant that the man has the responsibility to lead and to provide, and the woman orients herself around the man; therefore the woman has to adjust to the man's worldview. Counseling can help form relationships without passing over the differences. The differences make differentiation possible in the first place and show us the possibilities and the richness of human experience and existence. These abundances and the diverse possibilities can be discovered and made productive through intercultural and interreligious work.

The discussion in a study group: Discerning foreignness and entering into a relationship

This transcript was introduced and discussed in a discussion group in a course that I led. The transcript was initially discussed like all others. I usually proceed by having everyone in the group express how they were affected emotionally after the transcript has been read. The chaplain's confusion was reflected in the group's comments. I heard many of the questions mentioned above. In the next step of the discussion, the chaplain told us what he wanted to continue working on. The care-giver wanted to understand more clearly what the patient could have meant in order to gain access to him. At this point, the group's assumptions diverged greatly. In the end, however, it was clear that this was not helpful because the group only could have assumptions about the meaning of the patient's experience. I was telling the group that we could work with the chaplain on *his* understanding and perception—because *he* was present. We then came to the man's cultural and religious outlooks, which elicited reactions of defensiveness and astonishment. Once again, this reflected the chaplain's reactions. While the group was occupied with the patient and his images early on, the discussion turned more and more to the chaplain. It emerged that the participants also felt unsure of themselves and helpless. This comforted the chaplain; he felt solidarity with the others. The man's foreignness in his attitudes, his cultural and religious influences, and his path of life—in contrast to that of the course participants—was recognized and experienced. *It was important to not ignore or skip over this foreignness and this being different, but rather to appreciate it.* It was important to experience the differences that played an important role for the man in the conversation. Only after the foreignness was recognized did the first approaches begin to engage the man at an emotional level. The chaplain had rudimentarily attempted this a couple of times (S 4; S 14), but overall he asked about what he should do to understand rationally, or he instructed. Now, with the group he began to listen more to his own emotionality in relation to the man—and it emerged that an "understanding" arose. It was an emotional approach to the patient's confusion, the fear, and the insecurity. The stranger became a confidant and a human came into view with his humanity.

The result of this group discussion was that, even with all the cultural, religious, and biographical differences, interreligious counseling aims to perceive and accept the person in his or her humanness. It must be noted, though, that this succeeds sometimes, and sometimes it does not. It is most likely to succeed when it is possible to let someone in emotionally and enter into a relationship with them.

"I can't imagine it without her"

The female pastor Ulrike Mummenhoff works full time as a Protestant chaplain/counselor in a hospital in the Ruhr area in Germany, a region with many immigrant families. There is a special room in the hospital where the most seriously ill and dying patients are placed, so that their relatives can visit them at any time. This room is meant to communicate a homey atmosphere. The chaplain cares for the people in this room regularly regardless of their religion. This requires great sensibility because she has to adjust to the patients as well as the patient's relatives. The chaplain offers her accompaniment to all.

The pastor had heard that Mrs. A. (from Turkey) is unresponsive because of a brain tumor and is in the "accompaniment room" described above. She goes to the room every day until Mrs. A.'s death. She has much contact with Mr. A.

Day one

"I enter the room with mixed feelings. I know that Mrs. A. is unresponsive because of a brain tumor. I have heard from her sister that Mr. A. is with his wife. I am concerned with many questions: will Mr. A. understand me on the language level (many immigrants speak little or broken German)? How will he receive my attempts to establish contact (as a Christian, a woman)? How open-minded or fundamentalist is *his* faith? Can I shake his hand?"

Mr. A. sits at the foot of the bed in an armchair. His wife lies peacefully in bed.

I introduce myself and explain why I am here. Mr. A. is uncertain. The telephone rings. Mr. A. asks me to explain to his daughter on the telephone once more why I am there. An exchange between the two follows. Afterwards Mr. A. turns to me. We are standing at the bed and I ask if it is ok that I am here. Mr. A. nods. I ask him what happened and Mr. A. tells me: Mrs. A. had headaches for a long time. Three days ago she suddenly could not move her legs any more and was taken to the hospital. Two days ago they told him and his family that this woman is incurable. She has been unresponsive since yesterday. Today she was moved to the single room.

Mr. A. speaks haltingly, always searching for the German words. I feel like this searching for words reflects his innermost feelings: the desire to understand the situation and at the same time helpless pain about the loss which is hardly bearable. After a while I say good-bye and agree with Mr. A. that I will come tomorrow. I stretch out my hand and Mr. A. shakes it.

Day two

Mr. A. and his son are in the room. Our conversation concerns the question of whether Mrs. A should be moved home. Mr. A. asks his son (sometimes impatiently) to translate for him. Together we think about what would be the pros and cons of the decision (she would be close to the whole family, if Mrs. A. would open her eyes once more; her presumed wish to die at home; the fear if she would receive good medical care at home...). Mr. A. and his son initially have different opinions but the son changes his mind. Mrs. A. should move home. They tell about their family life. At the end of the conversation I ask if they have considered visiting a *Hodscha* (there are numerous mosques in the surrounding area). We talk about that and Mr. A. will establish contact. I promise to come by the next day. Shortly before I come a Turkish nurse that knows the family visits from another ward.

Day three

Mr. A. is alone. Mrs. A.'s condition has taken a turn for the worse. She can no longer be moved. I ask Mr. A. about their mutual history and where they met. Mr. A. tells about that and his children. "*I can't imagine it without her.*" The nurse comes and translates. Mr. A. tells stories about how fairly his wife dealt with the children, that she was the 'general' of the family. I ask him how a Muslim deals with this situation. Mr. A. knows that Allah is the Lord of the living that he gives and takes away, that there is a paradise. But he cannot understand why it has to happen so quickly and why he can't talk to her anymore. I ask him what he would like to tell her. He says: That she was a good wife. A good mother. A good grandmother. I ask him what she would tell him. He doesn't know for sure. He says that he tried to be a good man, father, and grandfather. I see tears in the corners of his eyes. I say that often the sense of hearing is the last to go, that his wife might not be able to understand everything but I believe that she can somehow sense his words. In my own words I try to emphasize the goodness and preciousness of the relationship. I say that I also sense how close he is to her and how he supports her and that this is good and precious. I am convinced that his wife senses that he is there and that his voice is good for her and perhaps his touch as well. The nurse cries and says that she needs a break but that she would gladly translate for us later. She leaves. We sit together a while. He tells how difficult it is to make the children understand that there is no cure. He also says how uncertain he is with his grandchildren without his wife. We sit silently for some time. Then I say goodbye.

Day four

As I come into the hospital late in the morning after an appointment, I hear that Mrs. A. died early that morning. Some of the children and extended family are still there—but not Mr. A. It is very peaceful in the room and it is difficult for me to not be able to see Mrs. A. anymore because the family has already covered her with a sheet. I introduce myself, give my condolences, ask if they need anything, and ask them to greet their father and extend my condolences to him and excuse myself.

Discussion in a group and general reflection

The group that discussed this accompaniment consisted of approximately 15 members, Muslims as well as Christians. The group came together just for this sitting lasting one and a half hours. For that reason it couldn't be concerned with viewing the case in connection with a lengthy training. It was primarily concerned with giving the chaplain answers to her questions: did I deal with these people with enough religious sensitivity? Was I helpful for them?

In the discussion, it became clear that this chaplain went into the situation very consciously—and that is a prerequisite for sensitivity. She is very aware of the differences: She, as a woman, encounters a man and family members whose culture normally lends men a higher level of authority. She encounters Muslim fellow humans as a Christian pastor. She establishes this contact with these differences and remains connected. At the same time, she leaves some space but repeatedly establishes a relationship. If this family had been Christian, she could have brought up and drawn significantly on Christian religious traditions and contents much sooner and offered to comfort them and strengthen them in the situation. She held back with religious statements in this situation. This was received very positively especially by the Muslims in the group. She referred to a Muslim clergy member and establishing contact with him. Whether or not this was successful was not reported. Cultural and religious sensibility was apparent in the chaplain's behavior.

Aside from the discussion about the current situation and the history of illness, aside from practical considerations about what can be done about the patient (which are important in such situations), the chaplain raises other points. She initiates a reflection of personal narratives and relationships. She clearly connects with some of the husband's basic human needs with these offers. He can experience his emotional state, express his relationship with his wife and recognize their shared history. In that way, the chaplain was helpful on a human, deeply emotional and spiritual level.

The fact that the chaplain asks how the man dealt with the situation as a Muslim was seen as important because he connects this situation with his faith. Mr. A.'s answer is impressive: *He knows that Allah is the Lord of the living, that he gives and takes away, that there is a paradise. But he cannot understand why it has to happen so quickly, why he can't talk to her anymore.* The chaplain gives her conversation partner space to express his own faith and questions.

The chaplain is integrated in a relatively intensive relationship process, which is meaningful for the family involved over the course of several days. But once the woman has died she has to remove herself from the process. After the death the family assumes other tasks, which are culturally and religiously ritualized—differently than for Christians. The chaplain's involvement would have been objectionable. The rituals following death are so deeply influenced by the individual religion that meddling would have been irritating and unwelcomed.

An important point for interreligious counseling emerges here; in interpersonal relationships which deal with cultural and religious differences, sensitivity can be helpful. Religiously influenced rituals, however, are fundamentally more exclusive and stimulate an "inward" identification. They tend to exclude people from other cultures. It is important to recognize and appreciate this.

Theological reflections on both cases

The fact that chaplains orient themselves around the patient's humanity and do not specifically bring their convictions into the conversation can be theologically justified by my Christian views in various ways. I would just like to hint at them here:

- Seeing people as God's creation uniquely applies to the interpersonal relationship of pastoral caregiving.
- God becoming human in Jesus Christ (incarnation) reminds us that everyone is a child of God.
- God's Spirit leads us toward human flourishing and toward an appreciation of all humans in their own ways.

Chaplains may sometimes introduce their own religious beliefs and interpretations as an expression of the search for meaning and salvation into interreligious and intercultural care giving. This would happen only when such disclosure seems helpful in light of the context, situation, and specific relationship of care. However, the main concern of the caregiver should always be to try to help the care receiver to reach his or her own meaning and own salvation.

Conclusion

Finally, I wish to offer the following observations in the manner of succinctly articulated theses:

- Interreligious and intercultural pastoral care (including counseling) is *contextual* care. The cultural and religious context of the respective persons is realized, observed and brought into the relationship.

- Interreligious and intercultural pastoral care recognizes *differences* on all levels of human relationships. The biographical and confessional differences are accepted and not ignored. At the same time, pastoral care seeks connections and interpersonal commonalities.

- Interreligious and intercultural care is relationship work on a rational and emotional basis. In all areas of difference, caregivers and conversation partners must look for points of mutual contact in understanding and for the common ground of our shared humanity.

- Interreligious and intercultural care takes place on the backdrop of an *"ultimate reality"* and receives its theological grounding for practice and understanding from it.

- Interreligious and intercultural care always has to be reconceived and reformulated in each societal context and is therefore focused on the *current situation* while seeking to find meaning in the future with hope.

Individualization—Migration—Globalization

A Protestant perspective on interfaith spiritual caregiving in the hospitals of Switzerland

Tabitha Walther

This essay will try to bridge continents in several ways. It has two playgrounds and you, the reader, will be invited to travel between two scenarios. The main focus is on interfaith spiritual care in Switzerland; the other focus is on a dialogue with interfaith spiritual care in the USA. I believe that bringing the two scenes together—Switzerland and North America—in dialogue will highlight the phenomenon of interfaith spiritual care in a useful way. I will first address the contextuality of interfaith spiritual care, then describe the Swiss situation and finally bring the Swiss situation into dialogue with the Stanford Model of interfaith spiritual caregiving.

The contextuality of interfaith spiritual care

Spiritual care always happens in a certain context. This context is multidimensional. Its different dimensions—historical, sociological, theological, pastoral, religious, political, and others—are crucial for understanding spiritual care practices. All these dimensions shape the practice and theory building of spiritual caregiving.[1] Obviously, spiritual care provided in hospitals is different between the contexts of Switzerland and of the United States.

Tabitha Walther, L.Theol., is an ordained minister of the Reformed Church of Baselland. She is Scientific Assistant for Practical Theology at the Theological Faculty of the University of Basel, Switzerland.

[1] In this essay "spiritual care" indicates care between a chaplain and a patient, each with an individualized spirituality. For the Swiss Protestant context professional spiritual care is always provided by an ordained pastor, a minister of the Protestant Church. Therefore in the Swiss context professional spiritual care is always *pastoral* spiritual care.

The place, function, individual adaptation, and institutional organization of religion within the societies of these two countries are different. The religious sociological structure is barely comparable. History has marked different tracks, with one track leading mainly to a plurality of religions (USA) and the other track leading mainly to a plurality of individualized faiths within the still dominant Christian religion (Switzerland).[2] Nevertheless, there are similarities within the two scenarios that will help us understand the profile of the other context.

What are these commonalities? Both societies, the Swiss and the North American, share significant migration movements and live under highly *globalized* conditions in a plurality of cultural and religious self-understandings in their each individually experienced spirituality. Their societies are *pluralistic*, in the sense of being multicultural and, to a growing extent, multireligious.[3] This is especially true for the large urban agglomerations[4] and less noticeable in rural areas.

Where are the big contextual differences in terms of religion and faith? Diana L. Eck labels the United States as the "most religiously diverse nation" due to their history of settlement, slavery, and migration. Added to the religiously diverse faiths of First Nation Americans were Christianity and Judaism with the first European settlers and Islam with Muslim African slaves. Centuries later, members of different religions live in the same neighborhoods as a matter of course. Furthermore, U.S. Americans are highly religious compared to the Swiss and other Europeans.[5]

In Switzerland today, modernity and postmodernity are reshaping a cultural landscape that has politically and religiously been fairly stable in the 20th century. The noteworthy shift in the religious landscape is not only the extended plurality of religions due to migration. The sig-

---

[2] For example, Wilhelm Gräb, *Sinnfragen. Transformationen des Religiösen in der modernen Kultur* (Gütersloh: Gütersloher Verlagshaus, 2006). For Gräb, religion today is adopted individually in its construction of meaning making (*Sinndeutung*) and Alfred Dubach and Roland J. Campiche, eds., *Jeder ein Sonderfall? Religion in der Schweiz. Ergebnisse einer Repräsentativbefragung* (Zürich/Basel: NZN Buchverlag, 1993).

[3] For the U.S. American context: Diana L. Eck, *A New Religious America. How a 'Christian Country' has Become the World's Most Religiously Diverse Nation* (San Francisco: HarperSanFrancisco, 2002). For the Swiss context: Martin Baumann and Jörg Stolz , eds., *Eine Schweiz–viele Religionen. Risiken und Chancen des Zusammenlebens* (Bielefeld: Transcript Verlag, 2007); Alfred Dubach Brigitte Fuchs, eds., *Ein neues Modell von Religion. Zweite Schweizer Sonderfallstudie–Herausforderung für die Kirchen* (Zürich: TVZ, 2005).

[4] Wilhelm Gräb, "Stadt," in Christian Fechter et.al., eds., *Handbuch Religion und populäre Kultur* (Stuttgart: Kohlhammer, 2005).

[5] Compare the results from the Religion Monitor of the Berthelsmann-Stifftung: http://www.religionsmonitor.com/index.php?lang=EN&sid=61359367768-9cf0550a.

nificant shift has to be seen in the plurality of self-understandings and the *individualized spirituality* within Christianity, the one and still dominant religion. Until the 1970s, Switzerland was a traditionally Christian country with two mainline churches: Catholic and Protestant.[6] The Protestant church was and is institutionally organized in cantonal[7] churches subsisting in autonomous local community churches. The Catholic church is organized in dioceses and their local parishes. They are administrated in cantonal structures. The Jewish community has been present since the Roman times and before Christianity. Marginal in number, they are publicly visible and institutionally organized, for example, in the synagogues of Zurich, Basel, Geneva, and Bern.

If we look at the last 30 years, membership of the so called "Volkskirchen" (mainline churches as public body corporate) is declining significantly in urban centers. Religion seems to be vanishing from the public sphere[8] and is being lived out individualized in the private sphere, in the form of a floating religiosity and in significant distance from institutions—churches, synagogues, mosques—or religious groups. But religion is by far not disappearing.[9] This religious change towards individualization of religion was and is still caused by the process of *secularization* that came with modernization and its functional differentiation of society.[10] Unlike North America, *Switzerland is not best characterized as multireligious but as secular and religiously individualized[11] and pluralistic[12] within a Christian cultural framework*, characterized by a low profile religiosity and without an explicit group affiliation. Switzerland has faced significant multireligiosity only in the last decades, mainly, but not only, through the migration of people with a Muslim background. These people come from countries such as Kosovo, Turkey, Serbia, and

---

[6] The two mainline churches have the status of public-law institutions. Other religious communities have only private-law status. Exceptions can be found in certain cantons, such as Basel City, where the Jewish community of Basel since 1972 and the Christ-Catholic Church also have the status of public-law institutions.

[7] Swiss Cantons are politically similar to U.S. states and in size comparable to U.S. counties.

[8] Thomas Luckmann, *Die unsichtbare Religion* (Frankfurt a.M.: Suhrkamp, 1991).

[9] Peter L. Berger, Der Zwang zur Häresie. *Religion in der pluralistischen Gesellschaft* (Frankfurt a.M.: S. Fischer Verlag, 1980).

[10] Niklas Luhmann, *Soziale Systeme. Grundriss einer allgemeinen Theorie* (Frankfurt a.M.: Suhrkamp, 2006) and Ulrich Beck, *Risikogesellschaft. Auf dem Weg in eine andere Moderm* (Frankfurt a.M.: Suhrkamp, 1986).

[11] Ulrich Beck, *Der eigene Gott: Die Individualisierung der Religion und der "Geist" der Weltgesellschaft* (Frankfurt a.M.: Verlag der Weltreligionen, 2007).

[12] Martin Baumann and Jörg Stolz, eds., *Eine Schweiz–viele Religionen. Risiken und Chancen des Zusammenlebens* (Bielefeld: Transcript Verlag, 2007).

others, many because of war in Kosovo. Compared to Judaism, Islam is new to the Swiss society and barely institutionalized. However, the number of people with a Muslim background is significant and constantly growing. After New Zealand and ahead of Australia, Switzerland has the highest migration rate in the world, relative to its population.[13]

Historically, Switzerland has been a multicultural country. A hint of this past are the four languages spoken traditionally and officially (German, French, Italian, and Romansh). These cultures coexisted side by side. Nowadays, the traditional four languages are heard more frequently in one and the same city. Due to migrants, asylum seekers, and the needs of the economy, new languages are heard in the streets and in the trams and buses of Zurich, Basel or Geneva. Every fifth person living in Switzerland is not Swiss. This proportion is much higher in the bigger cities. In Basel 58 percent of newborn children are not Swiss.[14]

Naturally, all these changes have had an effect on the situation in the hospital, especially because Swiss hospitals attract cheap labor and specialized professionals from outside Switzerland. The hospital staff and the patients represent the variety of cultures, languages, religious affiliations, and experienced spirituality of the Swiss and the foreigners living among the Swiss.

This is the situation spiritual care faces in Switzerland. The Swiss situation has shaped my understanding of spiritual caregiving. I have come to the conviction that the Swiss situation requires a new kind of spiritual care—interfaith spiritual care. I have also come to the conviction that the models of interfaith spiritual care which have developed in the United States of America can give helpful inputs for interfaith spiritual care in Switzerland. This conviction is sustained not only by reflection on pastoral care theories and praxis, but also by my biographical background. This is the second reason for bridging the continents and bringing the two playgrounds of Switzerland and North America into dialogue. After completing my Master in Theology I was trained as a minister of the Protestant Church in one of the cantons of Switzerland. After some experience as a pastor in Romansh and German Switzerland I was privileged to spend nine months of Clinical Pastoral Education (CPE) training at Stanford University Hospital and Clinics in California. There I worked as an interfaith chaplain. In my young ministry ca-

---

[13] Compare OECD, International Migration Outlook 2007.

[14] This number is also extremely high because Switzerland has much more strict migration laws than the USA. People living in Switzerland for decades sometimes still do not hold a Swiss passport.

reer I have experienced the contextuality of pastoral care through two significantly different models of spiritual caregiving in the hospital, dealing with their secularized and multireligious contexts respectively.

Understanding interfaith spiritual care in Switzerland

Spiritual care is always contextual. The first section of this essay has briefly introduced the Swiss context and described some of the significant analogies and differences compared to the North American scenario. This will help us understand what interfaith spiritual care could mean for the Swiss context. In Switzerland, theorizing about spiritual care in health care institutions happens interdisciplinarily and in relationship to the discussion of intercultural care in the nursing sciences.[15] Professional spiritual care practice from a Swiss Protestant perspective is pastoral care practice: an ordained pastor (female or male) providing spiritual care.

Interfaith—"Interreligious"—Spirituality: Sharpening diffuse and opalescent terms

As interfaith practitioners not only are we all challenged to be "multilingual,"[16] or at least bilingual, but also we are challenged to be researchers between the continents. This is meant literally. First of all, it is necessary to understand two or more languages to move into the other context and take part in its discourse. Furthermore, it makes sense to clarify some crucial terms first for the English speaking and the German speaking context.

The English term *interfaith* is widely used in common North American speech and means *interreligious*. Sometimes it is used in a wider sense and includes *interdenominational* as well as *interreligious*. The term does not seem to be systematically explored but rather practically used in the spiritual care debate and in spiritual care practices.[17] Within the discourse of pastoral care theory, Christian pastoral care for non-Christians is what I call *interfaith spiritual caregiving*.[18] In a postmodern

---

[15] One current example is the debate on equal opportunities of care in the hospital in a pluralistic society. Peter Saladin, ed., *Diversität und Chancengleichheit. Grundlagen für erfolgreiches Handeln im Mikrokosmos der Gesundheitsinstitutionen, mit DVD: Verstehen kann heilen* (Bern: Bundesamt für Gesundheit BAG, 2006).

[16] Leah Dawn Bueckert & Daniel S. Schipani, "Interfaith Spiritual Caregiving. The Case for Language Care," in *Spiritual Caregiving in the Hospital: Windows to Chaplaincy Ministry* (Kitchener: Pandora Press, 2006), 257.

[17] Compare Nancy J. Ramsey, ed., *Pastoral Care and Counseling: Redefining the Paradigms* (Nashville: Abingdon, 2004) and the Stanford example in this essay below.

[18] Compare Bueckert and Schipani, 245–263.

conceptualization every interaction between two individuals can be described as an interfaith encounter.[19] We can reconsider the individualization of spiritual self-conceptions of care receivers to the extent, where similarity of faith between care receiver and caregiver is less pronounced than difference. We name no longer the collective identification of a person with a specific religious preference but the individual (religious or non-religious) faith of a person. Then, interfaith chaplaincy in the hospital is defined as *pastoral care for all religions and all faiths*.

I use the term *interfaith* in spiritual care practice and theory in two dimensions: in interreligious encounters (where two individuals with two distinct religious traditions and with two distinct references to the Holy meet each other) and in interspiritual encounters (where two distinct individuals with two distinct spiritualities meet). *Spirituality* is as an anthropologically applicable construct, a faith that is not necessarily, but can be shaped by one or more religious traditions, and is applied and practiced by an individual.[20] The term spirituality is highly helpful in describing the general human reference towards meaning and transcendence and its consequences for life practice. The term is wide enough to embrace traditional as well as patchwork religiosity, independent of its group-sociological structure. Spirituality is therefore a useful category for describing a by now unclear globalized and multicultural religious landscape. Furthermore, the term is used in medical science, psychology, and nursing science (for example in the debate on religious coping and on spiritual health[21]). While the term spirituality is well established in U.S. American discussions (spiritual care substituting pastoral care for example) and in the health care context, the term still has to be established in the German speaking theological and philosophical debate.[22]

The focus in *this* book and in this essay is on encounters between a professional spiritual caregiver with a different religious tradition than the care receiver. To date, unlike the North American context, in the Swiss context the Protestant caregiver is always an ordained minister of the mainline Protestant Church.

The term *interfaith* is best translated into German by the term

[19] Ibid., 263.

[20] Ulrich Köpf, "Spiritualität," I. Zum Begriff, in RGG (*Religion in Geschichte und Gegenwart*) 7 (2004) 1589–1591 and more differentiated: Karl-Friedrich Wiggermann, "Spiritualität," in TRE (*Theologische Realenzyklopädie*) 31 (2000) 708–717.

[21] In 2008 the international congress on *Religion, Spirituality and Health* (RSH 08) took place in Bern, Switzerland.

[22] Spirituality as a scientific term: Karl Baier, ed., *Handbuch Spiritualität. Zugänge, Traditionen, interreligiöse Prozesse* (Darmstadt: Wissenschaftliche Buchgesellschaft, 2006).

interreligiös (interreligious). In the European academic field *Glauben* (faith) was substituted by *Religion*. This is due to different cultural connotations of the terms *faith* and *religion* and the preference of the term "religion" in the scientific discussion of comparative religious research.[23] In this essay *interfaith* is used synonymously with *interreligious*. Interfaith suits the North American context best while *interreligious* suits the Swiss German context.

The present situation in the Swiss hospitals

In Switzerland, hospital chaplains are ordained theologians of the mainline Protestant Church or qualified assigned theologians of the Catholic Church. In most cases they work in close ecumenical cooperation. Many hold a Master in Theology combined with a thorough training in Clinical Pastoral Education. They are highly professionalized and their pastoral service is surprisingly well-regarded in the secular and religion-critical environment of health care institutions.[24] They play a noteworthy role in the holistic care approach of most modern hospitals.

Hospitals in Switzerland have become multireligious institutions for reasons noted above. Numerous encounters at the hospital bed are encounters between members of different religious communities, and more often, of different spiritual self-understandings.[25] This is due, first of all, to the pluralization of Swiss society through the individualized religious lifestyles of the Swiss people.[26] Second, the increasingly multireligious character of hospitals is due to the migration of people from other cultures and religions; and third, this situation is due to the globalization of Swiss economy, politics, and cultural lifestyle.

---

[23] The term *faith* declined while the term *religion* was preferred in discussions of comparative studies on religions. For the success of the 19th century term *religion* in European intellectual history compare, for example, "Religion," in *TRE* 28 (1997): 513–559.

[24] David Plüss and Dominik Schenker, "Welche Seelsorge hätten Sie den gerne? Oder: Was willst du, dass ich für dich tun soll? (Lk 18,41) Ergebnisse einer Patientinnen- und Patientenbefragung im Kantonsspital Basel," in *PT* (*Praktische Theologie*) 37 (2002): 22–33.

[25] Albrecht Grözinger, "Seelsorge im multikulturellen Krankenhaus," in *WzM* (*Wege zum Menschen*) 47 (1995) 389–400; and Reinhold Gestrich, "Gedanken über die Seelsorge im multireligiösen Krankenhaus und einige praktische Hinweise," in *WzM* 47 (1995): 400–412; Karl Federschmidt, et.al., eds., *Handbuch Interkulturelle Seelsorge*, (Neukirchen-Vluyn: Neukirchener, 2002); Christina Kayales, "Interkulturelle Seelsorge und Beratung. Brücken zu Menschen aus fremden Kulturen," in Pohl-Patalong et.al., eds., *Seelsorge im Plural* (Hamburg: E.B.-Verlag, 1999): 63–73; Kurt W. Schmidt, ed., *(Klinik-)Seelsorge im multireligiösen Kontext*, (Frankfurt a.M.: Zentrum für Ethik in der Medizin, 1999).

[26] For a deeper look into the religious topography of late-modern Switzerland: Alfred Dubach and Brigitte Fuchs, *Ein neues Modell von Religion. Zweite Schweizer Sonderfallstudie–Herausforderung für die Kirchen* (Zürich: TVZ, 2005) and Alfred Dubach, et.al., eds., *JedeR ein Sonderfall? Religion in der Schweiz. Ergebnisse einer Repräsentativbefragung*, (Zürich/Basel: NZN Buchverlag, 1993).

There is a historical reason for the phenomenon of interfaith spiritual care practice of Christian caregivers at the hospital bed of non-Christians and of patients outside the church: mainline churches, Catholic and Protestant, make up 75 percent of the Swiss population. Until the 1970s, the percentage was over 90 percent. The mainline churches, historically and traditionally, have a legally established privileged position within the Swiss society. This situation has a historical basis and implies, for example, that the mainline churches have a societal task and the right to offer pastoral care within the hospital to a population beyond the boundaries of their churches. Hospital chaplains have access to patient data that a parish pastor does not have.

While the membership of mainline churches has declined considerably since 1970, all other significant denominations and religious communities have increased their numbers. The Islamic population for example has almost doubled in Switzerland. In Basel, people with no religious affiliation are by now the biggest minority, followed by Catholics and Protestants. The Muslim population in the city of Basel has increased from 463 individuals in 1970 to 12,643 in the year 2000.[27] This situation in our pluralistic society poses a challenge to all areas of the practical work of ministers and professionals. It is particularly true for the chaplain's situation in the urban hospital.

Interfaith spiritual care inevitably happens in the daily practice of the hospital chaplain. At the same time it is not yet clear how it can be done in a professionally competent and theologically responsible way. So far, the quality and effectiveness of an interfaith spiritual care intervention depends on the chaplain's intuition or self-training. Theory building on clinical training for interfaith encounters in the field of spiritual caregiving is not established yet. Therefore, it is not clear how the hospital chaplains, paid by the mainline churches and motivated by their social responsibility, should respond to the request for interfaith chaplaincy within the hospital as a public institution. The reason for this uncertainty can be found in the European past and more so in the emerging religiously pluralistic situation in the hospitals. So far there is a lack of differentiated reflection on the new pluralistic, multireligious, and multispiritual challenge in Swiss hospitals. In the following paragraph I will briefly address the marginal research done on interfaith (interreligious) spiritual care in the German-speaking context.

Theory building on interfaith spiritual care in Switzerland

The Swiss German discussion is traditionally linked most closely to the

---

[27] http://www.statistik-bs.ch/themen/16/sprachen/konfession.

discourse in Germany. Empirical studies and theoretical reflection on interreligious spiritual care are still in the very early stages, in Germany as well as in Switzerland.

Interfaith or interreligious chaplaincy is a special subject within the wider area of cross cultural chaplaincy.[28] Interfaith chaplaincy theory goes further as it does not simply see religions as part of culture. It sees sees religion as a distinct field within culture and has its distinct questions and challenges that cannot be answered without specific religious and theological competence. The German speaking discussion on *intercultural care* was weaker than in North America and followed with delay.[29] It was not scientifically established until 15 years after David Augsburger's seminal contribution.[30] Since 2001 with the publication of Christoph Schneider-Harpprecht's book on intercultural pastoral care and counseling[31] and the handbook of intercultural pastoral care and counseling,[32] the intercultural pastoral care debate has been established in the German speaking practical theological scientific community.[33] Still, it is not as comprehensive and effective as in the North American discussion.[34] It is noteworthy that the specific questions and problems raised by the interreligious challenge of intercultural pastoral care and counseling were not discussed.[35] Federschmidt analyzes a space that needs

---

[28] Tabitha Walther, "Interfaith Chaplaincy: Pastoral Care for all Religions and all Faiths. A New Perspective for Clinical Pastoral Care in 21ˢᵗ Century Western Europe? A Swiss Protestant View," in Wilhelm Gräb and Lars Charbonnier, eds., *Secularization Theories, Religious Identity and Practical Theology.* (Münster, Berlin, Hamburg, London: LIT, 2008), 416–423. This location of interfaith chaplaincy is also and independently used in the North American context: Bueckert and Schipani, pp. 245 and 262 and several contributions in Ramsay, *Pastoral Care and Counseling: Redefining the Paradigms.*

[29] The beginnings of the intercultural pastoral care debate are to be found in the writings of the *Gesellschaft für interkulturelle Seelsorge* in their journal *Zeitschrift Interkulturelle Seelsorge und Beratung,* Nr. 1–11 (Düsseldorf: SIPCC, 1996–2003).

[30] David W. Augsburger, *Pastoral Counseling Across Cultures* (Philadelphia: Westminster Press, 1986).

[31] Christoph Schneider-Harpprecht, *Interkulturelle Seelsorge* (Göttingen: Vandenhoeck & Ruprecht, 2001).

[32] Karl Federschmidt, et.al., eds., *Handbuch Interkulturelle Seelsorge.*

[33] For a more differentiated and still brief history on cross-cultural chaplaincy in German speaking Europe compare Christoph Schneider-Harpprecht, "Was ist Interkulturelle Seelsorge? Praktisch-theologische Annäherungen," in Karl Federschmidt, et.al., eds., *Handbuch Interkulturelle Seelsorge,* pp. 44–47.

[34] The *DPCC* (2004) mentions the intercultural aspect as one of two paradigmatic shifts in pastoral care since 1990. Compare Nancy J. Ramsay's preface to the second edition, XIII.

[35] Federschmidt states: "Die meisten der hier versammelten Beiträge beziehen den interreligiösen Aspekt selbstverständlich in ihre Überlegungen mit ein. Doch als eigenes Thema wird diese Fragestellung im vorliegenden Handbuch nicht systematisch vertieft.... Eine ... thematische

to be "systematized," "theorized," and "explored theologically."
There has been some literature on *interreligious spiritual care* and counseling and its practical implications in regard to spiritual care for Muslim
patients;[36] but otherwise, there is hardly any conceptualized systematic
reflection on the issue. The only systematic-theological publication on
interreligious spiritual care I am aware of and which tries to formulate
the questions interfaith spiritual care poses to systematic theology is a
"grey literature" booklet from 1999 on pastoral care in the multireligious
context of the hospital.[37] This booklet together with the *Ethik und Praxis
des Helfens in den verschiedenen Religionen*[38] is a good starting point to
explore the practice and theory building of interfaith spiritual care.
Protestant university theology welcomes ecumenical and interreligious approaches in theology. Still the area of theology of religion(s) is
an emerging subject and discussions are controversial. I suggest an empirical detour on the dialogical and theoretical interreligious construction area of the theology of Religion(s): a close description of how interreligious spiritual care happens concretely in Swiss hospitals. With this
empirical detour will we perhaps be able to provide a conceptualized
practical theological reflection on interfaith spiritual care in Switzerland.[39]

Behandlung der interreligiösen Fragestellung hätte … erforderlich gemacht, die sehr
umfangreiche und kontroverse theologische Diskussion zur Frage des interreligiösen Dialogs und
interreligiöser Begegnungen darzustellen." Federschmidt, Karl, "Einführung," in *Handbuch
Interkulturelle Seelsorge*, p 14.

[36] Ulrike Elsdörfer, "Die gläubigen Männer und die gläubigen Frauen sind untereinander
Freunde. Islamische Seelsorge und seelsorgerliche Begegnung mit Muslimen," in *WzM* 50 (2007)
342–353.

[37] Kurt W. Schmidt, ed., *(Klinik-)Seelsorge im multireligiösen Kontext*, (Frankfurt a.M.: Zentrum für
Ethik in der Medizin, 1999). It is a translation and abbreviation of one edition of the journal
Christian Bioethics from 1999 supplemented by a systematic-theological article. Maybe it is
symptomatic that the German discourse felt the need of adding a systematical founding of
interfaith chaplaincy. This booklet takes the US American and the German context into
consideration and puts the focus precisely on matters of inter-religious encounters in hospitals. It
explores generic chaplaincy (*allgemeine Seelsorge*) versus denominational, so called "brand name"
chaplaincy" in a post-Christian age. Furthermore, the booklet illustrates a German Protestant
view on inter-religious chaplaincy in the hospital and searches for Christian criteria in a pastoral
encounter with members of other religions than Christian, discussing the normative implications of an interreligious model. It demonstrates a shift towards a more differentiated perspective, which shows awareness of the tension between practices and theological reflection and
awareness of the tension between different religious self-understandings.

[38] Helmut Weiss, Karl H. Fedeschmidt, and Klaus Temme, eds., *Ethik und Praxis des Helfens in den
verschiedenen Religionen* (Neukircher-Vluyn: Neukirchen, 2005).

[39] Empirical theology starts being accepted in the theological canon of disciplines within the
German speaking practical theology. Astrid Dinter, Hans Günter Heimbrock, and Kerstin
Söderblom, eds., *Einführung in die Empirische Theologie: Gelebte Religion erforschen* (Göttingen:

Analyzing the Swiss situation

For the chaplaincy education of the future we need an educational concept at the university and in CPE training that deals systematically and practically with interreligious issues at the hospital bed. The German speaking research can profit immensely from a strong link to the English speaking spiritual care discussion and vice versa. It needs to overview the scientific discussion on interfaith chaplaincy in Northern America, Australia, the Netherlands, United Kingdom, and elsewhere, focusing on interreligious matters in specific contexts. I see empirical deficiencies in the German world and systematic reflective deficiencies in North America.

In the near future it would be desirable to have non-Christian chaplains in the hospital in order to provide adequate spiritual care to their respective faith tradition.[40] But it must be said that competent interfaith ministry by non-Christian spiritual professionals is not a realistic scenario for Switzerland at the moment. This is due to a lack of theological professionals outside the mainline churches. And this again is because of non-existent university education for other than Christian spiritual leaders. Institutionalized interfaith spiritual care is a reality in California and elsewhere in North America but not in Switzerland. Given the functional needs of the hospital combined with the process of religious pluralization going on in our society, it can also happen in Switzerland in the future.

Analyzing the situation in the Swiss hospitals and the on-going theory building, we understand that although pastoral care practices are highly professional, interfaith spiritual care is provided intuitively. Depending on the CPE supervisor, interreligious dimensions are duly thematized. There is a high and sensible awareness of the differences in an interfaith encounter and the given individual and theological limits inherent in the situation. However, students do not receive adequate systematic, in-

---

Vandenhoeck & Ruprecht, 2007). In the Netherlands, in contrast, a series of books on empirical theology have been published: Johannes A. van der Ven, ed., *Empirical Studies in Theology*, vol. 1–15 (Leiden: Brill, 1998–2007). A methodological problem is how empirical and theological methods inform and ground each other. There is one empirical-theological study on pastoral care in the Swiss hospital: David Plüss and Dominik Schenker, "Welche Seelsorge hätten Sie denn gerne? Oder: Was willst du, dass ich für dich tun soll? (Lk 18:41). Ergebnisse einer Patientinnen-und Patientenbefragung im Kantonsspital Basel," in *PT* 37 (2002), 22–33. There is no empirical data for interfaith pastoral care in the health care institutions. Therefore I cannot provide empirical data here. I claim this is a major task of the future of interfaith research in spiritual care.

[40] This is partly already the present situation in Basel, where a Rabbi and Jewish volunteers are available to care for the Jewish patients.

stitutionalized, and obligatory interfaith education—neither for hospital chaplaincy nor for chaplaincy in general. There are no articulated guidelines at hand for interfaith spiritual care giving. CPE students are trained in ecumenical groups, but they are all (almost exclusively mainline church) Christians. Professional interfaith practitioners could be more effectively trained through interfaith CPE groups and in group interfaith experiences. Most of all there is a lack of empirical data about how interfaith interventions happen in hospitals. Once empirical data are systematically gathered and evaluated, it will be possible to analyze care practices and to design manuals with guidelines for competent interfaith caregiving.

Swiss Practical Theology is in the early stages of conceptualizing interfaith practices in the hospital. It can, therefore, learn from an already existing and functioning interfaith model such as the model of the spiritual care department at Stanford University Hospital and Clinics. This model will be introduced in the following section and brought in dialogue with the Swiss situation.

In dialogue with a North American model of interfaith spiritual care

The Stanford University Hospital and Clinics are located in the multicultural and multireligious, pluralistic society of the San Francisco Bay Area. This area holds an immense spectrum of religious identities and self-understandings. This denominational and religious plurality at Stanford necessitates a distinct chaplaincy model within the hospital.

The Spiritual Care Department at Stanford University Hospital and Clinics employs, beside the Administrative Associate, six full-time chaplains with different religious affiliations: the Director (Presbyterian), Associate Director (Roman Catholic priest), the CPE Coordinator (African Methodist Episcopal Zion), the Decedent Care Chaplain (Lutheran), and the Cancer Care Chaplain (Jewish). In addition the Spiritual Care Department has three independently contracted chaplains who are not hospital employees but who are financially supported by their faith groups: one Episcopal, one Jewish and one LDS (Latter Day Saints/Mormon). Further, the Spiritual Care Department consists of about 250 volunteers who are divided into the following faith groups: Buddhist, Jewish, Interfaith (different Protestant and Charismatic Christian Denominations), Hindu, LDS, Muslim, Roman Catholic, and Sikh.

The hospital chaplains and the CPE students are responsible for medical units and therefore work as interfaith chaplains. The unit chaplain belongs to the medical team. The unit is the multireligious and multispiritual community of the interfaith chaplain. Patients with other religious preferences than the unit chaplain are also visited by a minister or volunteer of their respective denomination. All varieties of Protestant faiths (for example Pentecostal, Presbyterian, Baptist, Episcopal, Lutheran, Evangelical, and Methodist) are identified on the admittance sheet. All Protestant chaplains and volunteers serve all Protestant denominations. They form the so called "Interfaith" group which works mainly interdenominationally rather than interreligiously.

The educational concept at Stanford is embedded in the Spiritual Care Department. The CPE students are trained cross-culturally and interreligiously. Classes are taught on different religious preferences and their specific needs and spiritual resources. Students are trained in interfaith ministry during on-call duty at night and during weekends when they are the only hospital chaplain present providing spiritual care to patients of all religions and all faiths. The on-call chaplains in training reflect and share their interreligious experiences in the CPE group.

Different spiritual services can be offered by the Christian, Jewish or other interfaith chaplain. The chaplain is free to offer whatever is possible according to her vocation and faith-based standards. Patients are free to ask for or accept what fits their spiritual needs. They can also request a chaplain of their own faith group to be called to the bedside. For example, in the case of death in a Buddhist family the family can ask to have a monk of their specific tradition be called into the hospital. In that case the interfaith chaplain is responsible for triaging the request adequately. The chaplain can advocate the spiritual needs of the family towards staff and hospital, for example, by enabling a chanting ritual where the dead body is not touched by physicians and nurses during the Buddhist time of transition.

The general Stanford Hospital concept of spiritual care providing is to mobilize the spiritual resources of a patient and/or family in the time of crisis, illness, or loss, and to address and respond to their spiritual needs on their own terms.

The Stanford model is a pragmatic model of spiritual caregiving. It has grown organically out of the needs of the hospital. The overall approach is not, per se, oriented by theological views or filled with religious content, but with techniques and methods. In any event, through the educational process of CPE trained chaplains, mature spiritual caregivers are aware of their theological, cultural, denominational, and religious backgrounds and identities and have developed their cultural and religious profile as a major resource for spiritual care giving.

272 | Interfaith spiritual care

This pragmatic model at Stanford functions very effectively. It can offer its service to everyone who is willing to receive support, no matter what their religious affiliation (or non-affiliation) is. Quantitatively speaking, it can provide caregiving service to many. However, it is often unable to provide adequate *qualitative* service. This is frequently due to marginal and superficial knowledge or ignorance of the other faith traditions, and sometimes due to an uncritical approach towards religion and spirituality by some interfaith caregivers. Furthermore, Stanford provides no explicit understanding and conceptualization of either interreligious realities or a theological foundation for their model. Nevertheless, it provides and practices interfaith spiritual caregiving and holds a clear commitment to interfaith ministry. It leaves the question of the theological framing of the interreligious interaction to the chaplain's own truth claims and exclusively to the individual chaplain. Considering the affirmation of the equality of all faiths in light of the U.S. constitution, this is a politically appropriate understanding. In terms of professionalism and excellence it would be wishful to improve the quality of interfaith spiritual care through profound interfaith education.

Maybe it is an especially European preference and a fruit of the academic discipline of Practical Theology that a practical pastoral model must be sustained and founded by an interreligious theory that undergirds the mission of the spiritual care services and defines objective criteria. Still, to have the Stanford model translated and adapted to a European context practicality standing by itself cannot suffice. A critical theory of the interreligious practices at the hospital bed is expected for the Swiss context.

The Stanford model cannot be simply transferred to the Swiss hospital as such. It would not fit the Swiss religious landscape and the place of religion within the public sphere. However, the Stanford model can be translated into the religious landscape of Switzerland in terms of an important *transfer of experience and know-how*. The Swiss can assess a functioning interfaith model and learn from it and from its interfaith chaplains in order to design a Swiss model of interfaith chaplaincy under the highly individualized, postmodern, and globalized conditions of our pluralistic society. Interviews with members of the spiritual care team, especially the interfaith ministers, would help to reconstruct the inherent implicit theological foundation of the interfaith chaplain at Stanford and to understand how interfaith practice happens and what functions practically and what does not. At a future point, although ethically and politically difficult, it would be desirable to analyze the interfaith spiritual care situation as such, and to have the patients as well as hospital staff and hospital leadership interviewed.

Under the rainbow: Ideas for a theological foundation of an interfaith spiritual care model in the Swiss hospital

In this section I introduce the theological dilemma of interfaith spiritual caregiving and bring forth some ideas of how this practice could be theologically framed. The assumption is that there really is a systematic-theological dilemma in interfaith spiritual caregiving. The dilemma arises when the Christian spiritual caregiver comes in contact with members of other religious traditions. The dilemma is theoretically addressed in the *en vogue* theology of religion(s). This theology poses the following question: What is the relation between Christianity and other Religions? Or in other words: What is the status of non-Christians in terms of salvation, given that salvation is at the core of Lutheran and Reformed theology, the very gospel? This is the theological dilemma in very simple words if we look at religion(s) in terms of homogeneous entities with homogeneous convictions. It is not a new theological question, but one that became more crucial under globalized conditions and religious traditions living together in the same nations and neighbourhoods. Until 1900 an absolute truth claim for Christianity against other religious traditions was prominently put forth. Since then, new approaches to the problem are manifold.[41] The approach in Practical Theology can be characterized as such: Practical Theology no longer looks at faith systems and religions as such, but on the lived religion (*gelebte Religion*) of individuals, religious communities and societies. Practical Theology is interested in the concrete praxis of religion(s) in contact with other faith traditions. Practical Theology establishes a pragmatic and performative concept rather than a theological framework.

In the modern theological discourse there are mainly three models visible of how to interpret the status of non-Christians by academic theology as well as by individual and congregational convictions and their interactions with people from a religion other than their own.[42] The three models can be described as the *neutral position* (pluralist theology of religion), the *exclusive position* (exclusivist theology of religion) and the *intermediate position* (inclusivist theology of religion). The neutral

---

[41] Reinhold Bernhardt, *Der Absolutheitsanspruch des Christentums. Von der Aufklärung bis zur pluralistischen Religionstheologie* (Gütersloh: Gütersloher Verlagshaus Gerd Mohn, 1993) and Christian Danz and Ulrich H.J. Körtner, eds., *Theologie der Religionen. Positionen und Perspektiven evangelischer Theologie* (Neukirchen-Vluyn: Neukirchener, 2005).

[42] Alan Race, *Christians and Religious Pluralism. Patterns in the Christian Theology of Religion* (London: SCM Press, (1993).

position eases the Christological soteriology into a pluralist position, holding every religious truth claim democratically equal. This position is very popular with individuals holding a multireligious identity. The exclusive position conserves an absolute truth claim. It can be observed in certain congregations and individuals in the USA (i.e. new born Christians) but also in some Charismatic and Evangelical congregations and individuals in Switzerland.

I opt for an intermediate position. This position sustains the tension between the exclusivist claim of the biblical tradition, such as the Pauline *solus Christus* while holding reasonable respect and appreciation for other religious traditions and vitally counting on the healing and saving power that exists within them. It eschatologically expects the Holy to release the soteriological tension. Indeed, those holding this view propose to live out of such soteriological hope. An interfaith chaplain, working out of such concept is not in the need to missionize the other.

An example of a biblical founding of this understanding is the story of God's covenant with Noah after the flood (Gen 9, 8–17). According to the story every creature is included in God's covenant with Noah. Systematizing this story into New Testament theology, Christ does not realize God's salvation but reveals and symbolizes God's acceptance of every creature. In God's covenant with Noah the Jewish Israel is primarily included, then the other people (ethnoi) through participation in the covenant with Noah. Christianity has lived out of this participation in the Jewish story with God from the very beginning. Christ communicates the Good News of the Old Testament rather than bringing it forth. Out of this systematic theological argument hope is held that people (believing or not believing in Christ) are carried through God's covenant with the whole creation by God. As the sign of Gods invisible covenant the story tells that God sets the rainbow as a visible sign for this covenant. To put it metaphorically: I see interfaith spiritual care as happening under the rainbow. To have community with people from outside one's own faith tradition but under the same rainbow can be interpreted as a human covenant giving sign to God's peace creating acts.[43]

Practical-theologically these very short biblical and systematic walks have the following consequences for the practical work of interfaith spiritual caregivers: interfaith chaplains must learn to bear the potential in-

---

[43] Another New Testament passage encouraging interfaith relationships can be found in Paul's writings. Paul sees non-Christian spouses of Christians as sanctified through their believing spouse (1 Cor 7, 12–16). There is not enough time and space here to go further into details or other biblical examples.

ner conflict between their own religious identity and its possible intrinsic truth claim, on the one hand, and true respect for the otherness of the other on the other hand. I argue that a theology which denies differences and affirms sameness ("neutral" position) misses the heart of the Christian faith tradition and maybe the heart of any religious tradition. The same is true for a fundamentalist theology that cannot accept the possibility of religious truth in a faith outside his or her faith community (exclusive position). There interfaith pastoral care becomes easily an occasion to missionize and uses spiritual pressure rather than an option to grow spiritually and love the stranger. From a Swiss Protestant perspective much, if not all, soteriological tension can be released into Christ's open arms and into God's world embracing covenant. We are set free to search for human covenants with non-Christians, for example in the interfaith spiritual care situation.

Still, there might be individual religious and spiritual boundaries and limits that should not be crossed for the sake of the other or of oneself. These limits become most relevant in prayer, rituals, and sacraments. For example, it has to be respected if a devout Catholic wants the priest to conduct the sacrament of the sick or if a Jewish or Baptist chaplain cannot baptize a newborn child herself, but can guide a family in doing so.

Here again it becomes visible why empirical research needs to be undertaken and why case studies and qualitative interviews with spiritual care givers and patients should be done to explore sameness, overlap, and otherness in interfaith chaplaincy encounters when performing prayers and rituals or use of *religious myths*.[44] It will also help to understand to what extend it is a cultural otherness and to what extend it is a religious otherness. In my own experience as a former spiritual care giver at Stanford and Basel, interreligious encounters at the bedside can make the religiously different intuitively understandable. This religious difference is not only felt towards people of another religion, but also of a secular, low-profile religiosity combining elements and symbols from different cultures and religions. In Switzerland the majority of Jews, Christians, and Muslims are secular, though religious. The Holy can be met sometimes in an encounter with the stranger and sometimes not.[45] Every interreligious encounter bears the risk of learning something substantial

---

[44] Albrecht Grözinger, "Seelsorge im multikulturellen Krankenhaus," in *WzM* 47 (1995) 389–400.

[45] Theo Sundermeier, *Den Fremden verstehen. Eine praktische Hermeneutik* (Göttingen: Vandenhoeck & Ruprecht, 1996) and Heike Walz et al., eds. *Als hätten sie uns neu erfunden. Beobachtungen zu Fremdheit und Geschlecht*, (Luzern: Edition Exodus, 2003).

for my own spiritual path or even of things being created anew and of (my) human (Christian) existence being transformed.

Above, I gave the biblical example of God's covenant with Noah to sustain interfaith practices at the bedside of the non-Christian sick or dying. It could also be sustained through the most powerful construct of God within the Christian tradition: the notion of God as the Trinity. Here, we could argue that the trinitarian concept that sets the difference of personhood (*persona*) as explored in the concept of the Trinity in analogy to the three *personae* of God: If God is relationally differentiated as Father, Son, and Holy Spirit, the notion of relational difference is given in God's very being. In analogy to God's very being again, we can argue that every human being is a light to the other on the path to the Holy, and interfaith ministry tries to walk this path. It is a ministry that values and respects plurality with all its difficulties and beauties.[46] It will be most interesting to enter into conversation with non-Christian spiritual caregivers as they articulate their own understandings and design their own interreligious guidelines while seeking to provide competent professional care.

The arguments above lay it near that at least for the Swiss context a reflected confessional grounding is wanted and needed in contrast, for example, to a generic chaplaincy model with low profile chaplains. The reflection happens also through serious hermeneutics of classical and postmodern concepts of the theology of religion(s) and the reflection of the core of the Protestant faith, the sola fide.

Practical suggestions for future interfaith chaplaincy: Learning from Stanford without copying

Without having conducted empirical research in depth, only some modest practical steps can be outlined at this point for the Swiss situation.

- For the Swiss pluralistic society we need a new structural openness to serve people of other than mainline churches and other than Christian or not religious. This is only possible if we modify the educational paradigm and train theology students and CPE students in interfaith encounters as an inclusive part of spiritual care education. Chaplains from other religious traditions would take part and educate the others within the educational process. Protestant students for example will have to learn that they serve patients as Christians in the name and mission of their religious community, the Protestant Church. The soteriological question has to be some-

---

[46] Hans Joas, *Die Entdeckung der Werte* (Frankfurt a.M.: Suhrkamp, 2001).

how reflected as demonstrated above, but has to be eschatologically kept open.[47] In addition, the Jewish, Christian, and Muslim vocation to care for the stranger and the non-believer will be taken seriously.

• I opt for a close international conversation, not only between the English and the German speaking world of clinical pastoral care, but beyond that world as well. This way we have access to the best interfaith practices being linked to the best hermeneutics and systematic concepts through a mutual exchange of knowledge and expertise. Similar to every interfaith encounter, if we are open to listening to each other we can transform our practices and theories into a greater wisdom; and we can learn from each other and from the other context what we need to know as competent caregivers encountering patients with a different faith, while standing firm on our theological and existential foundation, namely, the Triune God who has chosen to manifest Herself in the plurality of Her creation. To the best of my knowledge, the North American Model of CPE operates with similar understandings whenever students are trained in interfaith groups.

• Further, I claim that sensitivity to religious difference should be part of the training right from the beginning of a chaplaincy career in a Swiss hospital. Therefore, ministers from other than Catholic and Protestant traditions who are religiously tolerant and are grounded in a religious tradition and hold a theological university education should be admitted to the CPE education, such as Jewish chaplains or rabbis, Evangelical and Charismatic pastors, as well as Muslim professional caregivers. Religious tolerance includes a care approach without missionizing.

• I am not suggesting that a Protestant or Catholic chaplain cannot serve the religiously different. They can and they do. It practically and intuitively works out in many situations. But, in pluralistic societies and under globalized conditions the spiritual needs of today's patients should be met by someone within their own faith tradition whenever possible, especially if patients have an exclusive and high religious profile linked to a specific faith community; for example, orthodox Jews or Evangelical Christians. Only if this service is not available should the Catholic or Protestant chaplain be responsible for *professional spiritual support*. As long as only the Catho-

---

[47] Christine Janowski, *Allerslösung, Annäherungen an eine entdualisierte Eschatologie*, 2 Vol. (Neukirchen-Vluyn: Neukirchener, 2000).

lic or Protestant professional chaplains are trained and available for institutionalized hospital ministry, the churches must take on the interreligious challenge and provide interfaith spiritual care as effectively as they can. This is particularly true in emergency situations.

- In any case, CPE students and spiritual care givers will have to engage in critical conversation with their traditional and modern concepts of interreligious encounters. For the most intimate interreligious encounter at the bedside Protestant ministers are expected to serve with compassion, respect and appreciation for any human being who is religiously grounded in a religious tradition other than their own or not religious, *and*, at the same time, to be aware of the unsolved and not understood differences revealed in the encounter with the stranger.

- In case of individual religious and spiritual boundaries and limits towards other religions, these limits should not be crossed for the sake of the other or oneself but be respected. These limits become most relevant in prayer, rituals, and sacraments and have to be respected in any case.

- Moving from intercultural towards interfaith spiritual care theory we are challenged to develop a concept for interreligious spiritual care for Swiss hospital chaplains that no longer works merely out of the intuition of the interfaith chaplain alone but provides certain criteria and guidelines for interfaith practice. This perspective can be offered to other hospitals with a similar sociological context.

Conclusion: reflective interfaith praxis in 21st Century Switzerland

Due to individualization, migration, and globalization of the Swiss society, Swiss Practical Theology will not only have to think about a new model of spiritual caregiving in the hospital that is able to embrace all faiths and all religious traditions. Rather, Practical Theology will have to think about *interfaith chaplaincy in general*, because the multireligious reality also touches Swiss school education and education of the adult, as well as multireligious wedding services and services of remembrance. I expect interfaith chaplaincy to become an essential professional competence of nowadays Swiss pastors and chaplains. Last but not least, the future will show if interfaith spiritual care will more and more become a professional reality, a reflective praxis rather than an intuitive practice of spiritual care providers in the Swiss hospital.

The junction of the seas
Interfaith spiritual care in the Netherlands

Ari van Buuren, Mualla Kaya and Bart ten Broek

This three-part essay reflects the collaborative work of the writers and is offered to the readers of this book as a joint contribution from the Netherlands. Ari van Buuren starts with a characterization of the Dutch context. His essay clarifies the developments in the Netherlands and the pioneering program he founded at the University Medical Centre in Utrecht. He then describes the salient features of the new model by highlighting core values that inspire and orient its implementation. In the second part, Mualla Kaya presents a gender specific approach in spiritual care from a Muslim perspective. Finally, Bart ten Broek discusses an educational model aimed at fostering community and formation in a multifaith society.

Part One:
A New Model of Spiritual Care for a Multifaith Society

Ari van Buuren

A few words about the setting where we practice interfaith spiritual care are in order. The UMC Utrecht functions as a medical training hospital serving thousands of in- and outpatients in various clinics on site. It

Ari van Buuren, Drs. Theol., is the Head of the Department of Guidance and Spiritual Care (DLGV: Dienst voor Levensoriëntatie & Geestelijke Verzorging) at the University Medical Centre (UMC) in Utrecht, the Netherlands.

Mualla Kaya, Drs. Theol., is a Muslim theologian and spiritual caregiver; she is a member of the spiritual care teams at the University Medical Center (UMC) located in Utrecht and in the Altrecht, the Netherlands.

Bart ten Broek is a Gestalt therapist and a former teacher and school administrator; he serves as educational advisor in The Hague, the Netherlands, and as a trainer in intercultural and interreligious communication. He is the secretary of the Dutch branch of the United Religions Initiative.

functions also as a medical training hospital with about twelve thousand employees. The Department of Guidance and Spiritual Care (DLGV) serves patients, helps train medical students and is especially available as a resource for ethical liaison with hospital staff. In the words of Donald M. Berwick, "as caregivers we are guests in the life of our patients."[1] This conviction informs the basic philosophy of the polyclinic.

The DLGV team is made up of a diverse group of ten spiritual care givers—four men and six women—representing five spiritual streams: Roman-Catholic, Protestant, Humanist, Muslim, and Hindu. The members of the team are highly conscious of the fact that they operate in a secular as well as a multireligious society; indeed, for us that is the essence of learning to live together with differences![2]

Interculturalization: The choice that makes a difference

The post-war years have brought about many changes in the Netherlands. De-colonization led to independence from the Netherlands of the largely Islamic Indonesia and later of multireligious Surinam. This, in turn, triggered a migration to our country from the former colonies for political or economic reasons. Many of these immigrants settled in the Netherlands such as Moluccans from Indonesia and Hindustanis from Surinam. Simultaneously, immigrants from the autonomous Dutch Antilles (Aruba, Curacao and Bonaire) also migrated. In later years there has been an influx of unskilled workers from Turkey and Morocco who also settled in the Netherlands. Due to the Dutch policy of universal acceptance there followed a large immigration of refugees from many international destinations. Since the events of 9-11 this influx has been severely curtailed by the Dutch government.

Of a total population of sixteen million people there are currently one million Muslims, a number close to that of Christian migrants, and about 150,000 Hindu immigrants from Surinam. All this means that other cultures and religions have been introduced through immigration and have an influence on Dutch society. Or, to be metaphorical about it, this shift can be likened to the junction of the seas as mentioned in koranic Surah 18:60.[3] To paraphrase:

---

[1] Donald M.Berwick is Director of the Institute for Healthcare Improvement (IHI) at Cambridge, Massachusetts. The awareness that we are guests in the life of our patients is foundational for Berwick. See www.ihi.org

[2] Together with his Humanist colleague Alphons van Dijk, Ari van Buuren discusses interculturalization in the Dutch New Handbook of Spiritual Care (*Nieuw Handboek Geestelijke Verzorging*, [Kampen: Kok, 2006]).

[3] The Dutch interdenominational broadcasting corporation IKON started in December 2007 a

as the water flows:
the riverbed leads the flow,
the flow changes the riverbed....

The fall of the Berlin Wall in 1989 has not seen the emergence of a better world. After anti-communism and Russia-phobia a new phobia has entered the arena: Islamophobia. This irrational fear escalated world-wide in the wake of 9-11 and still more in the Netherlands since the murder of film producer Theo van Gogh by a Muslim extremist in November 2004.

The political image of a multicultural society has been shattered and stranded somewhere between individualization and socialization. Many sought an escape in subcultures, prejudice or hatred. Right-wing nationalist politician Geert Wilders' controversial film "Fitna" (2008) documenting his one-sided crusade against Islam illustrates this trend.

The Dutch Ministry of Healthcare did not want to simply resign itself to these developments. Its report on the "Interculturalization of Healthcare" (2000) acknowledged the crucial importance of the Department of Interfaith Spiritual Care in the UMC Utrecht for the future. Currently the UMC Utrecht adheres firmly to the principles of cultural diversity. In fact, for having articulated and institutionally embodied such ideal, our Department was awarded the German INTR°A-Preis 2005 for the Complementarity of Religions.[4]

It thus appears that a new course for interculturalization is being charted. The UMC Utrecht Centre for Guidance and Interfaith Spiritual Care wishes to take the lead in this process. This stance contrasts with the alternative of non-committal co-existence; instead, a clear *choice* has been made. The Dutch model of interculturalization proposes a policy of active exchange and cross-fertilization.

This is also the aim of the new Dutch Integration Program for Immigrants introduced in January 2007. I am also involved in this endeavor as chair of the new Wico Bunskoek Academy (WBA) at the socio-cultural training center Kontakt der Kontinenten.[5] The WBA will become an institute with the mission of supporting religious leaders who have migrated from different countries. As the Lord Mayor of Amsterdam Job Cohen has repeatedly affirmed, these leaders are vital for promoting cohesion in society! This is one effective way to foster interculturalization

---

wonderful Koran and Bible side by side website, comparing Bible and Koran material; see www.quranandbible.net

[4] See www.interreligio.de

[5] See www.kontaktderkontinenten.nl, www.wbacademie.nl, and www.wrr.nl

and interreligious dialogue and collaboration.

Professionalization

Spiritual care in Dutch healthcare is no longer the domain of the Church. Pastoral care or hospital chaplaincy was traditionally part of the identity of Roman Catholic and Protestant hospitals. Originally there was no such care in non-denominational hospitals. But today spiritual care is part of the healthcare system as a whole.

For about thirty years, spiritual care in our secular society has been subject to a process of transformation, integration, and professionalization. This process was legalized in 1996 as part of the "Kwaliteitswet Zorginstellingen" (Quality Law on Health Care). Throughout the health care system spiritual care is financed by healthcare institutions and not by the churches as is the case in Germany, for example. Funding for health services in the Netherlands is starting to feel the limitations of the free market because of a new health insurance system. This situation presents a challenge for hospitals: to what degree should they specialize in providing spiritual care?

Professionalization has meant that Roman Catholic or Protestant chaplains and Humanist caregivers (if appointed) do not just serve their "own" people, but provide spiritual care to the public at large, including "non-believers." The exclusivity of spiritual care along denominational lines is definitely a thing of the past. That is a very significant change. Incidentally, many more people are now exhibiting a mix of spiritual convictions and lifestyles. The Christian and Humanist spiritual caregivers operate within a specified geographic area within the healthcare institution. Each of them is responsible for certain nursing units. Within the organization as a whole there is close and active contact with other disciplines.

This new approach to spiritual care provides patients with the space to find their own unique source of meaning and comfort in their life. Such type of care operates in a Socratic way and uses the *maieutic* or "midwife" method.[6] Secularization draws on and promotes this view. For that very reason the presence of Humanist, non-religious care giving is essential as a reflection of secular society.

Transformation

Society is not only becoming increasingly secular, it is also becoming

---

[6] The "Socratic way" is analogous to a dialogical and dialectical method of teaching in that listening well and asking certain questions help care receivers to tap their own spiritual resources for healing.

more and more multicultural. Both these aspects are reflected and taken into consideration in the approach adopted by the DLGV. Making spiritual guidance more multicultural begins by recognizing equal rights for all caregivers and therefore a transformation of the status quo. The "Interfaith Spiritual Care Project" led by Daniel S. Schipani and Leah Dawn Bueckert in the United States and documented in the first part of this book is a very good example of Christian pastoral caregivers being trained to engage in interfaith care with people of other faiths in a professional manner. However, from our perspective, that project is not transformative enough because we hold a more all-embracing concept of interfaith care. Our model calls for the broadest possible representation of care givers, all of whom enjoying the same status within the health care team.

When we look at the situation in Europe, it seems that the next step should be the appointment of non-Christian spiritual caregivers in health care centers. Only then will we see conditions to foster more professionalization. Initially, Muslim and Hindu caregivers in the Netherlands worked only for their own people (as their Christian and Humanist colleagues originally did). But the history of emancipation repeats itself: soon they will also work within a given area of the health care institution just as their Christian and Humanist colleagues do since the 1970s.

Emancipation from the limitations of the traditional model of spiritual care has made slow progress, however. The question is, are directors in the healthcare system properly prepared and willing to invest in interculturalization in all its various forms, including in its staffing policy? We believe that the DLGV at the UMC Utrecht is at the forefront of spiritual care provision. In spite of this, it was only in November 2007 that a hospital wide conference was held to implement interculturalization. The conference was organized by the DLGV in cooperation with the Patient Communication Department, the Training Department and the Management of the Children's Hospital.

The UMC Utrecht started to employ a Muslim colleague with Turkish background in 1996. His successor has a Moroccan background. The first female Muslim colleague—Mualla Kaya, who has a Turkish background—joined in 2005 alongside a Hindu caregiver with a Surinamese background. This way we have sought to ensure that our spiritual care services include not only various religious backgrounds and traditions but also diverse cultures and both genders. We hold that such representation makes the difference!

When Buddhist, Hindu, Jewish, Muslim, and Winti spiritual caregivers join the healthcare profession as well as the prison system and others, it immediately sets in motion an irreversible process of renewal, interaction, and interculturalization. In addition, in their role as advisors and consultants, the spiritual caregivers play an active role in setting values, norms and ethical standards for medical students and doctors, nurses, and other employees. The DLGV is also making a growing contribution to the teaching dimension that is so important for any University Medical Center. This development is giving new impetus to the field of spiritual care and the training of caregivers in the Netherlands. Muslim caregivers are currently being trained at the Free University of Amsterdam and the IUR/Islamic University in Rotterdam and also includes additional training in Clinical Pastoral Education.

At the forefront

I do not underestimate the fact that some more traditional types of caregivers have been somewhat marginalized, either because they are unable to position themselves adequately as competent professionals, are too modest or, possibly, even theologically frustrated by the changing environment of our multifaith society. In any event, consistently intercultural and interfaith spiritual care has come to the fore. This type of care and counseling has become the way of the future. We wholeheartedly promote it but not as in a kind of holy war against other models. It should be noted, however, that there is an internal "holy war," as it were, in both the Christian and Islamic faith that seeks to focus on a blessing (*zegen*) rather than a victory (*zege*). For his part, Jesus did not encourage a crusade; rather he made a call to follow his way of life. Similarly, properly understood, a "jihad" in Islam points to nothing but the struggle against the tyranny of one's ego.

In short, human interaction could be determined by what Jacob said in his spiritual wrestling with the unknown at the Jabbok River: "I will not let you go unless you bless me" (Genesis 32:26). Who is this unknown person? Is it God, an angel, a demon, his brother Esau hurt by Jacob himself, his alter ego or his shadow side? The interpretation is not exclusive "or/or," but inclusive "and/and." In other words, each individual can be viewed as a mixture of multiple selves.

This Jacob narrative is a model Bible story foundational for a theology of interpersonal, intercultural, and interreligious encounter and interaction. The essence is not the victory but welcoming the other and celebrating the blessing! Later on Jacob says to his brother Esau: "to see your face is like seeing the face of God...." (Genesis 33:10) The biblical Hebrew says literally and clearly that we must seek grace and God's peace in each other's eyes. It is the art of living and the art of living together to seek grace in each other's eyes on all levels: on the micro-, mid-, and macro-level.

Now more than ever, there is a need to learn to live together with differences by learning a common human language to help bridge-building. The French-Lebanese writer Amin Maalouf[7] and the French inter-religious writer Eric-Emmanuel Schmitt are great examples in this hermeneutical field.[8]

All this can take place at the grassroots of every interreligious meeting. This kind of grace occurs on a daily basis in hospitals. Healthcare, then, can function as a fertile proving ground for interreligious synergy. It is an opportunity for patients from different spiritual backgrounds to meet each other, and sometimes engage in a mini dialogue. Hospital employees also have to work together to discuss and adapt norms, values, and ethics. Guidance from the DLGV and training in spiritual and ethical issues faced by medical and nursing staff, make possible to foster and develop those interaction skills and to apply them to the caregiving relationship. That process can enhance treatment offered to patients at a deeper level.

Illness or death can become the occasion for a deepening of the psyche. As the American psychiatrist Jean Shinoda Bolen suggests, every crisis or illness could mean the beginning of a spiritual journey. This reflects the belief that the psyche frees herself like a butterfly out of her cocoon. In Greek, the word *psyche* means both soul and butterfly. For Theresa of Avila it is *the* metaphor for spiritual transformation and it happens in only half an hour. Authors such as Elisabeth Kübler-Ross and Raimon Panikkar often refer to this metaphor.[9]

Passion and compassion

At the level of the soul we are finding our way out of the cocoon of wounds to that of wonderment, out of the cocoon of human passions into the realm of godly compassion. Compassion goes much deeper than having pity. My Dutch language therefore makes a difference between "mede-lijden" and "mede-dogen." Compassion means *mededogen*, as the

---

[7] Amin Maalouf has been living in Paris since the start of the Lebanese Civil War (1975-1989). Among other works, he wrote *The Crusades Through Arab Eyes* (New York: Schocken Books, 1984) and *In the Name of Identity: Violence and the Need to Belong* (New York: Arcade, 2000).

[8] Eric-Emmanuel Schmitt (1960) wrote in *Le Cycle de l'Invisible* (Paris: Albin Michel, 2002) a series of four novels dealing with childhood and spirituality: "Oscar and The Lady in Pink," "M. Ibrahim and the Flowers of the Coran," "Noah's Child" and "Milarepa." These plays are very well-known in Europe and also often staged.

[9] See Kübler-Ross and Panikkar, passim. See especially Jean Shinoda Bolen's classic book, *Close to the Bone: Life-Threatening Illness as a Soul Journey*, rev. ed (San Francisco: Conari Press, 2007).

Dalai Lama emphasizes, for example. Christ demonstrates compassion. Every Surah of Koran opens with the words, "in the name of Allah, the Compassionate."

I have learned to practice the way from passion to compassion in spiritual exercises within the United Religions Initiative (URI). To play with words, I would say, yes: URI = You Are I![10] I suggest we should allow ourselves to be surprised by the differences between religions. These differences reflect the diverse qualities of religious and spiritual traditions. They reflect the unique value and riches of those traditions. Let us mutually seek to experience the "amazing grace" of this all. It can happen in only half an hour....

As I have experienced, let's allow ourselves to be surprised by

- the religious surrender in Islam
- the guarding of autonomy in Humanism
- the wisdom of love in Buddhism
- the reverence for life in Hinduism
- God's partnership in Judaism
- the power of love in Christianity

Isn't this wonderment actually enriching rather than threatening?

This enriching spiritual plurality is reflected in the intercultural Center of Silence of the UMC Utrecht (at the AZU-location). The DLGV had decided to relinquish the idea of a mono-cultural Christian chapel in favor of a multicultural and interfaith Centre of Silence. This Center of Silence is the architectural creation of Jack de Valk, who is a Roman Catholic colleague as well as an architect. The Board of Directors authorized him to erect it when the UMC moved to the new campus situated at "De Uithof" in 1989.

Jack de Valk has applied the philosophy of the *agora* (the Greek word for "market"), the open space with room for the soul. He formulated the following "Ten Commandments for a Center of Silence":

I. The spiritual caregivers present their program requirements with the directors responsible for construction. Part of the motivation is that, among others, the human being is not like a repairable mechanism or object of medical care. The Center of Silence is open seven days a week, twenty-four hours a day, as material space shows the immaterial (spiritual) aim.

II. The Center of Silence must be easily accessible and centrally

---

[10] The author chairs the Dutch branch of the United Religions Initiative. See www.uri.org

situated in the hospital. clearly demarcated, accessible to wheel-chairs and partially see-through doors.

The greater the contrast of the surroundings—for example the nearby-situated shops and restaurant—the greater the expressive nature of the Center.

III. In contrast to the interior decoration of the general building the Center needs to be given its own interior identity with, for ex-ample its own shape, special lighting, characteristic color scheme, solid floor, clearly demarcated walls, and comfortable furniture. A balance needs to be maintained between too luxurious or too monastic.

IV. The interior of the Center needs to have a focal point. To main-tain a sense of calm, excessive devotional paraphernalia, flowers, plants, and functional furniture have to be avoided. The space has to be empty and in this way open for individual thoughts, musing, reflection, and meditation.

V. If adequate space is available differentiation may denote Chris-tian devotion or meditation, Islamic prayer, Jewish lamentation, Humanist introspection, etc.

This, however, remains always in open relation to each other: one unified space means solidarity, tolerance, and respect in or-der to promote interculturality.

VI. In a paradoxical way the archetypical symbols always signify good and bad.

Water means freshness and drowning: baptism and cleansing ritu-als have to do with it. Fire stands for warmth, light, and destruc-tion: Mecca, Easter Candle, incense. Space can be breath-giving and breath-taking. Note that the presence of symbols can cause uniform interpretation, this may be desirable or not....

VII. In smaller spaces the different accents are to be concentrated together to strengthen each other. Wide distribution leads to dis-traction.

VIII. In spite of the focus of the Center of Silence the furniture needs to be movable in connection with different uses such as baptism, unction, bereavement counseling, etc. Besides chairs and seats for meditation a comfortable couch is needed for individuals to lounge in.

IX. Space for Holy Books: Torah, Bible, Koran, Bhagavad-Gita, Veda and for Humanist literature etc. According to the aim of the Center specific literature is accentuated or lies beside on a bookshelf. A book for prayers or thoughts on a desk (accessible by a wheel-chair operant) can be helpful for people to express themselves; it also can be used in worship.

X. The Center of Silence is not a church, chapel, mosque, temple or synagogue. Rather, it functions as an open space where people can refresh themselves from their own source as well as enrich themselves with the sources of others.

The Center is open 24 hours a day, 7 days a week and is not to be used in a multifunctional way.

Dag Hammarskjöld, former Secretary General of the United Nations, formulated some subtle thoughts about the UN's Meditation Room in 1957. "We all have within us a centre of stillness surrounded by silence. This house, dedicated to work and debate in the service of peace, should have a room dedicated to silence in the outward sense and stillness in the inner sense. It has been the aim to create in this small room a place where the doors may be open to infinite lands of thought and prayer. People of many faiths will meet here and for that reason none of the symbols to which we are accustomed in our mediation could be used. But the stone in the middle of the room has more to tell us.... We may see it as an altar, empty not because there is no God, not because it is an altar to an unknown god, but because it is dedicated to the God whom man worships under many names and in many forms. There is an ancient saying that the sense of a vessel is not in its shell but in the void. So it is with this room. It is for those who come here to fill the void with what they find in their centre of stillness."[11]

The Golden Rule

Since autumn 2007 we have displayed a special poster of the Golden Rule in our Center of Silence. For thirteen religious and spiritual traditions the core motif, fundamentally, is: "Do not do unto others what you would not want for yourself." Karen Armstrong, the well-known re-searcher of religious traditions and author, finds inspiration in the Golden Rule and illustrates this with the story of Rabbi Hillel: One day a goy, a non-Jew, challenged the Rabbi to recite a summary of the Torah rules standing on one leg. Rabbi Hillel didn't succumb to cramp and quickly replied: "Do not do unto others what you would not want for yourself. That is the Torah. The rest is commentary. Just go and do it!"

---

[11] This quote is from a text written by Dag Hammarskjöld for distribution among visitors to the UNs Meditation Room.

This message is found in almost identical terms in all thirteen source texts. Other phrases and words expand upon and elucidate this concept.[12] The texts make clear our interdependence. To summarize: Prosperity and the loss of nearest ones may be deemed your own personal prosperity or loss. This revolves around respect. Do not hurt others with that which hurts you. Do not burden the soul of another whose burden you do not wish to carry yourself. We are not strangers to one another. Those who treat their neighbor badly, treat themselves badly. Such a Golden Rule serves as a wonderful and powerful binding factor between religions and cultures, furthermore, between all human beings!

Karen Armstrong follows in the footsteps of the philosopher Karl Jaspers (as does Hans Küng in different writings) when she asserts that the Golden Rule is the dismantling of egotism. She characterizes the rule as a form of empathic spirituality. In summary, Armstrong affirms that, essentially, religion equals compassion. The Golden Rules helps one to step outside of one's own self-centered consciousness to live a life full of compassion.[13] In the thirteen source texts, I am particularly touched by the sentence, "Don't hurt others with the things that hurt you."

Pope Benedict XVI spoke on the Golden Rule to American Roman Catholics in April, 2008: "The world has greater need of hope than ever: hope for peace, for justice, and for freedom, but this hope can never be fulfilled without obedience to the law of God, which Christ brought to fulfilment in the commandment to love one another. Do to others as you would have them do to you, and avoid doing what you would not want them to do to you. This Golden Rule is given in the Bible, but it is valid for all people, including non-believers. It is the law written on the human heart; on this we can all agree, so that when we come to address other matters we can do so in a positive and constructive manner for the entire human community."[14]

Enlightened political leaders also refer to the Golden Rule. For example, recently elected U.S. President Barack Obama highlighted the Golden Rule in his eloquent speech on race: "In the end, then, what is called for is nothing more, and nothing less, than what all the world's great religions demand: that we do unto others as we would have them

---

[12] According to Matthew 7:12, Jesus' teaching of the Golden Rule is stated positively and in a radical way: "In everything do to others as you would have them do to you; for this is the law and the prophets."

[13] See Karen Armstrong, *The Great Transformation: The Beginning of Our Religious Traditions* (New York: Alfred A. Knopf, 2005).

[14] Message sent by Pope Benedict XVI on April 8, 2008 (Vatican City: Libreria Editrice Vaticana, 2008).

do unto us. Let us be our brother's keeper, Scripture tells us. Let us be our sister's keeper. Let us find that common stake we all have in one another, and let our politics reflect that spirit as well."[15]

There is an exercise practiced within the United Religions Initiative (URI) that trains people to develop sensitivity to this. Participants share experiences where they felt hurt by people from a different religion. Next the group reflects on those incidents where one, in turn, may have hurt others. This experience can have a deeply healing and cleansing effect. The next step in this process may be sharing two positive qualities of one's own spiritual tradition. Subsequently participants share two positive qualities that touch them in another religion or spiritual perspective.[16]

Ultimately, the Golden Rule can assist us to leave the road of passion, which often causes clashes and is used to manipulate others. Rabbi Hillel chose not to remain standing on one leg. Instead he chose to become aware of what it is to stand on two feet and what it is to move. Such stance makes possible and guides (or provides a compass for) the movement from passion to compassion; from deadly passion to the mercy of inevitable and amazing grace! This is where the seas meet, as the Koran says....

Mobilization of spiritual power

A common spiritual concept for multicultural spiritual guidance in the Netherlands has proved its worth over the past several years. In 1994 I developed a new working definition of spiritual care: *The mobilization of the spiritual forces which are hidden in every individual.*

All colleagues, both from religious and humanist traditions, can work together on this basis. It is essential in the context of a religion or worldview to create space for dealing with matters of life and death, illness and suffering. In doing so, we experience the emotional, spiritual,

---

[15] Barack Obama, Speech on Race in Philadelphia, March 18, 2008 (New York: CBS Interactive, 2008).

[16] For the Golden Rule Campaign and a multilingual version of the Golden Rule see www.tannebaum.org/goldenrule.html.

Here is a practical suggestion for a workshop in which a group considers the Golden Rule:

Step 1: How to live together with differences: Share positive experiences and negative experiences.

Step 2: Living with the Golden Rule as guide: How does it make a difference?

Step 3: Being hurt and hurting: How have you been hurt? How did you hurt others?

Step 4: Sharing traditions: Discuss two positive qualities from your own tradition and two from another.

and mystic aspects of life. Visiting the sick allows us to find or even discover God. Jesus emphasizes this in the parabolic reference to the Last Judgment in Matthew 25. The Hadith of Islam makes the same point. At the Kirchentag 2007 in Cologne I listened to South African Archbishop Desmond Tutu speaking passionately along the same lines. And I think that is what Albert Schweitzer meant when he spoke about God incognito. God is present at the bottom of the soul....

All caregivers, including medical students, should be required to reflect carefully on the experience of being ill or undergoing surgery. In this manner, as Jean Shinoda Bolen points out, one is brought into a deep contact with one's soul. I myself had this experience when I had an operation in 2001. After the anesthesia wore off I wrote the following poem. I include the original version in my native language, Dutch, because poems often get lost in translation:

Simplification	*Vereenvoudiging*
is my life	*is mijn leven*
no longer what it is?	*niet meer wat het is?*
it's even more what it is	*het is méér wat het is*
I enjoy the	*ik geniet van de*
simplification	*vereenvoudiging*
pasture of life	*de weide van het leven*
loses my eagerness	*verliest mijn gretigheid*
she recovers	*zij herwint*
her "grassiness"…	*haar grazigheid…*

The richness of the meadow of life, its tapestry, or spiritual detachment is the way we benefit from intercultural society, education, and policy. This is the great added value that makes the difference.

Part 2
Muslim caregivers and the road to a new cultural climate: A gender specific approach in spiritual care

Mualla Kaya

Islamic spiritual caregiving is undergoing a transformation process. The health care sector is often reticent to invest in intercultural and spiritual care. When it does occur it is still too isolated, of too little consequence and not consistently structured. This essay is a report on a project introduced as a model focused on spiritual growth to optimally treat female patients with an Islamic background.

The project "Muslim Spiritual Caregiver"[17]

Late in 2005, the University Medical Center in Utrecht approached me to participate in a project aimed at optimally treating female patients with an Islamic background. This invitation came from the Department of Guidance and Spiritual Care (DLGV) in conjunction with the Division of Women and Infants and funded by the WKZ Children's Hospital Scientific Fund. I was asked to consider a number of developments while working on the "Muslim Caregiver Project." Over the last few decades the patient population of the UMC has undergone significant changes that have consequences for the future. These were the reasons for recruiting me to identify the changing care needs.

The main objective of this Project was to gain insight into how the Division of Women and Infants as well as the DLGV could meet the needs of female patients with an Islamic background. The overarching goal was to strengthen spiritual care and so create and stimulate a new cultural climate at the UMC. I asked myself the following question: how can the interculturalization policy of the DLGV enhance the Medical Center's commitment to engage with diversity? To answer this question I concentrated on my practical work experience as a spiritual caregiver. In this article I will refer to some of these experiences. Conclusions and recommendations found at the end of the Muslim Caregiver report present a possible way forward for caregiving institutions for the next few years. They reflect the character and power of a model consistent with social and institutional development.[18]

An intercultural perspective in spiritual care

Since the 1960s migrant workers from Turkey and Morocco have had an influence upon the already existing multicultural Netherlands society. Because of this, the Dutch people became more familiar with Islam. The inevitable and necessary interaction between the Western and Islamic

---

[17] The "Moslima GV Project (2005–2007)" was carried out in the UMC. It focused on the Adult Clinic at the main campus and the Wilhelmina Children's Hospital. In this article it will be referred to as the Muslim Caregiver Project.

[18] The Utrecht University Medical Center and its caregivers seek to identify and anticipate significant changes in the Dutch society and in its own population. The Muslim Caregiver Project is therefore a special expression of the UMC's overarching commitment to multicultural care.

cultures manifests itself in all segments of society.

In 1996 the Quality Law on Health Care was introduced that requires that all hospitals deliver quality care. In spiritual care, hospitals are therefore required to attend to the diverse spiritual backgrounds and spiritual needs of their patients. Since the early 90s the health sector has paid more and more attention to multicultural and multireligious aspects. The willingness to do so is driven by necessity: our society is changing drastically. On the one hand, secularization manifests itself in an increasing spiritual openness, on the other hand there are one million people with an Islamic background in the Netherlands. The fastest growing part of the Dutch population are the non-Dutch groups. They live mostly in the bigger cities. As a result, a large number of patients come from diverse immigrant backgrounds. The known patterns of illness, care, and treatment are shifting due to migration and spiritual processes of change. The goal of the Medical Center and the Spiritual Care Department is to tune into the spiritual care needs of the patients in a way that best reflects the intercultural or life attitude of the individual.

Culture specific care

The DLGV regularly evaluates the care and counseling given to patients to remain abreast of changing circumstances and needs. The Department currently is faced with numerous changes including medical technology and techniques, changes in the health system, demand for and availability of health services, demographic changes, and the upcoming ageing of the population, to name but a few. In this manner the DLGV of the Medical Center in Utrecht remains in close contact with the diverse Dutch society and has been performing a pioneer function since 1996 in this field of intercultural diversity, specifically in Islamic spiritual care.

My esteemed former colleague, Dr. Arslan Karagül, was the first Muslim caregiver from 1996 to 2007 and he came to the conclusion that he could not reach all patients with an Islamic background in his work. With the exception of critical cases, patients in Obstetrics, Fertility and Gynecology, the domain of female patients, were difficult to reach. Also, when there was need for Islamic death rituals, it was difficult to care well due to the Islamic requirements that surround female patients. In spite of my male colleague's professionalism, the request for a female spiritual caregiver was frequent due to principle-related preferences, and religious or cultural requirements. Women who in daily life live strictly separated from men indicated, both implicitly and explicitly, their difficulty in communicating with a male Muslim caregiver. It was extremely difficult for these women to relate intimate details with regard to the wish to have children, pregnancy, gynecological oncology, marital relationships, domestic violence, and so on. Karagül's view was that a female Islamic caregiver would be more able to reach this group of female patients who cannot or do not want to collaborate with a male caregiver due to their religious convictions or cultural background.

In the course of the Muslim Caregiver Project, I was assigned to various specific departments such as: *Obstetrics*, including outpatient clinics for midwifery, nursing care for pregnancy-related matters and the University Obstetrics Center; *Neonatal Department*, including the intensive, high, and medium care units; and *Fertility and Gynecology*. During this period I was involved with the department for Women & Infants and Pediatrics. My affiliation with the departments mentioned above and my availability to female patients helped me to adopt a professional approach and an open attitude. I made myself available, and I also counseled male patients with an Islamic background. In the last two years I cared for patients through various channels in both the main hospital campus and the Children's Hospital.

My experience as a Muslim caregiver

How can one measure the benefits of having a female Islamic caregiver on staff? An empirical approach for this project was decided upon by the DLGV in conjunction with the Muslim Advice Committee for Spiritual Care with whom I worked closely. From the beginning, specific attention was paid to the religious, cultural, and ethnic backgrounds and contexts of patients. In addition to my main task as spiritual caregiver I counseled and gave advice to other disciplines and colleagues. My role also included providing education to the broader Islamic society and their Imams regarding the health care context.

Women to women: A universal phenomenon

Both professionals and patients reacted positively to my availability in the Medical Center from the start. Doctors and professionals were pleased with the extended availability of multicultural services offered to patients of the Center in Utrecht. According to the professionals female patients with an Islamic background have benefited from my presence, especially those who in their daily lives have chosen to live separately from their male counterparts. It also became apparent that female patients from all cultural and religious backgrounds prefer to speak about intimate matters with a female professional.

According to an article that was published on the website of MI-

KADO[19] (a national center for intercultural spiritual care), Dutch female patients in the Erasmus Medical Center ask for a female gynecologist as often as non-Dutch female patients. The same is true in the Amsterdam Academic Medical Center and most definitely also in the Utrecht University Medical Center. It appears that women, regardless of their ethnic, cultural or religious background prefer to be treated by female professionals. It also goes without saying that as a woman, I have more affinity with the problems of female patients. Therefore, in addition to my role as a spiritual caregiver I often mediate between the patient and medical personnel when interaction with male doctors is seen as problematic.

Nonverbal and physical communication

The spirit is indefinable and cannot be isolated; but it can be felt in the touch of a hand, a gesture, a look, or in the sound of a voice. Too easily in our culture we associate the spiritual with a message in words, a message that can be spoken or written down. Essentially, spiritual care would consist of delivering this message, speaking the words that confer the meaning of that message. The physical aspect would be merely the arrangement of chairs for the conversation that needs to take place there. But even when we give preference to the word, how often do we engage the body at the heart of communicating? Speaking is breathing formed in the stomach, chest, throat, mouth, and head, gesturing with the face and looking with fingers and hands; a pantomime from the tip of ones toes to the crown of the head. The body is not merely the package from where the words are transferred: it is the words we speak or write. The message includes our physical enactment, our shared movements, our shared warmth, our shared melody and our shared silence.[20]

In the New Handbook for Spiritual Care (*Nieuw Handboek Geestelijke Verzorging*) Dr. H. Coenen highlights two important aspects of communication, namely the attitude and the non-verbal aspects. In our interaction with patients, the verbal aspect naturally plays a major role, but often contact is established by touch or a hug. Silence can be essential to effective communication.

Not all people like to be touched. Yet often touch can play a large role in effective communication, for example with patients suffering from dementia, holding a persons hand or taking their arm can be the best

---

[19] http://www.mikado-ggz.nl/artikel.php?artikel_id=776.

[20] H. Coenen, 'Lichamelijkheid in de geestelijke verzorging," *Nieuw Handboek Geestelijke Verzorging*, p. 909.

way to show support and to communicate effectively.[21]

Female Islamic patients who are open to touch find it preferable to be counseled by a professional female caregiver. In Islam physical contact knows many restrictions and can have inevitable social consequences. Therefore, an Islamic woman without an escort cannot be in a closed room with a male Islamic caregiver. Eye contact is another sensitive area when counseled by a male spiritual caregiver as this is viewed as unacceptable.

Activities and themes in counseling contacts: "we culture"

Not only do I provide care and counseling, strictly speaking; I often offer additional services to the patient such as listening to music or taking walks together. Other activities that require mention are crisis intervention, contact with family and relatives, mediation and advice on medical and ethical issues, assisting in rituals and prayer, assisting when a death occurs, and after care, to mention a few. Below follows an overview of my activities documented in the Muslim Caregiver Project report as well as a reference to the various themes that were encountered during this period.

Number of contacts per activity	
1. Offer of spiritual care	40
2. Getting acquainted	29
3. Scheduling a meeting	16
4. Maintaining contact	28
5. Discussions with clinical patients	50
6. Discussions with patients and family	10
7. Discussions with outpatients	19
8. Telephone contact with ex-patients	32
9. Discussions with a family member	38
10. Discussions with several family members	40
11. Psycho-social consultation (multi-disciplinary)	10
12. Discussions with doctors	14
13. Discussions with nursing staff	98
14. Discussions with social services	5
15. Discussions with internal colleagues	7
16. Discussions with external colleagues	2
17. Religious discussions/jurisprudence	14
18. Religious discussions (narrative)	1
19. Prayer (non-ritual)	20

[21] J. Hettinga, "Een sprakeloos gevoel…Over communiceren met dementerende mensen," *Nieuw Handboek Geestelijke Verzorging*, p. 386.

20. Prayer/seminar (ritualistic)	29
21. Birth ritual and naming	1
22. Assistance with death	7
23. Leave-taking upon death	12
24. Death rituals	1
25. Burial/funeral service	6
26. After-care for family and friend(s)	3
27. Silence	4
28. Wake	1
Total	**538**

According to the figures, discussions with nursing staff scores the highest. The nursing staff is mostly responsible for communicating relevant information to patients, identifying patient needs, and referral of patients. I maintained regular contact with patients and nursing staff before as well as during counseling to ensure feedback and tuning in to needs.

It can also be concluded from the figures that in 88 cases one or more family members of the patient were involved in conversations. This can be explained by the cultural characteristics of the people who adhere to a "we culture" (collective culture): they are more involved with each other. In the we culture, the group is essential, which manifests itself also in the care for sick and elderly Islamic patients. The group in the we culture adheres to a hierarchical structure the members of which are closely involved with each other. This characteristic comes about not only out of responsibility, involvement, and charity, but originates in the need to survive. Each member is thus directly involved with others and indirectly with him or herself. Furthermore, it is important to note that the activities identified in numbers 17 to 28 have an overt religious and spiritual character.

Number of contacts per theme	
Experience of being ill	2
The course of and experiencing illness	80
(Future) expectations/ self-diagnoses/ life plan	22
Meaning	11
Experiencing support	11
Comfort/inspiration/support and strength	13
Loneliness/disorientation/feeling of being uprooted	7
Far-reaching change	8
Religious experience	2
Giving over to faith/surrender	5

Prayer/healing prayer	8
Guilt/shame/ punishment/ responsibility/ penance	1
Letting go/ saying farewell/loss (of another)	8
Becoming dependant/ restrictions/ loss of self	5
Pregnancy/birth	20
Biography	6
Personal growth/ awareness	1
Autonomy/freedom	3
Ethics/ making choices/ decision over life, death, and treatment	16
Religious institute institute/ mosque	2
Fear/ desire	7
Bad news	14
Dying	23
Social bonds	5
Important others	16
Conflict(s)	13
Thankfulness	9
Grief/ coping with grief	4
Profession/ job/ work	5
Hobbies	2
Total	**329**

The themes addressed during counseling will receive attention in the following section. An important point to be explicitly mentioned is that the spiritual caregiver has relatively less time pressure than other caregivers who are closer to market- and product-related time pressures. Spiritual caregivers can afford and want to spend the time necessary to address the situations mentioned above in order to contribute to the alleviation of human suffering.

Social, religious, and ethical contexts

Social context

In reviewing the content of the discussions, it became apparent that many of the themes touched upon the results of migration. Themes such as biography, loneliness, disorientation, a feeling of being uprooted, religious experience, social bonds, conflicts, and profession, job, or work are influenced by migration to a foreign country. It is therefore possible to group these themes and name them migration—related themes.

It is not strange that in my counseling with both male and female patients migration-related themes regularly arose. During their stay in a hospital patients encounter different people in a strange environment. Patients with an Islamic background who often have a non-Dutch background, find themselves in an unfamiliar environment where the language and culture are not their own. Memories and hopes, images and expectations, norms and values that they have internalized in the past now emerge, causing serious discomfort.

Many questions arise, such as: Why did I come to the Netherlands? What have I achieved? What is the cost to myself? What would have happened had I stayed in my own country? What would happen if I returned? Have I changed (much) in the past few years? If not, can I live or learn to live with it? Why are these changes so painful to deal with? The attraction and nostalgia, especially longing for the known and trusted, now plays its part.

In addition to the above themes, there were also the themes of autonomy, freedom, dying, letting go, farewell, loss, comfort, inspiration, support, and strength. These themes, in addition to being gender specific also have a social, religious and/or ethical dimension. In these instances my being of the same sex, culture, and religion positively facilitated the conversations.

In their practice, medical staff and other professionals come into contact with patients whose vision is shaped by Islam. Themes such as self-determination and freedom, dying and euthanasia can cause a chasm of misunderstanding between the parties.

Medical staff may view the treatment of a patient, whether an adult or infant, as not medically viable, when there is the prospect of hopeless and unbearable suffering. The suggestion of ceasing treatment or active euthanasia might clash with the convictions of the patients or their parents due to a difference concerning ethical beliefs.

Spiritual and religious counseling of patients and the communication with doctors are extremely meaningful. Before I introduce the ethical context, I wish to focus on the religious context from which Islamic patients derive their ethical views.[22]

Religious context [23]

Belief in God. "La ilaahe illa Allah": this Arabic sentence in essence reflects the Islamic belief in God, namely the Unity of God: "There is no God, except Allah." *God is The Creator, The Controller, and The Absolute Master. God is The Most Charitable, The Most Merciful, and The Most*

---

[22] On this issue, A. van Dijk and A. van Buuren, "Identiteit en Interculturalisatie," *Nieuw Handboek Geestelijke Verzorging*, pp. 185–186.

[23] The content of the following paragraphs is based on the Koran, especially suras 2 (Al-Baqaarah) and 4 (An-Nisa). *The Qur'an*. Text, Translation and Commentary by Abdullah Yusuf Ali (Elmhurst, NY: Tahrike Tarsile Qur'an, Inc. US Edition, 2001).

Righteous. God is The First, The Last[24] and God is the same God as The One who Revealed Godself to Moses and Jesus and all the other prophets, whether their names are known or not. *In spite of God's transcendence, God may be directly approached and stands close to humankind.*

Humanity. Human beings are a creation of God, born pure and without sin with an intrinsic goodness and value. Their mental capabilities and freewill lift them to the crown of creation. They are the stewards and representatives of God. The world is their garden, the land is on loan to them, and they act charitably to those who live on earth. The goal for every person is to become better both physically and spiritually. Upon death the person returns to God to atone for his deeds.

Illness and suffering. The reality of illness and suffering is no reason for rebelliousness. There is divine wisdom behind illness and suffering. Through illness and suffering, faith and trust in God are put to the test. Complete surrender and patience, combined with an active attitude towards healing are reasons for mercy.

Life and death. The life of any living being can neither be prolonged nor shortened, unless God has already given permission for that. Contrary to life on earth, the afterlife is unending. Death is therefore not an ending, but the beginning of a new life. And every being will return to God after a period of living on earth. Killing another human being or the unnatural ending of life is a great sin that is equal to killing humanity.

Ethical dilemmas regarding informed consent and euthanasia

On the subject of euthanasia and discontinuing life support with patients who are not mentally competent, many difficult ethical questions are raised. Can a doctor end the life of a child who is suffering excruciating pain or will die within a short period of time? Can euthanasia be applied if the child will not die of his illness but faces an "unlivable" life? What constitutes an unlivable situation? Does it involve physical pain? Or does "unlivable" imply that the child will never be able to think or communicate, even though he or she does not suffer?

The disputable unlivable prognoses may be confronted with the conviction that each life has an intrinsic value. The action of the doctor based on professional intuition and the foundations of the Hippocratic Oath—"act and do not harm, and when in doubt, do not act"—in order to prevent unnecessary suffering may well encounter tension in the reli-

[24] The ninety-nine names of Allah are the names for God which are used in Islam. These names reflect the properties and qualities related to God's divinity, love and mercy, greatness and honor, knowledge, creativity and power.

gious convictions of the patients or their parents.

In practice, the principles of "when in doubt do not act" and "prevent unnecessary suffering" seem to stand in opposition to "autonomy" and "informed consent." Guaranteeing the interests of the diverse people involved—individual patients as well as parents and caregivers—may prove problematic.

What does jurisprudence prescribe in such circumstances? The decision of the medical practitioner to cease treatment in certain situations, believing it would be medically fruitless, is a legal professional decision presumably "in the interest of the patients." In those cases, no consent is required from either the patients or their representative. The practitioner merely needs to "inform" the patients or their representative.

In spite of the jurisprudence, parents are burdened with a right that they do not seem to have, namely to agree with the decision to discontinue treatment. In an effort to achieve consensus, pressure tactics may be resorted to, leaving the parents feeling torn apart and powerless. "Is not the medical professional in a better position to judge the situation?" they may ask themselves. Are parents not asked the impossible when their interests and that of the child are inextricably intertwined?[25] This is an extra burden for parents of an Islamic, non-Western background. In addition to the restrictive determinations surrounding euthanasia, decisions to cease treatment and active ending of life in Islam, the parents deal with a cultural heritage wherein hierarchy, relationships, and language play a vital role.

The principle of "informed consent" leads to great confusion and insecurity for parents with an Islamic background. Not only are the parents informed, they are asked for an opinion in an attempt to reach consensus over the decision to cease treatment. This leads to the suspicion that the medical professionals do not know what they are doing. Asking for their permission gives the parents the impression that the doctor is not capable.

Some parents will not ask questions if they do not understand. This attitude stems from their respect for the doctor's authority, but it is also due to language difficulties and to the embarrassment of admitting to not having understood everything. This situation may lead parents into

---

[25] The duty to inform the patient has been linked inseparably with the authorization requirement. Without adequate information, authorization is not possible. And, in principle, without authorization, treatment is not permitted. This combination of information and authorization has also been called "the requirement of informed consent." Authorization is therefore a requirement for a treatment, but is not required for a "stop treatment" policy, thus becoming a source of confusion and disorientation.

emotional isolation which in turn enhances the feeling of powerlessness. Clear and careful communication can thus avoid undue stress.

It is important to consider the role differentiation in the family, and the emotional bonds that exist between men and women. In my experience, it can be beneficial in some cases to employ a gender specific approach. Patients or parents who are unfamiliar with the phenomenon of a Muslim spiritual caregiver in a hospital regularly consult their Imam on medical-ethical issues. The lack of medical knowledge and practical hospital experience of these Imams does not always make them the most competent to advise their clients. A Muslim spiritual caregiver can play a vital role in advising the parents, and in addition serve in an educational capacity for the Muslim society at large.

Conclusions and guidelines[26] stemming from the report

The following conclusions and guidelines are presented together with the following assumption: It is envisioned that the initiative articulated in the Muslim Caregiver Report fosters a new cultural climate and optimizes the input of the Department of Guidance and Spiritual Care (DLGV) concerning interculturalization and engagement with diversity.

Mission and strategy of the UMC Utrecht

The DLGV appropriates the mission and strategy of the University Medical Center in Utrecht.
The overarching objective is to provide a qualitatively high-level, patient-directed care, resulting in the development and implementation of innovations to improve health care.

The growth of culture-specific care

The Muslim Caregiver Project pioneers the way forward in providing culture-specific care. The DLGV has chosen a growth model as a framework and instrument to improve the quality of healthcare.
The DLGV promotes the assistance that medical staff requires from spiritual caregivers as consultants in situations requiring a culture-specific approach.

Interculturalization

In view of an existing multicultural society the DLGV has chosen an intercultural approach. The choice was made as a way of fostering mutuality and social interdependence and cohesion. In the future, intercultural policy and engagement with diversity will expand within the orga-

---

[26] The actual guidelines are the summary statement in italics preceded by an asterisk.

nization of patient care.

In education and interdisciplinary cooperation the DLGV offers a multicultural contribution.

Uniqueness of each individual

In order to optimize treatment of care receivers we need to tune into the patients' personal needs that parallel their life convictions and cultural background. As professionals we should realize that we are guests in the lives of our patients.

Each person is unique and should be approached as such.

Anticipation and emancipation

Islamic spiritual care is currently undergoing a process of emancipation and development. With the exception of the Utrecht University Medical Center, the health care sector has not been well prepared to invest in the future in terms of intercultural and spiritual care. Due to some stagnation and political ambivalence in the health care sector concerning a multicultural society, diversity management is now once again experiencing growth.

The DLGV promotes timely and coherent engagement with diversity.

Muslim spiritual caregivers

The DLGV feels that Islamic spiritual care by a female Muslim caregiver is especially liberating and exemplary. Female patients from a Muslim background who have chosen a strict separation from men benefit greatly from the presence of a Muslim female caregiver. Common issues for discussion include the wish to have children, pregnancy, gynecological oncology, marital relationships, domestic violence, and so on. These patients would otherwise not have access to spiritual care.

Often a gender specific approach is preferred. There is no other conclusion than that a Muslim female caregiver is not a luxury. The implicit or explicit demand of female patients with an Islamic background needs to be answered by a Muslim female caregiver who can contribute positively to their well-being.

The DLGV has chosen to embrace a broadening of the spectrum of Islamic spiritual caregiving with respect to gender as well as cultural background.

We-culture (collective culture)

The we-culture is characterized by a specific trait: each member is directly involved with the other and indirectly with him or herself. Being male or female determines the status and the place of the persons in their context, old or young, learned or illiterate.

The difference between the we-culture and the teachings of Islam require some attention. Religion and culture are not always synonymous. The we-culture is characterized by an extended system of family care that can also be religiously motivated. Often we see entire families and groups of friends visit patients. Medical staff needs to be able to identify the hierarchal key figure(s) in the family.

Due to the lack of a support system, it is important for immigrants to have contact with the spiritual caregiver in the hospital. As already indicated, migrant-related situations and themes are often considered.

Islamic spiritual care devotes adequate attention to the we-culture in patient care and provides information to medical staff.

Communication

Knowledge of the Islamic background of a patient is an important means to promote effective communication. It is recommended that doctors caring for patients who are not fluent enough in Dutch to understand information or to express emotions, utilize the services of an interpreter or counselor instead of family and friends.

A key rule is to ascertain which language the patient speaks at home.

The patient needs to be protected so that the illness does not gain the upper hand. Background information helps explain the patient's behavior. Knowledge of interpersonal relations also serves as an important tool for the caregiver.

The DLGV offers a course in effective communication with migrant patients.

Indicators, case histories, multidisciplinary discussions

It is often difficult for medical staff and other professionals to identify the implicit need for spiritual counseling. In addition to referrals by medical and other professionals, the case histories taken by the nursing staff are very important for the referral of patients to Islamic spiritual care. During the taking of case histories, patients are often not well informed of the availability of a spiritual caregiver.

Multidisciplinary meetings also do not function optimally, partly due to the fact that the Muslim spiritual caregiver cannot be present at all meetings.

The DLGV has developed a set of guidelines for indicators, case histories and multidisciplinary meetings on the availability of Islamic spiritual care.

Availability-directed service

The non-Western patient with an Islamic background does not possess much information about spiritual care in a hospital. In light of our experience, information via brochures and posters is not very effective. It is much better to provide verbal information face to face.

The need for spiritual care often remains latent in patients from an Islamic background as, culturally, one hesitates to ask. The Muslim spiritual caregiver is expected to remain involved after initial contact, sometimes in the role of social counselor.

Counseling on demand is not effective with patients from an Islamic background; therefore we offer an availability-directed service combined with problem-oriented service. This availability-directed service has priority and tends to uncover hidden needs.

Counseling function

Medical doctors and other professionals have indicated that they have benefitted greatly from the presence of a Muslim spiritual caregiver in connection with a gender specific approach. They can count on her to establish connections as a consultant in medical-ethical questions and to function as an intermediary.

The personal approach of the spiritual caregiver works best with medical and other professionals. Where ethical dilemmas exist, especially around decisions about discontinuing treatment, contact with the spiritual caregiver is vital and, for example, prevents emotional isolation on the part of parents.

Muslim spiritual caregivers can provide information and education for patients and hospital staff and build a bridge between the different sexes, cultures, languages and religions.

Education

Imams normally have limited competence regarding knowledge of medical-ethical situations and basic medical knowledge. Therefore:

Muslim spiritual caregivers can play an educational role towards the broader Muslim society.

Part 3
Fostering community and formation in a multifaith society: Towards a new educational model

Bart ten Broek

A tale of two cities

The Hague. The Hague is a city in the Netherlands that likes to introduce itself as the International City of Peace and Justice. This is the city where the Roman Catholic elementary school, "De Wereldwijzer" received the designation "Wide World School" in October 2008.[27] It should be noted that the Dutch name *WijDe Wereld School* may be translated as either "Wide World School" or "We the World School." De Wereldwijzer has gone through some efforts to achieve this. That is what this article is about. It is a somewhat personal story, because the author was the director of a school that developed from a Christian Protestant elementary school into a Christian-Islamic cooperative school, and then evolved further from an interfaith school to a pluriform cooperative school. Some of these processes will be described and the connection between both models will show how schools have the opportunity to evolve in Dutch society. Due to the fact that schools are at the center of social reality, there is some resistance to be felt. At the same time, the Dutch educational system allows broad parameters for schools to further develop themselves.

Ede. Ede is a large village with a population of more than one hundred thousand people. It is situated in the nature-rich region in the central part of the Netherlands, known as the Veluwe. The village population consists largely of orthodox Christians. This is the setting in which a radical change occurred on the premises of the Christian Protestant Juliana van Stolberg elementary school in the last twenty years of the last century. The influence of the developed model continues to the present day.

In the 1980s people from Turkey and Morocco moved to the Netherlands to join family members who were already living here. Schools were not really prepared for this development. In addition, the Dutch educational system is organized in accordance with the principles according to which Protestant-Christian, Roman Catholic, Waldorf, and Public Schools have equal rights and duties. Without the school forming some kind of plan, children from Turkish and Moroccan backgrounds enrolled at the Juliana van Stolberg elementary School. These children brought Islam with them. This became apparent around Good Friday and Easter. Muslim children voiced their doubts about a God, who would let himself be crucified in the person of Jesus. This resulted in fights among the children. The Director of the school then invited all the parents to discuss this issue. Dutch, Turkish, and Moroccan parents attended the meeting with many preconceived, and potentially antagonistic, ideas. People of the same nationality gathered in separate parts of the hall. The Director initiated the conversation indicating that religious dogma of the various religions was not up for discussion but, instead, that as religiously

---

[27] The author of this article is the Chairman of the Foundation that issued that designation.

motivated parents they might wish to contribute to religious understanding and acceptance of differences in the education of their children. The
parents came out of their corners and mingled. They ended up talking
for a long time about their religious traditions. It was in the daily practice of communing with God that they found each other. That night saw
the beginning of the creation of a new school.

A Protestant Christian junior school

In 1956, the Juliana van Stolberg School was founded in Ede as part of a
group of twelve schools affiliated with the "Vereniging voor Christelijke
Nationaal Schoolonderwijs (CNS)"[28] located in Ede. Change began to
take place in 1979 as society encountered changes. Some of the pupils
came from a neighbourhood with many families with a socio-economi-
cally deprived background. One-parent families lived in smaller flats and
experienced socio-emotional problems. In the same year the family re-
unions of people from Turkey and Morocco took place. It was at this
time that the author of this article started at this school and with the
assistance of a team formulated a new policy.

The first objective was: "Each pupil needs special attention". It was
not the intention to stigmatise the pupil as a problem child; on the contrary, the intention was to create personalized education for each pupil.
Furthermore it served to reflect the experiences that the pupil brought
with him/her from the home situation. This meant that the Protestant
Christian school needed to take Islam seriously. A larger role was allo-
cated to the parents to develop a new educational syllabus. The school
was awarded an experimental status by the Department of Education,
which in turn created more teaching positions.

This elicited many questions from the minority of Orthodox Christian parents as well as several teachers and board members. The question
arose as to how the school could maintain the original objectives of the
CNS. The first protocol stated that Muslim children were considered as
'guests.' This was based on the assumption that the migrant labourers
would return to their home countries.

For the existing teaching staff this meant the start of adjustment.
Every day school started with a prayer, a Psalm (one that the children
learned by heart that week) and a Bible story. The Lord's Prayer and
Confessional also were taught. One Muslim pupil remarked, "You can
also pray with your eyes open." That helped everyone. When the pupils
in Grade 8 were challenged to learn their Confessional, a Turkish boy

---

[28] CNS: Association of Christian National Schools.

remarked, "I know that!" Directly after he said "But I will not say it aloud." This led to a beautiful discussion about the meaning of the Confessional and the Soera 1 of the Koran.

All these experiences were recorded and discussed with the parents. This in turn led to the need to incorporate this knowledge into the educational process and syllabus whereby both religions could be taught. During this period the pre-schoolers (4–6 years) and the junior school (6–12 years) were integrated into one large elementary school (4–12 years). The Department of Education was then approached for the school to be allowed to continue with the experimental status for another year and to work on a new concept: "ontmoetingsonderwijs" (education of meeting and dialogue).

Each week one lesson was reserved for each group wherein stories of 'meeting' were told. Corresponding stories were found in the Bible, the Koran and children's literature.

Pupils then had the opportunity to verbalize what they brought to school from their own traditions. This was a great success and the results were recorded in a Book of Ontmoetingsonderwijs that was later presented to the State Secretary of the Department of Education.

A Moroccan father regularly visits the school on Monday mornings to speak with the director. He says: *"This is the only place where I can speak freely about Allah, God."*

The board of a local mosque responded to this Education of Meeting and Dialogue, and praised the concept. They did, however, point out that Biblical education was still presented but that this did not pose a problem. They did not feel that they were able to adequately teach their children themselves. To ensure more equality, they requested one hour of Islamic religious teachings per week. The team felt that this was a reasonable request, even though the school board resisted. How could a Christian School allow for Islamic religious teachings?

Initially the school board decided to grant this one hour per week. This caused some commotion in the various Orthodox Christian communities in the region. The CNS Board decided to discuss the terms with the board members of the mosque. When the question was asked by one of the CNS Board Members, "Would you like more lesson hours?" The logical response of the Turkish board members was "Yes, of course!" At the end of the meeting one of the CNS Board Members remarked, "Give them one finger, and they take your hand!"

Eventually the Board decided not to give permission. Some parents from Turkish descent were so offended that they withdrew their children from the school. Parents from Moroccan descent supported the school during this period. Due to the tense situation that had occurred, the Board decided to authorize an experimental lesson-hour of Islamic religious teachings to be conducted by an imam. A commission was formed of board members and external members to guide the process! These actions did not resolve the situation, however. Eventually the director wrote a protocol that stated the options of the school as follows:

1. Forbid Islamic teachings
2. Discontinue the school or integrate it with another Christian school
3. Present the school with a special status within the United School Association (CNS)
4. Make the school independent

This situation led to exhaustive discussions. The Department of Education and public schools administrators critically followed the ensuing events. During this period there was much speculation about Islamic and "black" schools.[29] Termination and integration, many feared, could mean that Turkish and Moroccan pupils would move towards the public schools. They did not want to have more "black" schools in Ede. Eventually a special decision was made: the Juliana van Stolberg School was to become independent!

A new challenge

This process cost a lot of energy or, more accurately, blood, sweat, and tears. Still, we can conclude that the school is not just a center for knowledge but can also make an essential contribution to society. If all the institutions were mentioned that were involved in this project to give children a better chance in life, the article would be too long. Even Queen Beatrix of the Netherlands visited the school to witness how it had managed, outside of the Randstad (the area between Amsterdam, Rotterdam, The Hague and Utrecht) to place itself in the center of a network. Rejection and acceptance alternated.

In March 1990 the first Christian-Islamic school in the Netherlands opened its doors. The board consisted of representatives from Moroccan, Dutch, and Turkish people with Muslim and Christian backgrounds. Television, radio, and newspapers rushed to the school to find out how this form of education could be the answer to the discussion surrounding the so-called "black" and Islamic schools.

---

[29] In the Netherlands it is common to speak about "black" and "white" schools. A "black" school has a mixed population, with a majority of migrant children.

One day as the school presented itself to the outside world, a five-year-old Moroccan girl grabbed the director's hand and skipping alongside said, "My father has also become the boss of the school, has he not?" Her father was one of the board members.

Not only did the management composition change but also the curriculum. The objective was to really implement equal participation. Naturally, the school continued to work with all didactical requirements, but the religious curriculum was completely revised. Socio-emotional development was to form part of this.

Earlier it was mentioned that the school worked closely with the parents to determine the content of the curriculum. In the same way, recognition education was approached. Two members of the team were asked to search stories and themes that originated both from the Koran and the Bible. These stories and themes were closely associated with the socio-emotional experiences of the children. The Public Library searched for stories in worldwide children's literature. Events pertaining to the neighbourhood were also included. Both the local imam and the Protestant minister, sometimes assisted by an external theologian, contributed by explaining the meaning of these stories. The stories of Joseph (Yusuf) and Moses (Musa) were told first, as they are both presented in the Bible as well as in the Koran.

Each week, a theme is chosen for all children. The theme is presented to and by the pupils in story-telling, drama, song, and music. During the week the Christian pupils receive further Biblical lessons about the theme by their teachers while an imam teaches pupils from the Islamic heritage. A Moroccan father and a Turkish mother with imam qualifications undertake the furtherance of these lessons. A recognition lesson is then organized for the whole class and herein lies the heart of the religious education. Together the children explore the similarities and differences and discuss these with each other. Sometimes, there is reason to rejoice and sometimes there is pain because of the differences. In these lessons a field of surprises is uncovered (as put forward by the philosopher Martin Buber).

The surprise is remembered! The lessons are creatively processed and the results contribute to the joint weekly meeting held on Fridays.

Recognition education creates new rituals and symbols, and teaches children at an early age to interact without prejudice. The teaching staff is supported by stories from Hans Kung who proposes the Rock Dome as the common symbol for the three monotheistic religions.

We also know that a similar symbol can be surpassed by world history. Therefore it is important to give a form to the meeting of religions on the level of children. Later, in high school, the pupils of the Juliana van Stolberg School often act as "peace negotiators" when religious themes cause disunity. Both Christian and Islamic feasts are elaborately celebrated. Parents very often take the initiative in this. It is clearly anticipated that children participate in the religious expressions of the others, but they are a witness to these expressions and join in the celebrations by eating Turkish fruit, the hamburger at the festival of offering, the eggs at Easter, and so on.

After ten years of successful recognition education at the Juliana van Stolberg elementary school, the school had to close down due to various reasons, including politics. Many parents greatly regretted this. It was widely stated that this educational model was born too early!

WijDe World School

The influence of the Juliana van Stolberg elementary school in Ede spread widely, in the Netherlands as well as to other countries, especially Germany. Many education specialists, pedagogues, theologians, and philosophers visited the school. A Centre for Intercultural Cooperation, Juliana van Stolberg, was founded to present and share the knowledge attained. The director had his duties partially freed for this purpose and gave many presentations in both the Netherlands and other countries. Various universities closely followed the progress of the school; the University of Utrecht and the school participated together in an European educational project. The director had to leave the school for health reasons. He moved to The Hague and was not present at the time of closure. He did, however, continue to present the model to schools of higher education.

In The Hague a teacher from a Waldorf school was investigating whether it would be possible to establish an intercultural and interreligious school! She was motivated by the multicultural cooperation taking place in The Hague and eager to leave her current limited space. During her research she often came across the name Bart ten Broek, the director of the interreligious school in Ede. When she realized that he lived in The Hague, contact was soon established. To establish a new school was not possible.

The search was on to more closely integrate the philosophy and qualities of the Waldorf school (working with head, heart, and hands), the knowledge acquired by the school in Ede and the unification attempts of The Hague. A Catholic school, by the name of "de Wereldwijzer," was founded. This school wished to promote this combination of qualities. An institution was founded to guide and advise schools that choose to receive the title of a WijDe Wereldschool. An independent commission determines whether this title applies in each case.

What is the WijDe Wereldschool?

The WijDe Wereldschool stands for creative education that is rich with culture and raises children to be world citizens. At WijDe Wereldschool teachers, parents, pupils, and other people involved work together to create a school that offers a practice ground for a "new communal society," a society in which people are "free" to be themselves, but take responsibility for each other as well as for their direct and worldwide environment.

Existing schools can be awarded the title WijDe Wereldschool via a developmental process. The title WijDe Wereldschool is awarded when the school has developed or strengthened the following areas:

- A mixed pupil population or regular meetings with a partner school with a different school population.
- Culture-rich education whereby art, stories, celebrations, and traditions from many cultures of the world are used as a source of learning.
- Education to raise world citizens, whereby children gain insight into the social, economic, and ecological coherence of the world.
- Lessons wherein pupils are brought into contact with various religions and universal human values and where they experience these as guiding principles to peaceful and meaningful coexistence.
- Attention to dialogue and socio-emotional development. Pupils can thus develop a strong own identity and an attitude of respect for another person's identity.
- Learning with their head, heart, and hands. In this manner children are addressed in all areas of their "being" and can develop into balanced, creative individuals.
- Individual, self-discovering, and cooperative learning and practice in free and independent thinking and judgement.
- Attention to multilinguism, both Dutch and a second language, modern languages and mother tongues that are spoken at home.
- A broad school with a large offering of after-school activities that further the cohesion in the neighbourhood.
- Extended parent involvement where the parents actively add to the intercultural and interreligious character of the school.

Every school can become a WijDe Wereldschool. If a school chooses this model, it will have to undergo a re-orientation of its identity. In any event the school will open itself to other cultures, in the broad sense of the word, and to a renewed educational culture that allows space for diversity.[30]

Conclusion

The experiences and knowledge generated in Ede some years ago make it now possible for a school to clearly position itself intentionally within the multicultural society. It is also personally fulfilling for the former director at Ede to realize how the prematurely born educational model is now flourishing and growing in The Hague.

Teachers and parents can experience a spiritual formation and community-building process together in which equality is central to the values and norms of interaction. We thus reaffirm that it is indeed essential to acknowledge and appreciate each other, including the richness and challenges of the differences.

---

[30] For example, the Catholic elementary school the Wereldwijzer was awarded the title on October 17, 2008. Over the previous two years, the teaching staff had worked very hard to integrate the above objectives into their curriculum. The foundation had been laid and further development would follow. In the presence of parents, local authorities and the press, the school was festively opened.

Epilogue
Growing in *wisdom* as spiritual caregivers

Daniel S. Schipani and Leah Dawn Bueckert

As indicated in the Introduction, the research and writing project leading to the publication of this book was designed with three goals in mind: to explore the dynamics of interfaith spiritual care as a work of practical and pastoral theology; to identify reliable guidelines for the competent, and duly contextualized, practice of interfaith spiritual care; and to invite further collaboration on this subject among practitioners and scholars. Thanks primarily to the wonderful work of numerous colleagues whose writings are included in the volume, we are confident that those goals have been met.

The following paragraphs highlight a picture of excellence and growth in professional wisdom. We will thus conclude the discussion of understandings and practices of spiritual care with a profile of competence that describes our common and ongoing vocational commitment.

The notion of *professional wisdom* helps us to refocus our attention on the spiritual caregiver. We introduce it here as a way to restate concisely certain guidelines for excellence discussed and illustrated in this book.[1] Wisdom in interfaith care involves not only what we know but also what we are and what we do. In other words, we may view professional (clinical as well as ministerial, broadly speaking) wisdom for interfaith care as the integration of three domains—*knowing, being* and *doing*.

On *knowing*

In order to grow in pastoral wisdom, spiritual caregivers must participate in so-called "circles of learning," which include four dimensions: actual experience of being cared for and caring for others (learning by "feel-

---

[1] For the following understanding of "professional wisdom" in terms of knowing, being and doing, we are indebted to John Patton's thought as presented in his book, *Pastoral Care: An Essential Guide* (Nashville: Abingdon Press, 2006), chapters 1, 2, 3.

ing"); observation and reflection on care provided by others (learning by actively "seeing" and "hearing"); systematic analysis of those practices of care (learning by "thinking"); and active experimentation with new ways of caring well for others (learning by "doing"). The more intentionally and consistently we participate in the four dimensions of the "circle," the more likely that our knowing of interfaith care will increase. That is why supervision, seminars and consultation groups are fertile settings for developing knowledge and understanding related to spiritual care in interfaith situations.[2] A sample of indicators of professional wisdom directly connected with this domain (*knowing*), include the following:

- A philosophy of spiritual care, including a view of human wholeness, truth, the good life, and excellence in professional work (as seen especially in an ethic of care), grounded in one's faith tradition.

- Optimal theoretical integration of spirituality, human science and theological perspectives.

- Understanding of the complexities, dynamics and richness of interfaith situations, with appreciation for human and spiritual commonalities and due consideration to gender, culture, religious, family and social contexts.

- Theological assessment that includes: revisiting the validity of certain absolute, normative doctrinal claims; selective reappropriation of theological and religious convictions; rediscovery of the simplicity and beauty of core spiritual clues for interfaith care, etc.

- Linguistic-conceptual and "multilingual" competency (knowing a variety of psychological, theological and spiritual languages) born out of theological and human science perspectives and resources.

- Clinical ways of knowing, such as interpretive frameworks (psychodynamic, systemic, etc.), that enhance understanding, communication, and ministerial practice of spiritual care.

Such comprehensive ways of *knowing* in turn must always be closely related to the *being* and *doing* dimensions of professional wisdom, as briefly

---

[2] As indicated above, the editors co-led a year-long seminar group jointly sponsored by the Associated Mennonite Biblical Seminary and the Pastoral Care Department of Lutheran Hospital of Indiana. Activities aimed at increasing the theoretical and practical-clinical knowledge of interfaith spiritual care included preparation and analysis of spiritual care situations, discussion of readings and special topics of concern, and engagement in conversation with other health care professionals.

considered in the following two sections.

On *being* (not-knowing?!) non-action

Professional wisdom is also a matter of "being" as well as "being with" that defines *presence*. Caregiving in interfaith situations involves special sensitivity and self-awareness regarding what one feels and experiences in the relationship. It also involves the sense that one represents not only a religious tradition and community but also, somehow, healing Grace. Indeed we deem such embodiment essential to remind care receivers that a caring Presence is available. Therefore, the sense of personal and professional (ministerial) identity is an essential component of being and presence. It is in fact indispensable to engage the care receiver in a relationship characterized first of all by respectful attending and listening. Such relationship allows the spiritual caregiver to be a witness, not primarily to "tell" things, let alone to tell care receivers how to cope with or fix their situation, but rather to "admire," to behold with love and hope the mystery that is the stranger. Among the traits related to the *being* dimension of professional wisdom, we find the following essential:

- Self-awareness, including: acknowledgment of strengths and limitations; movement beyond preoccupation with one's "ministerial-therapeutic" self (while maintaining clarity regarding identity as spiritual caregiver); and recognition of ways in which that ministerial self influences the interfaith encounter;

- Moral character that integrates a plurality of attitudes and virtues such as: capacity for wonder and respect in the face of the stranger; sensitivity and receptivity; courage to risk and to be surprised; freedom to be vulnerable and open to learning and growth; disposition to recognize, accept, and honor those deemed to be different; hospitality grounded in compassion, humility, and generosity; passion to care and creative energy to transform the inherent violence of separation, prejudice, and alienation into a way of being with (empathy) and for (sympathy) the other as neighbor and partner in care and healing; etc.

- Spirituality defined in part in terms of a "conjunctive faith"[3] which informs ministry style: ability to embrace ambiguity and

---

[3] The conept of *conjunctive faith* comes from James W. Fowler and denotes a desirable level of faith development, as briefly characterized here. See Fowler's *Stages of Faith: The Psychology of Human Development and the Quest for Meaning* (San Francisco: Harper & Row, 1981), pp. 184–198.

paradox; a sense of truth that is multiform and complex; post-critical receptivity ("second naiveté") and readiness to partici-pate in the reality expressed in symbols, myths and rituals of one's own tradition; genuine and disciplined openness to the truths of communities and traditions other than one's own (not to be equated with relativism); movement from the prevalence of certainty to the centrality of trust; etc.

- Sense of personal and spiritual wellbeing, integrity and growth.

On *doing*

Accompaniment and *guidance* are words that name well what we actually do in spiritual care. On the one hand, spiritual caregivers are responsible for attending to, and guiding the actual caregiving process as such. In that sense, guidance is a form of leading which includes, for example, setting appropriate boundaries of time, space, contact, and remaining fully aware of what is going on in the caregiving process. Guidance may of course include gently probing questions, encouragement and support, instructing, confronting, and mediating. On the other hand, except in certain emergency or crisis situations, spiritual caregivers will not be di-rective and try to resolve the problems and struggles faced by care re-ceivers. Especially in interfaith situations, wise caregivers will rather help patients and others to use the specific spiritual resources that have been part of their lives or that may be now available for them. In short, ac-companiment and guidance will optimally be a practice of wisdom—to know how to relate and act in order to care well in interfaith situations.[4] Therefore, among other competencies and skills, effective caregivers will be able to:

- Relate to care-seekers, their relatives, and colleagues in ways that engage their spirituality and facilitate spiritual assessment, including the skill to articulate desired outcomes of spiritual care.

- Internally monitor ongoing caregiving practice so as to remain care receiver-centered, avoid cultural and spiritual invasion or intrusiveness, and be open to receiving manifold gifts from care receivers even as we care well for them.

- Actively listen and discern the appropriateness and timeliness

---

[4] There is actually an interesting etymological connection between *wisdom* and *guidance*. In English, the words *wisdom* and *wise* derive from an Indo-European root, *weid-*, which means *to see* or *to know*. They are related to the Greek *eidos* (idea, form, seeing), to the Latin *videre* (to see), and to the modern German *wissen* (to know). And the word *guide* comes from an ancient Romanic word, *widare*, which means to know. The words *wise*, *wisdom*, *wit*, and *guide*, all share the same origin.

of specific caregiving gestures, use of language and action (probing, supporting, encouraging, comforting, guiding, confronting, mediating, reconciling, evoking, advocating; praying, blessing, etc).

- Reflect pastorally-theologically on ministerial practice on an ongoing basis and continually develop a practical theology of interfaith care.
- Actively partner with the Spirit of God while anticipating and participating in caregiving ministry.
- Maintain patterned practices (i.e. discipline) of self-care with adequate attention to emotional and relational needs and to spiritual nourishment.

Finally, it is clear that the education of interfaith spiritual caregivers in professional wisdom requires that theological education and ministerial formation be holistic and comprehensive. Indeed it must include three equally important and interrelated dimensions, namely, academic, personal-spiritual, and professional. The *academic* formation is obviously indispensable because, among other contents, it includes learning about one's own (religious or nonreligious) faith tradition and heritage and as much as possible about other traditions; it also includes learning about the social and cultural contexts of our work. The *personal-spiritual* formation focuses on our identity and integrity as spiritual caregivers who represent a given tradition; it involves nurturing our moral character. And the *vocational-professional* formation centers on the development of those clinical and other competencies necessary for caring effectively and faithfully wherever we serve as spiritual caregivers.

Spiritual Caregiving in the Hospital
Windows to Chaplaincy Ministry

Leah Dawn Bueckert and Daniel S. Schipani, editors

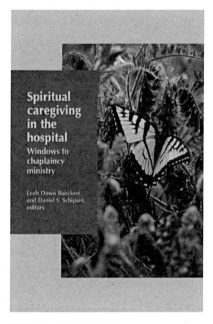

ISBN 1-894710-65-7
272 pages – Softcover
$28.75 Cdn.
$26.00 U.S.

For ordering information contact
Pandora Press
33 Kent Avenue
Kitchener, ON
N2G 3R2

Telephone: 519.578.2381
Fax: 519.578.1826
Toll Free: 866.696.1678
E-mail: karl@pandorapress.com
Web site: www.pandorapress.com

Even as hospitals increasingly recognize spiritual care as an essential component of holistic care, chaplains are still in the process of defining their role. This book acknowledges and celebrates the unique contribution of hospital chaplains, fosters understanding and support for their work, and seeks to elicit interest in their ministry of spiritual caregiving.

The writers bring together a wealth of conceptual and practical information for those engaged in the challenging ministry of caring for persons in crisis. Required reading for any chaplain or spiritual care provider, this book is also an excellent resource for those training professional caregivers.

Teresa E. Snorton,
Executive Director,
Association for Clinical
Pastoral Education